Microprocessors: Essentials, Components and Systems

R Meadows

BSc, MSc, PhD, MIEE, CEng, MInstP, ARCS
Head of Electronic and Communications Engineering
The Polytechnic of North London

A J Parsons

BSc, PhD, MIEE, CEng
Principal Lecturer in Communication Engineering
and Microprocessor Applications
The Polytechnic of North London

Pitman

PITMAN PUBLISHING
128 Long Acre London WC2E 9AN

First published in Great Britain 1983
Reprinted 1984, 1985, 1987

ISBN 0 273 01904 X

Printed in Great Britain at The Bath Press, Avon

Contents

Preface

Despite the recent, rapid growth in microprocessor-related literature, the user, from beginner to specialist, often still experiences difficulty in obtaining a text to suit his or her particular needs. The main reason for this is that current books tend to fall into one of two categories. The first category are those books which cover in a general and descriptive manner the basic concepts of microprocessors and microprocessor-based systems. Whilst such texts are of use to the novice, who requires answers to such questions as "What is a microprocessor?" and "In what circumstances can a microprocessor be of use?", they nonetheless often fail to provide the information necessary for the beginner to both understand and *use* a simple microprocessor system. The second category are those books which cover, in considerable technical detail, one or a few aspects of a particular microprocessor or its related systems. This category contains the many books which cover the programming of a specific microprocessor and the few, highly technical texts dealing with specialised topics such as interfacing, system design, etc.

The purpose of this book is to try to bridge the existing gap between these two categories and provide a broadly-based text of value and, more important, of direct use to a wide cross-section of users and aspiring users.

R G M & A J P

January 1983

1 Introduction to Digital Computers; Overview of the Book

1.1 Introduction

Digital computers are basically electronic calculating and data processing machines that work with instructions and data which are coded in simple binary digit form—hence the characterisation "digital". It is, however, misleading and certainly very short-sighted to think of digital computers solely in their calculator–processor role—they are very readily adapted to act as the complete controller in a very wide and ever-increasing number of applications.

Digital computers may be loosely classified into three broad classes according to cost and degree of sophistication:

Microcomputers currently costing from approximately £50 (sterling) upwards.

Minicomputers costing from approximately £1000 to £5000 upwards.

Mainframe computers costing from the order of £100 000 upwards.

The **microprocessor**—an integrated circuit containing all the computational and control circuitry on a single silicon chip—is the heart or rather the "brains" of a microcomputer. The microprocessor provides all the control, processing and computing power required in all types of applications, e.g. in controlling washing machines, ovens, central heating and air-conditioning systems; in computing in weighing machines and petrol pumps; in electronic instruments; in electronic games; in word processors; and in microcomputers for all types of business, engineering and scientific calculations and processing.

The unit cost of the actual microprocessor chip is now so low—from a few pounds upwards—that its inclusion adds little cost (and often considerable saving) to providing a "computer-controller on a chip" in modern products. One essential advantage of a microprocessor is its versatility. The same microprocessor chip can be programmed to control a very diverse number of processes using only the appropriate software (programs); a change in application means a new program, but no physical changes in the computing and control circuits are required.

Minicomputers are used for more extensive applications where, for example, greater speed, greater memory storage and/or more diverse control functions are required. Mainframe computers are even larger-capacity machines used, for example, for very-large-scale commercial data processing and for running simultaneously several tens or even hundreds of computer terminals for individual users.

1.2 Block Schematic of a Digital Computer System and the Function of its Basic Units

Regardless of size, cost, application and detailed structure, any digital computer can be represented by the simple block diagram of fig. 1.1a; while b shows in greater detail a typical microcomputer system and some of the commonly used peripheral equipment.

To introduce some of the basic terms associated with computer systems, and also to gain an initial insight into how a digital computer operates, let us explain the function of the basic units shown in fig. 1.1.

Input devices Input devices are required to input data, instructions, programs, etc. to the central processing unit of the computer. They enable the user to communicate with computers. Examples of input devices include:

Keyboard devices (similar to electric typewriters).

Transducers plus analogue-to-digital (A-to-D) converters to convert the transducer signals, e.g. electrical signals from temperature, light, pressure sensors, to the digital binary-coded signals that the computer can "understand".

Tape recorders or cassette players containing programs, data, etc. in digital form stored on magnetic tape.

Disc drive units—more readily accessible from the computer's point of view and therefore much speedier than cassettes—where programs, etc. are stored on magnetic discs.

Output devices Output devices are required to translate the computer output, which is in binary form, to human-recognisable form or a form suitable for controlling a machine, etc.. Examples of output devices include

Printers (to provide "hardcopy" of results).

Visual display units (normally abbreviated to VDU, which display results, graphics, games, etc. on a tv-type screen).

Lamps

Light-emitting diodes (LEDs).

Liquid-crystal displays (LCD).

Speech devices.

Digital-to-analogue (D-to-A) converters for converting the computer output to an analogue or continuous-type signal form, which, for example, may then be amplified and used to control a specific function in a process or machine.

Input/output unit (I/O unit) The input/output (normally abbreviated to I/O) unit forms the interface between the computer and the input and output devices. The I/O unit feeds information in the correct binary-coded form and sequence into the central processor unit from input devices, and also outputs results from the computer to output devices.

The input and output lines may enter a common I/O unit which may be programmed to control both the input and output data flow to and from the

Fig. 1.1 Digital
computer system
hardware

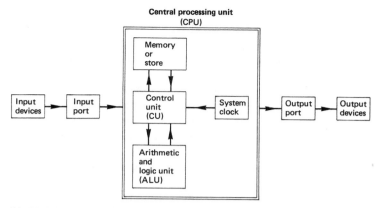

(a)   Block diagram of a fundamental digital computer system

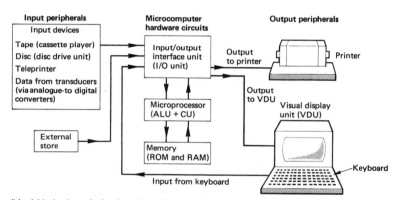

(b)   A block schematic showing units making up a microcomputer system
plus some typical peripherals

central processor; or, alternatively, the I/O unit function may be split into
two separate devices. The term *input port* is used to denote both the entry
point and/or the device handling input data; the term *output port* to denote
the output point/device for output data.

Peripheral devices   All devices, such as input and output devices, connected to the I/O ports are known as peripherals.

The central processing unit (CPU)   The actual computer, as distinct from
its peripheral devices, is known as the central processing unit, the CPU. The
CPU consists essentially of three basic units: a *memory* unit, an *arithmetic-
logic* unit, and a *control* unit. The operation of these three sub-units making
up the CPU are closely interrelated. In many microcomputers all three may
be contained in as few as two or three or even a single integrated circuit
chip.

For example, a microprocessor chip would certainly contain the required control circuits, the arithmetic-logic circuit and limited storage (memory) capacity (e.g. a number of "working" registers for holding data, single program instructions, intermediate results) and can therefore be thought of as a processor unit in its own right, i.e. as a microprocessor unit (MPU). The MPU then has the role of a CPU and, with the addition of memory and I/O interfaces, can form a very powerful computer-controller system.

However, regardless of the degree of integration it is very useful to understand the basic function of the three sub-units making up a CPU:

1 The store or memory unit The store or memory holds the data and instructions of the program which have been fed into the CPU via the I/O unit. It also holds the permanently stored programs (*operating systems programs*) that permit the operation of the computer system immediately after switch-on.

2 The arithmetic and logic unit (ALU) The ALU performs arithmetic operations $(+ - \times \div)$ and logic decisions on the data fed to it from the memory unit, according to the instructions of the program.

3 The control unit (CU) The control unit interprets and carries out the instructions of the program in the exact sequence—instruction by instruction—as stated by the program held in the memory unit. The CU is the master unit controlling the processing of all instructions and the movement of data to and from the input/output devices to the memory unit and to and from the ALU.

The clock A digital computer is the prime example of a digital-logic sequential system and as such requires a very accurate timing source to ensure perfect synchronism of all its step-by-step operations. The timing source controlling these operations in the CPU is known as the clock. The clock invariably consists of a crystal-controlled oscillator circuit which generates a continuous wavetrain of rectangular pulses of very stable frequency. These pulses are fed to all circuits in the computer system to ensure that they work in exact synchronism.

Auxiliary storage devices In many applications the internal store or memory unit of the CPU will prove inadequate. There will not be enough memory space to store *all* program instructions, data, results, etc. To overcome this problem, auxiliary stores are used. These consist of magnetic devices where programs, data, etc. are stored on magnetic tapes and magnetic discs. A tape of 100 m length is capable of storing about one million characters, whilst a disc may store 200+ million. Information from auxiliary stores is fed via the I/O unit to the internal store when it is called upon by the CPU. It must, of course, be split into suitable blocks to avoid swamping the available memory space in the CPU.

1.3 Explanation of Some Important Computer Terms: Hardware, Programs, Software

There are a number of computer jargon terms which are very widely used to describe the physical components of computer systems and the instructions used to program the system.

Hardware Hardware is used to describe any component or unit used in the construction of a digital computer system. Input devices, microprocessor chips, memory chips, I/O chips, auxiliary stores, output devices are all examples of hardware.

Program Any list of instructions or routines or actions set out in a logical order to solve a particular problem is known as a program. All digital computers work on a sequential basis. Each instruction is carried out one by one until all the instructions making up the program have been executed.

Machine code and machine instructions The CPU itself works with programs coded in binary form, i.e. each instruction and every piece of data is represented by a unique pattern of 1–0 binary digits. The binary codes used to represent instructions, data, etc., are known as machine codes.

The CPU can perform only a limited number of instructions, the number being determined in the case of a microcomputer by the actual microprocessor used. These instructions are known as machine instructions and the complete set available for a given microprocessor is known as its *instruction set*.

Object program A list of machine instructions set up in a logical order to solve a given problem is known as the object program.

Source programs Machine code programs (i.e. object programs) are very tedious to compose directly since they consist entirely of binary 1–0 patterns. Programming is normally done using one of the following two language forms:

a) High-level Languages
Such as BASIC, PASCAL, ALGOL, FORTRAN, etc.
These languages are very much easier for humans to understand and use. However, the computer cannot work directly with programs composed in a high-level language. Such programs must first be translated into machine code before the CPU can begin its work.

Programs written in a high-level language are known as **source programs**. A program which translates the source program into the machine code program (the object program) for execution by the computer is known as a **compiler**. Each high-level language requires its own compiler.

b) Symbolic or Assembly Codes
Symbolic or assembly code programming is essentially a half-way stage

between using a high-level language and preparing the final machine code programs. Every type of microprocessor has its own set of symbolic instructions, in many cases similar to abbreviated English, which may be used to write programs. Programs written in symbolic code are known as **assembly code programs**. They must, of course, be first translated into machine code for direct use in the computer. A program which prepares the machine code program from a symbolic language program is known as an **assembler**.

Software   Software is the general term used to denote all forms of program associated with computing systems, just as hardware is used to denote all forms of physical component.

Software is also often used to include not only programs but any documentation associated with the computer, such as manuals, circuit diagrams, compilers, assemblers, library routines, etc.

Firmware   Firmware is the term frequently used to describe those programs which are permanently stored in the CPU and are necessary for the control of start-up, switch-off, input/output procedures, etc. in the computer. Firmware programs are "burnt in" the ROM sections of the central store, usually at the time of manufacture and cannot normally be altered.

Applications programs, as distinct from firmware, can normally be freely altered by the user and are normally stored in the RAM sections of memory. Programs stored in RAM memory are normally "lost" on switching off the computer; firmware stored in ROM memory is always retained. (ROM and RAM are explained in Chapter 4).

1.4   Overview of the Book

In this introductory chapter we have described very briefly the basic hardware units making up a typical digital system and introduced some important terms associated with computing systems.

We expand this material with the aim of providing a text which will give you a real understanding of both hardware and software concepts and techniques currently used in modern microprocessor-based computer systems.

Chapter 2: **Computer arithmetic**   Here we start with basic concepts concerning binary numbers and computer arithmetic. We introduce the idea of binary numbers, show their relationships with decimal numbers, and then consider the closely related octal and hexadecimal numbers, which are used in practice to represent binary "word" patterns in more concise form. We consider the processes of binary arithmetic—the arithmetic the computer uses—and finally binary codes, used to represent alphabetical characters and other non-numerical data.

Chapter 3: **Logic devices, circuits and operations**   This chapter is essentially concerned with general hardware fundamentals; we consider the basic building blocks and concepts associated with digital logic circuits and systems.

In a practical microprocessor-based computer system, the control and arithmetic-logic units are now integrated and put down on a single integrated circuit chip (the microprocessor), and a powerful microcomputer can then be designed on a suitable printed circuit board containing the necessary conductor tracks by adding ROM and RAM memory chips, I/O chips, etc. It is, nevertheless, essential to have a sound understanding of the basic gates and circuits making up the medium, large and very large-scale IC chips used in modern microcomputer systems.

The aim of Chapter 3 is to achieve this understanding: it considers in simple terms the fundamental "decision-making" gates and some practical applications involving these gates; it introduces the idea of how "memory" may be achieved in digital circuits and considers in detail the basic flip-flop elements—the memory elements of sequential logic circuits. It also gives some examples of practical applications: counting circuits, shift registers (for storing and manipulating binary data); and introduces the concepts of arithmetic circuits capable of adding, subtracting, multiplying and dividing binary numbers.

Chapter 4: **Microprocessor architecture and system operation** In this chapter we consider the basic architecture (i.e. layout of the microprocessor and its support chips) and the principles of operation of a microcomputer system. This important chapter provides a link between the general concepts contained in the first three chapters and the more detailed software and hardware topics presented in the succeeding chapters.

The introduction to the chapter explains how the concept of a low-cost general-purpose computer-controller (the microprocessor) was made possible by the advances in large-scale integrated circuit technology. This is followed by a description of the basic function of the microprocessor and its support chips and how these chips are interconnected in a typical system. We also consider in detail the internal architecture of two widely used microprocessors, the Z80 and 6502. We explain the operation of microprocessor-based computer systems: the fetch-execute cycle, I/O routines and interrupts. Finally we consider some of the "tools" used for fault-finding and checking the system operation.

Chapter 5: **Microprocessor programming** Here we consider the methods used to program the microprocessor to perform its tasks: types of instruction, addressing modes, machine and assembly code programming.

It is fundamental to the microprocessor philosophy to appreciate that, once we have put the systems hardware together, problem solving is then implemented by software. A given microprocessor may be programmed to execute many different control/computing functions; if changes are to be made these are effected by changing the software, not by changing the microprocessor circuits (as may be the case in "random" logic systems), although we may change some memory chips containing firmware.

In this way a given microprocessor system may be programmed for many diverse applications: from purely dedicated roles such as a washing machine or petrol pump controller to a full-scale microcomputer capable of undertaking the control of a complex industrial system or for use as a scientific/business computer able to process fairly large volumes of data and solve complex calculations.

Chapter 6: **Computer storage devices**   In this chapter we consider, in some detail, storage devices—magnetic disc, tape and semiconductor memories—all the devices commonly employed to store programs, data and results.

Chapter 7: **Peripheral equipment**   In Chapter 7 we describe in detail the construction and operation of peripherals (other than stores)—the support units connected to the input and output ports which feed information, etc. to and from the computer. We include input keyboard devices; the various printers used for recording output data; LEDs, LCDs and 7-segment displays; visual display units; graph plotters; light pens. We also consider interfacing techniques and A-to-D, D-to-A conversion.

Chapter 8: **Microprocessor applications**   Finally we complete our coverage by giving some practical examples of the use of microprocessors: in weighing, in central-heating control, and in waveform synthesis, chosen to illustrate the versatility and advantages of microprocessor-based computer-controlled systems.

2 Computer Arithmetic

2.1 Introduction to Binary Numbers; their Relationship with Denary Numbers

The denary or decimal system of numbers is the everyday system we work with. We have been taught to think in terms of these base-10 numbers. Digital computer circuits—"machines"—however, employ a much simpler system of numbers. They work with binary numbers and instructions coded in binary number form. It is therefore very important that we develop an understanding of binary numbers, binary arithmetic and instructions—"machine instructions"—coded as binary patterns, so we can begin to comprehend how computers and microprocessors operate.

The binary system is the simplest of all number systems. Binary numbers contain only two different digits 0 and 1; whereas decimal numbers contain 10, i.e. 0, 1, 2, 3, 4, 5, 6, 7, 8, 9. The total number of different digits used in a number system is known as the **base** or *radix* of the system; the base of the binary system is therefore 2 and the base of the decimal system 10. Other number systems widely used in connection with computers, and which are closely related to binary and indeed used as short-hand codes to represent binary patterns, are octal, base-8 numbers, and hexadecimal, base-16 numbers.

In the binary system we write numbers as a sequence of 1s and 0s. Zero in the binary system may be represented by a single 0 or by a succession of 0s, e.g. 0, 00, 000, 0000, $\cdots$ all represent 0.

1 represents powers of 2, i.e. 2^0, 2^1, 2^2, $2^3 \cdots$. It is the position of a 1 digit in a binary number that determines its weighting value. For example, the 4-digit binary number has the following meaning:

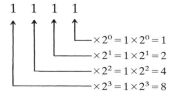

$$1 \quad 1 \quad 1 \quad 1$$

$$\times 2^0 = 1 \times 2^0 = 1$$
$$\times 2^1 = 1 \times 2^1 = 2$$
$$\times 2^2 = 1 \times 2^2 = 4$$
$$\times 2^3 = 1 \times 2^3 = 8$$

so the binary number $1111 =$ decimal number $(8+4+2+1) = 15$.

Each binary digit in a binary number is referred to as a **bit**. The right-hand bit having the least weighting is known as the **least significant bit** (LSB); the left-hand having the most weighting is known as the **most**

Table 2.1 Decimal (base 10) and corresponding binary (base 2) numbers

Decimal number	Binary number	Decimal number	Binary number
0	00000	9	01001
1	00001	10	01010
2	00010	11	01011
3	00011	12	01100
4	00100	13	01101
5	00101	14	01110
6	00110	15	01111
7	00111	16	10000
8	01000	17	10001

significant bit (MSB). As we progress from right to left, successive bits increase their weighting value in powers of 2. For example, in the binary number

10101101

the weighting is as follows:

2^7	2^6	2^5	2^4	2^3	2^2	2^1	2^0	← weighting expressed as powers of 2
128	64	32	16	8	4	2	1	← decimal equivalent
1	0	1	0	1	1	0	1	← binary number

so the 8-bit binary number

10101101

$$= (1 \times 2^7) + (0 \times 2^6) + (1 \times 2^5) + (0 \times 2^4) + (1 \times 2^3) + (1 \times 2^2) + (0 \times 2^1) + (1 \times 2^0)$$

$$= 128 + 0 + 32 + 0 + 8 + 4 + 0 + 1$$

$$= 173 \quad \text{in the decimal number system}$$

Conversion from a binary to its equivalent decimal number is then very straightforward. All we need to remember is the factor of 2 increase in weighting as we move from right to left away from the least significant bit. A binary 1 in a given position must be multiplied by the relevant power of 2, a binary 0 in any position indicates zero. Table 2.1 lists the decimal numbers 0 to 17 and gives their binary equivalents.

Example 2.1

Binary number	*Decimal equivalent*
1000000	$1 \times 2^6 = 64$
10000000	$1 \times 2^7 = 128$
100000000	$1 \times 2^8 = 256$

Using the above results, state how many bits are required to represent all the decimal numbers in the range a) 0, 1, 2, 3, $\cdots$ 127 and b) 0, 1, 2, 3, $\cdots$ 200

a) 7 bits   zero would be represented as 0000000
               127 would be represented as 1111111
b) 8 bits   decimal numbers from 0 to $2^8 - 1 = 255$ can be represented by 8-bit binary patterns, e.g.

$$200 = 128 + 64 + 8$$
$$= 2^7 + 2^6 + 2^3 = 11001000 \quad \text{in binary}$$

2.2 Conversion of Decimal Numbers to Binary Numbers

We can convert a decimal number into its binary equivalent by trial and error methods, as illustrated in the last example, by splitting the decimal number into the sum of powers of 2. For example,

$$43 = 32 + 11 = 32 + 8 + 3$$
$$= 32 + 8 + 2 + 1$$
$$= 101011 \quad \text{in binary}$$

so $43_{10} = 101011_2$.*

A more systematic method consists of dividing the decimal number successively by 2 and noting the remainders. The equivalent binary number is then found by writing these remainders in the *reverse* order.

Example 2.2   Convert 37_{10} into binary.

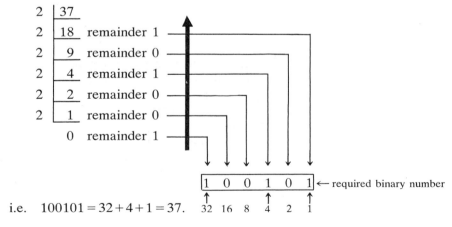

i.e. $100101 = 32 + 4 + 1 = 37.$

---

* To distinguish between different number systems we can write the base of the number as a subscript at the lower right of the number, so
    43_{10} denotes that 43 is a decimal number
    101011_2 denotes that 101011 is a binary number.
In practice, however, the base subscript is normally omitted and taken as understood. It is included only when confusion could occur.

Table 2.2 Decimal and corresponding binary fractions

Proper fraction	Power of 2	Decimal fraction	Binary fraction
$\frac{1}{2}$	2^{-1}	0·5	0·1
$\frac{1}{4}$	2^{-2}	0·25	0·01
$\frac{1}{8}$	2^{-3}	0·125	0·001
$\frac{1}{16}$	2^{-4}	0·0625	0·0001
$\frac{1}{32}$	2^{-5}	0·031 25	0·00001
$\frac{1}{64}$	2^{-6}	0·015 625	0·000001
$\frac{1}{128}$	2^{-7}	0·007 812 5	0·0000001
$\frac{1}{256}$	2^{-8}	0·003 906 25	0·00000001
$\frac{1}{512}$	2^{-9}	0·001 953 125	0·000000001

2.3 Binary Fractions

Just as we use a decimal point to separate the whole and decimal fraction parts of a decimal number, we can use a *binary point* in binary numbers to separate the whole and fractional parts. The significance of the weighting of the bits behind the binary point is illustrated below, and also summarized in Table 2.2.

$$
\begin{array}{l}
\times 2^{-1} = \frac{1}{2} \\
\times 2^{-2} = \frac{1}{4} \\
\times 2^{-3} = \frac{1}{8} \\
\times 2^{-4} = \frac{1}{16}
\end{array}
$$

$$0\cdot1 \quad 1 \quad 1 \quad 1$$

so $\quad 0\cdot1111_2 = \frac{1}{2} + \frac{1}{4} + \frac{1}{8} + \frac{1}{16} = 0\cdot5 + 0\cdot25 + 0\cdot125 + 0\cdot0625$
$$= 0\cdot9375_{10}$$

To convert a **decimal fraction to a binary fraction** we employ the following rule. Multiply the decimal fraction repeatedly by the base 2. The whole number part of the first multiplication gives the first 1 or 0 of the binary fraction; the fractional part of the result is carried over and multiplied by 2; the whole number part of the result gives the second 1 or 0, and so on.

For example, convert $0\cdot375_{10}$ to a binary fraction.

0·375	0·750	0·50
×2	×2	×2
0·750	1·50	1·00
↓	↓	↓
0 (MSB of fraction)	1 (next bit)	1 (LSB of fraction)

so $\quad 0\cdot375_{10} = 0\cdot011_2$

Check $\quad 0\cdot011_2 = (0 \times \frac{1}{2}) + (1 \times \frac{1}{4}) + (1 \times \frac{1}{8})$
$$= 0 + 0\cdot25 + 0\cdot125 = 0\cdot375_{10}$$

Example 2.3 Determine the equivalent decimal numbers of the following binary numbers:

a) 111·1   *b*) 101·001   *c*) 1001·01

a) $111\cdot1 = 4+2+1+\frac{1}{2} = 7\frac{1}{2} = 7\cdot5$
b) $101\cdot001 = 4+1+\frac{1}{8} = 5\frac{1}{8} = 5\cdot125$
c) $1001\cdot01 = 8+1+\frac{1}{4} = 9\frac{1}{4} = 9\cdot25$

Example 2.4   Convert $60\cdot625_{10}$ into binary.

Consider first the whole number part:

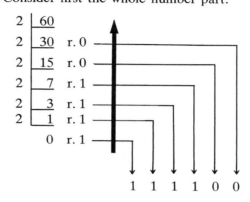

$$1\ 1\ 1\ 1\ 0\ 0 \qquad \text{so} \quad 60_{10} = 111100_2$$

Then the fractional part:

0·625	0·250	0·50
×2	×2	×2
1·250	0·500	1·00
↓	↓	↓
1 (MSB of fraction)	0	1 (LSB)

so $0\cdot625_{10} = 0\cdot101_2$

and combining whole and fractional parts, we have

$$60\cdot625_{10} = 111100\cdot101_2$$

2.4 Octal Numbers

Although digital computers handle binary 1s and 0s with ease, we as humans find binary patterns difficult to handle both mentally and physically, especially when dealing with 8, 16, 24 or even 32 bit numbers or machine instructions coded into binary form. For this reason octal and hexadecimal numbers are frequently employed. We can greatly simplify binary 1–0 patterns by using higher-order base numbers which are closely related to the binary system. Octal (base 8) and hexadecimal (base 16) number systems are essentially used as a shorthand representation for binary coded numbers and instructions.

2.4.1   Relationship of Octal with Decimal Numbers

In an octal number there are only eight possible digits 0, 1, 2, 3, 4, 5, 6, 7. The position of a digit in front of the octal point carries a weighting in ascending powers of 8, i.e. $8^0 = 1$, $8^1 = 8$, $8^2 = 64$, $8^3 = 512 \cdots$
For example,

$$8^2 \quad 8^1 \quad 8^0 \leftarrow \text{weightings expressed as powers of 8}$$
$$64 \quad 8 \quad 1 \leftarrow \text{decimal equivalent}$$
$$3 \quad 2 \quad 7_8 = (3 \times 64) + (2 \times 8) + 7 = 215_{10}$$

Digits behind the octal point are employed, just like the decimal and binary points, to separate whole and fractional parts, and carry weightings of

$$8^{-1} = \tfrac{1}{8} \qquad 8^{-2} = \tfrac{1}{64} \qquad 8^{-3} = \tfrac{1}{512} \cdots$$

For example,

$$0 \cdot 53_8 = (5 \times \tfrac{1}{8}) + (3 \times \tfrac{1}{64}) = \tfrac{5}{8} + \tfrac{3}{64} = \tfrac{43}{64} = 0 \cdot 671875_{10}$$

Decimal to octal conversion follows the process of decimal to binary but in this case we divide by 8, writing out the remainders in reverse order, e.g.

$$
\begin{array}{r|l}
8 & 247 \\
\hline
8 & 30 \quad \text{r. 7} \\
\hline
8 & 3 \quad \text{r. 6} \\
\hline
 & 0 \quad \text{r. 3}
\end{array}
\qquad \text{so} \quad 247_{10} = 367_8
$$

To convert a decimal fraction to an octal fraction we multiply repeatedly by 8 and note the whole number "spill-over" part in exactly the way we used for binary. For example, to convert $0 \cdot 48_{10}$

$$
\begin{array}{cccc}
0 \cdot 48 & 0 \cdot 84 & 0 \cdot 72 & 0 \cdot 76 \\
\times 8 & \times 8 & \times 8 & \times 8 \\
\hline
3 \cdot 84 & 6 \cdot 72 & 5 \cdot 76 & 6 \cdot 08 \\
\downarrow & \downarrow & \downarrow & \downarrow
\end{array}
$$

so $0 \cdot 48_{10} = 0 \cdot 3656_8 \cdots = 0 \cdot 366_8$ (to three significant figures).

2.4.2   Conversion from Binary to Octal and vice-versa

1   To convert **from binary to octal**, we group the binary number starting from the LSB in groups of three bits; each of these groups is then expressed by its equivalent octal digit. For example,

$$\underbrace{101}_{5} \quad \underbrace{110}_{6} \quad \underbrace{011}_{3_{8 \text{ (or 10)}}}$$

is expressed as

$$011 = 3_{10} = 3_8 \qquad 110 = 6_8 \qquad 101 = 5_8$$

i.e. $101110011_2 = 563_8$

With whole and fractional parts we group in threes, starting from the octal point, moving left for the whole part, right for the fractional part, e.g.

$$\underbrace{010}_{2} \; \underbrace{111}_{7} . \underbrace{101}_{5} \; \underbrace{001}_{1}{}_8$$

2 The reverse process—**octal to binary**—consists simply of writing the 3-bit binary number for each octal digit. For example, 4037_8 converts as

4   0   3   7

100 000 011 111

i.e. $4037_8 = 100\,000\,011\,111_2$

2.5 Hexadecimal Numbers

Hexadecimal numbers are base-16 numbers employing 16 distinct digits to represent the decimal numbers $0, 1, 2, 3, \cdots 12, 13, 14, 15$. The least significant digit in front of the hexadecimal point is weighted $16^0 = 1$ (i.e. units), the next is 16^1, the next 16^2, and so on. For example,

$$16^2 \quad 16^1 \quad 16^0 \leftarrow \text{weightings expressed as powers of 16}$$
$$256 \quad 16 \quad 1 \leftarrow \text{decimal equivalent}$$

hence $3 \qquad 6 \qquad 8_{16} = (3 \times 256) + (6 \times 16) + 8 = 872_{10}$

Successive hexadecimal digits behind the point are weighted

$$16^{-1} = \tfrac{1}{16} \quad 16^{-2} = \tfrac{1}{256} \quad 16^{-3} = \tfrac{1}{4096} \cdots \text{and so on.}$$

There is, however, a problem of notation. Using the digits available in the decimal system, what do we do to write down the double figures in the range 10 to 15? This is overcome by assigning the first six letters of the alphabet:

A in hexadecimal represents 10
B in hexadecimal represents 11
C in hexadecimal represents 12
D in hexadecimal represents 13
E in hexadecimal represents 14
F in hexadecimal represents 15

Table 2.3 gives the hexadecimal numbers from $0–17 \cdots 32$, together with their decimal and binary equivalents.

2.5.1 Hexadecimal to Decimal Conversion and vice-versa

1 To convert **from hexadecimal** (normally abbreviated to hex) **to decimal** we multiply each hex digit by the relevant power of 16. For example,

$$16^3 \quad 16^2 \quad 16^1 \quad 16^0$$

$$
\begin{aligned}
\text{C} \quad 4 \quad \text{B} \quad \text{A}_{hex} &= (\text{C} \times 16^3) + (4 \times 16^2) + (\text{B} \times 16) + (\text{A} \times 1) \\
&= (12 \times 16^3) + (4 \times 16^2) + (11 \times 16) + 10 \\
&= 49\,152 + 1\,024 + 176 + 10 \\
&= 50\,362
\end{aligned}
$$

so C4BA_{16} or $\text{C4BA}_{hex} = 50\,362_{10}$

2 The inverse procedure, **decimal to hex**, is similar to binary and octal except that we use the base 16 divisor, i.e. divide the decimal number successively by 16 and write down the remainders in the reverse order. For example, to convert 268_{10} to hex:

$$
\begin{array}{r|l}
16 & 268 \\
16 & 16 \quad \text{r. } 12 = \text{C} \\
16 & 1 \quad \text{r. } 0 \\
& 0 \quad \text{r. } 1
\end{array}
$$

so $268_{10} = 10\text{C}_{hex}$

Check $10\text{C} = (1 \times 16^2) + (0 \times 16) + 12 = 268_{10}$

2.5.2 Binary to Hexadecimal Conversion and vice-versa

1 **Binary to hex** conversions are very similar to binary to octal but, to form the hex number equivalent, we group the binary bits in groups of 4 and then replace each group by its equivalent hex digit. For example,

$$
\begin{array}{cccc}
\underline{1011} & \underline{1000} & \underline{1111} & \underline{0011} \\
11_{10} & 8_{10} & 15_{10} & 3_{10} \\
= \text{B}_{hex} & 8_{hex} & \text{F}_{hex} & 3_{hex}
\end{array}
$$

i.e. $1011\ 1000\ 1111\ 0011_2 = \text{B8F3}_{hex}$

Note how much easier it is to comprehend the hex equivalent of the 16-bit binary pattern.

2 The inverse process, **hex to binary**, is illustrated below. The corresponding 4 bits for each hex digit are written

$$
\begin{array}{cccc}
\text{F} & \text{A} & \text{E} & \text{C} \\
1111 & 1010 & 1110 & 1100
\end{array}
$$

i.e. $\text{FAEC}_{hex} = 1111\ 1010\ 1110\ 1100_2$

Table 2.3 Decimal–hexadecimal–binary numbers

Decimal	Hexadecimal	Binary
0	0	0000
1	1	0001
2	2	0010
3	3	0011
4	4	0100
5	5	0101
6	6	0110
7	7	0111
8	8	1000
9	9	1001
10	A	1010
11	B	1011
12	C	1100
13	D	1101
14	E	1110
15	F	1111
16	10	0001 0000
17	11	0001 0001
31	1F	0001 1111
32	20	0010 0000

2.6 Nibbles, Bytes and Words

Three terms concerning binary coded patterns are frequently used in computer jargon: the nibble, byte and word.

1 A sequence of 4 bits is known as a **nibble**.
0010, 1010, 1111 can be described as nibbles.
2 A group of 8 bits is known as a **byte**.
0001 1010, 1110 0101 can be described as bytes.
3 The number of bits used to convey data in a computer or microprocessor is known as its **wordlength**. In many microcomputers (microprocessor-based computers), a wordlength of 8 bits or 1 byte in used; some simpler microprocessors use 4 bits or 1 nibble, whilst the latest use 16 bits or 2 bytes. Mainframe computers use 24 to 60 bit wordlengths.

Example 2.5 Binary patterns representing numbers and instructions are stored in the memory of a computer. Each binary pattern or word, consisting typically of 1 or 2 bytes for microprocessor systems, has its own location in the memory and each location is given an address. These addresses are normally quoted as hex numbers.

Determine for a 1-byte microcomputer, which stores data in memory from address locations $B000_{hex}$ to $BFFF_{hex}$, the following:

a) The decimal equivalent for the first and last addresses.
b) The number of individual word locations between these addresses.
c) The amount of binary data in bits and bytes that can be stored in this memory space.

a) The address $B000_{hex}$ corresponds to the decimal address

$$16^3 \quad 16^2 \quad 16^1 \quad 16^0$$
$$B \quad\quad 0 \quad\quad 0 \quad\quad 0 = (11 \times 16^3) + 0 + 0 + 0 = 45\,056_{10}$$

The address is

$$BFFF = (11 \times 16^3) + (15 \times 16^2) + (15 \times 16) + 15 = 49\,151_{10}$$

b) The number of individual locations between B000 and BFFF is

$$49\,151 - 45\,056 = 4095$$

so including 1 for the first location, the total number of storage locations is 4096.

Check: we could of course find the difference using hexadecimal subtraction (virtually identical to decimal subtraction):

$$\begin{array}{l} BFFF \\ \underline{B000} \\ 0FFF \end{array} = (15 \times 16^2) + (15 \times 16) + 15 = 4095_{10}$$

c) The total amount of data that can be stored

$$= (\text{number of locations}) \times (\text{no. bits or wordlength per location})$$
$$= 4096 \times 8 \text{ bits} \quad \text{or} \quad 4096 \text{ bytes}$$

Note The size of a computer memory is often measured in units of $2^{10} = 1024_{10}$ locations. This unit is designated 1K.

$1K = 1024 = 2^{10}$

Thus in our example, the storage space between B000 and BFFF is

$$4096 = 4K$$

and since the microprocessor has a wordlength of 1 byte, the amount of information stored is

$$4K \text{ bytes} = 4K \times 8 \text{ bits} = 32K \text{ bits}$$

2.7 Binary Coded Decimal (BCD)

So far we have considered the encoding of numbers in pure binary form. Because of the everyday use of decimal numbers it is very useful in many microprocessor–computer applications to code each decimal digit by an individual group of 4 bits or by a nibble. Such codes are referred to as **binary coded decimal** codes, normally abbreviated to BCD. BCD is a special

Table 2.4 Examples of three binary coded decimal (BCD) codes

Decimal number	8421 BCD	2421 BCD	XS-3
0	0000	0000	0011
1	0001	0001	0100
2	0010	0010	0101
3	0011	0011	0110
4	0100	0100	0111
5	0101	1011	1000
6	0110	1100	1001
7	0111	1101	1010
8	1000	1110	1011
9	1001	1111	1100

form of binary code in which each decimal digit is expressed as a 4-bit pattern.

A number of different BCD codes are used, three of which are given in Table 2.4. Perhaps the most popular is the **8421 BCD**. In the 8421 BCD, the most significant of the 4-bit group is weighted 8, the next is weighted 4, the next 2, and the LSB 1. It allows us to define uniquely any decimal digit by 4 bits. Multi-digit decimal numbers are represented as illustrated in the following three examples:

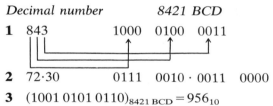

Decimal number   *8421 BCD*

1   843   1000   0100   0011

2   72·30   0111   0010 · 0011   0000

3 $(1001\ 0101\ 0110)_{8421\ BCD} = 956_{10}$

Note the distinction from pure binary coding: in BCD, each decimal digit is always represented by its defined 4-bit BCD code. Note also that 10 of the 16 possible 4-bit binary groups are used. The groups 1010, 1011, 1100, 1101, 1110, 1111 are not used. They are forbidden or illegal groups in the 8421 BCD code.

In the **2421 BCD** code (third column in Table 2.4), the MSB has a weight of 2, the next a weight of 4, the next a weight of 2, and the LSB a weight of 1. For example,

$$687_{10} = (1100\ 1110\ 1101)_{2421\ BCD}$$

BCD codes having positive and negative weights are also used. The **excess-3** code (XS-3) is such an example (see fourth column in Table 2.4), where 3_{10} or 0011_2 is added to each 4-bit group of the 8421 BCD code.

Example 2.6 Represent 258_{10} in *a*) 8421 BCD   *b*) 2421 BCD   *c*) XS-3 *d*) in pure binary   *e*) in octal   *f*) in hexadecimal.

a) In 8421 BCD:

$$2 = 0010$$
$$5 = 0101$$
$$8 = 1000$$

so $258_{10} = (0010\ 0101\ 1000)_{8421\ \text{BCD}}$

b) In 2421 BCD:

$2 = 0010 \qquad 5 = 1011 \qquad 8 = 1110$

so $258_{10} = (0010\ 1011\ 1110)_{2421\ \text{BCD}}$

c) In XS-3 code:

$2 = 0101 \qquad 5 = 1000 \qquad 8 = 1011$

so $258_{10} = (0101\ 1000\ 1011)_{\text{XS-3}}$

d) In pure binary:

2	258	
2	129	r. 0
2	64	r. 1
2	32	r. 0
2	16	r. 0
2	8	r. 0
2	4	r. 0
2	2	r. 0
2	1	r. 0
	0	r. 1

so on writing the remainders in reverse order,

$258_{10} = 100000010_2$ in pure binary

e) In octal:

$$\underbrace{100}_{4}\ \underbrace{000}_{0}\ \underbrace{010_2}_{2_8}$$

so $258_{10} = 100000010_2 = 402_8$ in octal

f) In hexadecimal:

$$\underbrace{1}_{1}\ \underbrace{0000}_{0}\ \underbrace{0010}_{2_{\text{hex}}}$$

so $258_{10} = 102_{\text{hex}}$

2.8 Introduction to Binary Arithmetic

Table 2.5 Rules of binary arithmetic

Addition

$0+0=0$
$0+1=1$
$1+0=1$
$1+1=0$ and
   carry 1

Subtraction

$0-0=0$
$1-0=1$
$1-1=0$
$0-1=1$ and
   borrow 1

Multiplication

$0\times0=0$
$1\times0=0$
$0\times1=0$
$1\times1=1$

Division

$0\div1=0$
$1\div1=1$

All digital computers and microprocessors work on a binary basis, processing numbers and instructions coded in 1–0 patterns. They can, in fact, carry out only a relatively small number of operations, but perform them at astonishingly high speeds—typically some million or so every second!

The binary addition operation is the fundamental process carried out in the arithmetic logic unit (ALU) in the central processor of a computer. Binary subtraction, multiplication and division, as we shall see in the following sections and also when we investigate the logic circuit used in Chapter 3, are essentially performed by repetitive sequences of binary addition.

Binary arithmetic is very similar to "normal" decimal arithmetic, perhaps even easier, since we are only dealing with 0s and 1s. The four basic operations, which we now discuss in detail, are summarized in Table 2.5.

2.9 Binary Addition

To introduce the idea of **binary addition**, which is virtually identical to decimal addition, let us recap on the processes used in finding the sum of two decimal numbers, for example $698+547$:

$$
\begin{array}{cccc}
10^3 & 10^2 & 10^1 & 10^0 \leftarrow \text{decimal number weightings} \\
1000 & 100 & 10 & 1 \quad \text{i.e. units, tens, hundreds, thousands} \cdots \\
 & 6 & 9 & 8 \\
 & 5 & 4 & 7 \\
\hline
1 & 2 & 4 & 5 \\
\hline
 & 1 & 1 & \leftarrow \text{the "carry ones"}
\end{array}
$$

To obtain the answer we proceeded along the following lines:

Units column: $8+7=15$, put down the 5 and carry the 1 (in fact a ten)

Tens column: $1+9+4=14$, put down 4 and carry 1 (in fact a
       ↑   hundred)
  the "carry 1"

Hundreds column: $1+6+5=12$, put down 2 and the "carry 1"
         ↑   in the next column
   the "carry 1"   (the thousands column)

The same approach is used in binary addition. We arrange the binary numbers in vertical columns, bits of the same power of 2 being under one another. We then follow the basic rules:

$$0+0=0 \qquad 1+0=1$$

$$0+1=1 \qquad 1+1=0 \quad \text{with 1 to carry to next column}$$

and in general, "carry 1" for every 2 obtained in the individual column sum.

Example 2.7 *a*) Find the sum of binary 011 and 010.

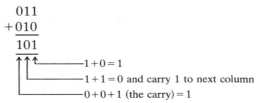

b) Add the following 8-bit numbers:

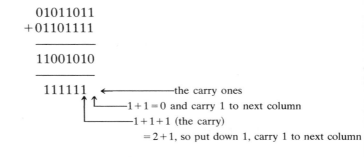

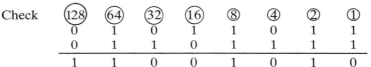

2.10 Binary Subtraction

Binary subtraction where the number to be subtracted is the smaller of the two, so that we obtain a positive result, can be achieved using the same approach as for "normal" decimal subtraction. When a "borrow" in binary is required, then we can think of this as a (decimal) value of 2, and this 2 is added to the relevant bit in the "top" number. Subtraction is then performed but we must remember to return the borrowed 1 to the next higher bit in the "lower" number by adding 1. The rules for binary subtraction (see Table 2.5) are

$$0-0=0 \quad 1-0=1 \quad 1-1=0 \quad 0-1=1 \text{ and borrow 1}$$

Difficulty with binary subtraction arises when the number to be subtracted is the larger and so a negative result should be obtained. So far we have not discussed any binary representation for negative numbers. In most ALUs binary subtraction is performed by complementing the number and then adding—we explain these ideas in sections 2.13 and 2.14. This enables subtraction to be accomplished using only adder circuits and auxiliary logic circuits for complementation—a much simpler solution than the circuits that would be required for "direct" subtraction.

Example 2.8   *a*) Subtract 1010 from 1101.

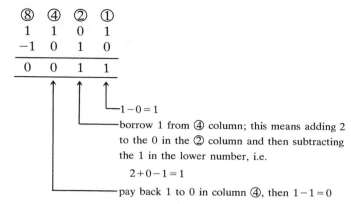

$$1 - 0 = 1$$

borrow 1 from ④ column; this means adding 2 to the 0 in the ② column and then subtracting the 1 in the lower number, i.e.

$$2 + 0 - 1 = 1$$

pay back 1 to 0 in column ④, then $1 - 1 = 0$

Check $1101_2 = 8 + 4 + 0 + 1 = 13_{10}$
$\quad\quad\quad 1010_2 = 8 + 0 + 2 + 0 = 10_{10}$
$\quad\quad\quad 0011_2 = 0 + 0 + 2 + 1 = 3_{10}$

b)   Evaluate $1101100 - 0111111$.

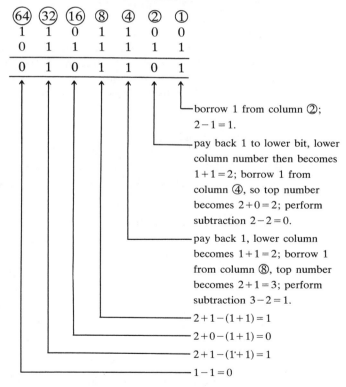

borrow 1 from column ②;
$2 - 1 = 1$.

pay back 1 to lower bit, lower column number then becomes $1 + 1 = 2$; borrow 1 from column ④, so top number becomes $2 + 0 = 2$; perform subtraction $2 - 2 = 0$.

pay back 1, lower column becomes $1 + 1 = 2$; borrow 1 from column ⑧, top number becomes $2 + 1 = 3$; perform subtraction $3 - 2 = 1$.

$2 + 1 - (1 + 1) = 1$

$2 + 0 - (1 + 1) = 0$

$2 + 1 - (1' + 1) = 1$

$1 - 1 = 0$

Check $1101\ 100_2 = 64 + 32 + 8 + 4 = 108_{10}$
$\quad\quad\quad 0111\ 111_2 = 32 + 16 + 8 + 4 + 2 + 1 = 63_{10}$
$\quad\quad\quad 0101\ 101_2 = 32 + 8 + 4 + 1 = 45_{10}$

2.11 Binary Multiplication

Binary multiplication can be accomplished using the same method as for the long multiplication of decimal numbers with the advantage that the binary multiplication table is very much simpler:

$$0 \times 0 = 0 \qquad 0 \times 1 = 0 \qquad 1 \times 0 = 0 \qquad 1 \times 1 = 1$$

The multiplication process is illustrated in the following example in which we find the product of 1011×1101:

```
   1011     multiplicand
   1101     multiplier
   1011  ← × by LSB of multiplier
  0000   ← shift one place and × by next significant bit ⎫ partial
 1011    ← shift and × by next significant bit           ⎬ products
1011     ← shift and × by MSB                            ⎭
10001111    product = sum of partial products
  111
```

Thus we see that multiplication is essentially a series of repeated additions of the multiplicand appropriately shifted. Use of the add-shift principle is in fact made in the ALU of a computer where multiplication is performed using adder and shift circuits (see section 3.25).

Note, also, that the product is a much longer number than the individual numbers multiplied. In general the product of two n-bit numbers will require up to $2n$ bits to accommodate the result.

2.12 Binary Division

Binary division can be accomplished using similar methods to the long division of decimal numbers as illustrated in the following two examples.

$a)$ $\underbrace{1111}_{\text{dividend}} \div \underbrace{100}_{\text{divisor}} = \underset{\text{quotient}}{\text{answer}}$

```
                                               11·11
                                     100 |1111·00
        Subtract divisor from dividend → 100↓
                    Partial remainder →  111
           Shift divisor and subtract →  100 ↓
                    Partial remainder →  11 0
           Shift divisor and subtract →  10 0↓
                    Partial remainder →   1 00
                 Divisor and subtract →   1 00
                    Zero remainder →       0 00
```

Note that the division process is analogous to binary multiplication in that the divisor is repeatedly shifted but subtracted rather than added. The individual quotient bits—either 1 or 0—are determined by repeatedly subtracting the appropriately shifted divisor from the partial remainders.

Check on result

$$1111 \div 100 = 11 \cdot 11 = (2 + 1 + \tfrac{1}{2} + \tfrac{1}{4})_{10} = 3 \cdot 75_{10}$$

$$15_{10} \div 4_{10} = \quad 3\tfrac{3}{4} \quad = 3 \cdot 75_{10}$$

b) $11011 \div 111$ i.e. $27_{10} \div 7_{10} = 3 \cdot 857 \cdots$

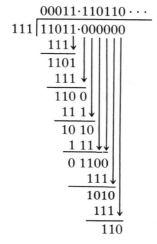

Note that our answer

$$11 \cdot 110110 \cdots = 2 + 1 + \tfrac{1}{2} + \tfrac{1}{4} + \tfrac{1}{16} + \tfrac{1}{32} \cdots \approx 3 \cdot 844_{10}$$

worked to 6 places after the binary point, still has an appreciable error, showing that it is necessary to take many more binary than decimal places to achieve comparable accuracy.

2.13 Representation of Positive and Negative Numbers in Binary

2.13.1 Unsigned Binary

So far we have considered only positive or unsigned binary numbers. **Unsigned binary** is the most basic form and for microprocessors one of the most common forms of number representation. In unsigned binary, all numbers are assumed positive and the 1s carry the appropriate power of 2 weightings as previously discussed for "pure" binary numbers. For example, the following 8-bit unsigned binary numbers represent the positive decimal numbers given in the right-hand column:

2^7	2^6	2^5	2^4	2^3	2^2	2^1	2^0	weighting
1	0	0	0	0	0	0	0	$= 128_{10}$
0	0	0	0	0	0	0	0	$= 0$
1	1	1	1	1	1	1	1	$= 255_{10}$
0	0	1	1	0	0	1	1	$= 51_{10}$

2.13.2 Sign-and-Magnitude Binary

Although for some applications simple unsigned binary is adequate, in almost all computer applications where arithmetic operations are involved, there is a need to represent both positive and negative numbers and produce the correct signed result.

The simplest form of signed binary representation is where the sign of the number is indicated by the most significant bit (MSB). This bit is reserved not to denote any numerical value but simply to indicate the + or − sign of the number. In the **sign-and-magnitude** convention for binary numbers:

The MSB is set to 0 to indicate a positive number and a 1 to indicate a negative number; all other bits indicate the magnitude of the number in the normal way.

For example, the 8-bit numbers using the sign-and-magnitude convention:

sign bit	2^6	2^5	2^4	2^3	2^2	2^1	2^0	
↓	64	32	16	8	4	2	1	weightings
0	1	0	1	0	1	0	1	$= +(64+16+4+1) = +85_{10}$
1	1	0	1	0	1	0	1	$= -85_{10}$
1	0	0	1	1	1	0	1	$= -(16+8+4+1) = -29_{10}$
0	0	0	1	1	1	0	1	$= +29_{10}$
0	0	0	0	0	0	0	0	$= 0$
1	0	0	0	0	0	0	0	$= 0$

Note that there are two possible representations for zero.

Example 2.9

A A register is a circuit in the central processor of a computer that temporarily stores 1–0 binary information. In a particular microcomputer, registers employing sign-and-magnitude binary numbers can store and manipulate 8 bits. Determine the maximum positive and negative numbers that can be held in the registers.

The maximum positive number is

$$0 \; \underbrace{1111111}_{} = +127$$
$$\uparrow$$

sign bit   7 magnitude bits

The maximum negative number is

$$1 \; 1111111 = -127$$
$$\uparrow$$

sign bit

B Determine for the general case the number range that can be accommodated in an n-bit register using (i) unsigned binary and (ii) sign-and-magnitude binary.

(i) For unsigned binary all n bits can be used to represent numerical information. The total number of different 1–0 combinations that can be obtained with n bits is 2^n. Hence 2^n numbers from zero to maximum number

$$N_{max} = 2^n - 1$$

can be accommodated.

(ii) In the sign-and-magnitude representation the MSB is used to denote the sign of the number so $(n-1)$ bits are available to represent the magnitude. Hence the maximum positive and negative numbers are

$$N_{max} = 2^{n-1} - 1 \quad \text{positive} \qquad N_{max} = -(2^{n-1} - 1) \quad \text{negative}$$

e.g. for a 16-bit register, the number range is

$$\pm(2^{16-1} - 1) = \pm 32\,767_{10}$$

2.13.3 Ones and Twos Complement Forms

Unfortunately the sign-and-magnitude representation has limitations. It is not possible to perform the basic arithmetic operations with positive and negative numbers and automatically provide the correct sign for the results. For this reason, twos complement representation for signed binary numbers is preferred. When dealing with this representation we can automatically produce the correct sign for arithmetic calculations.

As with sign-and-magnitude, the MSB of the number is used as a sign bit: MSB is 0 for a positive number, and 1 for a negative number. For positive numbers, all other bits are used to represent the magnitude in the normal binary way. For negative numbers we represent the number in twos complement form, which is obtained by applying the following simple rules:

1 The positive binary number (i.e. the number of the same magnitude as the negative number) is first inverted or complemented, that is, change all 0s to 1s in the number and all 1s to 0s.

This gives what is known as the **ones complement** representation of the negative number.

2 Then increment, i.e. add 1 to the LSB of the result (the ones complement). This gives the **twos complement** representation for the negative number.

Note: If there is a fractional part, then the 1 must be added to the furthest right-hand bit behind the binary point.

Example 2.10 Find the twos complement representation of a) -127_{10} and b) -81_{10}.

a) -127_{10}

sign bit
↓

$$+127 = 0\underline{1111111}$$
$$\left.\begin{array}{r} 10000000 \\ 1 \end{array}\right\} \begin{array}{l} \text{invert or complement} \\ \text{add 1} \end{array}$$
$$\overline{10000001} = -127_{10} \text{ in twos complement form}$$

b) -81_{10}

sign bit
↓

$$+81 = 0\underline{1010001}$$
$$\left.\begin{array}{r} 10101110 \\ 1 \end{array}\right\} \begin{array}{l} \text{complement} \\ \text{add 1} \end{array}$$
$$\overline{10101111} = -81_{10} \text{ in twos complement form}$$

Note that, after the complementation process, the MSB automatically becomes a 1, indicating a negative number. It must also be noted that, although the other bits essentially contain the magnitude information, this is *not* the same as in pure binary. The magnitude is found by "twos complementing" the negative number representation. For example, to find the decimal number represented by the twos complement binary number

1011 0001   the MSB is a 1 so the number is negative

To determine its magnitude, find its twos complement, i.e. complement the number and add 1 to the LSB of the result:

10110001	the negative number
01001110	after complementation
1	add 1
$\overline{01001111}$	magnitude of number $= 64+8+4+2+1 = 79_{10}$

so $1011\ 0001 = -79_{10}$

The reasons why the twos complement representation can be used for negative numbers can be reinforced by considering, for example, how we might represent -79_{10}. In 8-bit signed binary,

$$+79 = 0100\ 1111$$

It is plausible to assume that -79_{10} in binary could be found by subtracting $+79$ from 0, i.e.

$$\begin{array}{r} 0_{10} = 00000000 \\ +79_{10} = \underline{01001111} \\ \overline{10110001} \end{array} \quad \text{on subtracting and ignoring final borrow}$$

Table 2.6 Representation of signed binary numbers in sign-and-magnitude and twos complement forms

Decimal number	Sign-and-magnitude	Twos complement
+127	01111111	01111111
⋮		
3	00000011	00000011
2	00000010	00000010
1	00000001	00000001
0	00000000 ⎫ 10000000 ⎭	00000000
−1	10000001	11111111
−2	10000010	11111110
−3	10000011	11111101
⋮		
−127	11111111	10000001
−128	——	10000000

and $1011\,0001 = -79_{10}$ in twos complement form.

Table 2.6 summarizes the representation of signed 8-bit numbers in sign-and-magnitude and twos complement form.

Note that, by using 8-bit and twos complement representation, the range of numbers is from -128 to $+127$. It is very important to remember in carrying out arithmetic operations that results must always lie within this range. If not, errors will occur. For example, $108_{10} + 47_{10} = +155_{10}$ cannot be accomplished directly using only 8-bit signed numbers, since the maximum 8-bit signed number is $+127$. Likewise $-78 - 53 = -131$ cannot be worked out since the maximum twos complement 8-bit number is -128.

2.14 Binary Subtraction Using Twos Complements

Using twos complement representation, binary subtraction simply becomes an addition process, i.e.

$$A - B = A + (-B)$$

↑—negative number in twos complement form

The rules for subtraction (and addition) for twos complement binary numbers are as follows:

1 The numbers A and $-B$ are represented in twos complement form. For positive numbers the sign bit is 0, and the remaining bits represent the magnitude with the normal binary weighting. For negative numbers, form the twos complement from the positive number by complementing, i.e. change 0s to 1s and vice-versa, and add 1 to the LSB.

2 Add $A + (-B)$ and if the sign bit is

0   then the result is positive and the *true* difference of $A - B$.

1   then the result is the twos complement of the *difference* and is negative, with magnitude equal to the twos complement of the result; any final carry produced in the addition is ignored.

3 Note that the correct result can only be obtained for subtractions and additions lying within the permissible range of the twos complement representation:

for 8-bit numbers -128 to $+127$

for 16-bit numbers $-32\,768$ to $+32\,767$.

The processes of addition and subtraction using twos complement numbers is illustrated in the following examples.

A   *Five-bit numbers*

```
                  sign
                  bit  magnitude bits
                   ↓   8   4   2   1
     +15₁₀ = 0   1   1   1   1
     −15₁₀ = 1   0   0   0   1
      +9₁₀ = 0   1   0   0   1
      −9₁₀ = 1   0   1   1   1
```

(i) Hence to determine $15_{10} - 9_{10}$

```
     +15₁₀ = 0   1   1   1   1 ⎞
      −9₁₀ = 1   0   1   1   1 ⎠ add
       (1)   0   0   1   1   0   answer, i.e. +(4+2) = +6₁₀
             ↑
     neglect final carry
```

(ii) To determine $-15_{10} + 9_{10}$

```
     −15₁₀ = 1   0   0   0   1 ⎞
      +9₁₀ = 0   1   0   0   1 ⎠ add
               1   1   0   1   0   answer in twos complement form
```

The true difference is therefore negative since the sign bit is a 1. The magnitude of the difference is the twos complement of 11010, i.e.

$$00101 + 1 \text{ to LSB} = 00110 = 6_{10}$$

Hence true difference is $11010 = -6_{10}$.

B *Eight-bit numbers*

	sign bit ↓	64	32	16	8	4	2	1
			magnitude bits					
$+101_{10} =$	0	1	1	0	0	1	0	1
$-101_{10} =$	1	0	0	1	1	0	1	1
$79_{10} =$	0	1	0	0	1	1	1	1
$-79_{10} =$	1	0	1	1	0	0	0	1

(i) To determine $101_{10} - 79_{10}$

$$\begin{array}{rcccccccc}
+101_{10} = & 0 & 1 & 1 & 0 & 0 & 1 & 0 & 1 \\
-79_{10} = & 1 & 0 & 1 & 1 & 0 & 0 & 0 & 1
\end{array} \Big\} \text{ add}$$

$$(1) \quad \underline{0 \quad 0 \quad 0 \quad 1 \quad 0 \quad 1 \quad 1 \quad 0} = +(16+4+2) = +22_{10}$$

(ii) To determine $-22_{10} - 79_{10}$

$$\begin{array}{rcccccccc}
+22_{10} = & 0 & 0 & 0 & 1 & 0 & 1 & 1 & 0 \\
-22_{10} = & 1 & 1 & 1 & 0 & 1 & 0 & 1 & 0 \\
-79_{10} = & 1 & 0 & 1 & 1 & 0 & 0 & 0 & 1
\end{array}$$

invert and add 1 / add

$$(1) \quad \underline{1 \quad 0 \quad 0 \quad 1 \quad 1 \quad 0 \quad 1 \quad 1} \quad \text{answer in twos complement form}$$

$$1001\ 1011 = -(0110\ 0101) = -101_{10}$$

magnitude of difference
found by twos complement of result 1001 1011

2.15 Fixed-point and Floating-point Numbers

2.15.1 Fixed-point Numbers

The binary numbers and arithmetic we have so far been dealing with utilises what is known as fixed-point notation. The term fixed-point is used to indicate that the binary point (whether or not it is actually used) is fixed at the position where the power of the base 2 weighting changes from positive to negative, i.e. at the point between the 2^0 and 2^{-1} bits.

$$0110\ 1111 = 111_{10}$$
$$0110\ 0111 \cdot 101 = 103 \cdot 625_{10}$$

are examples of **fixed point binary numbers**.

Fixed-point notation has two major disadvantages. Firstly, the range of numbers that can be represented is restricted by the number of digits or bits used, e.g. in 2s complement 8-bit binary we can only accommodate the range:

$$1000\ 0000 = -128_{10} \quad \text{to} \quad 0111\ 1111 = +127_{10}$$

Secondly, in carrying out calculations involving fractional parts, it is necessary for the arithmetic logic unit circuits to keep track of the binary point so that it can be correctly positioned in the final result. Whilst it is relatively easy for us to deal with the "point" in calculations, it can be relatively costly in additional circuitry and processing time in a computer.

To represent even modest number values in fixed-point notation requires a large number of bits, including bits, for example, to denote the sign and binary point position. The example below illustrates how $-58 \cdot 97_{10}$ might be coded in 8421 BCD using 28 bits (or 7 nibbles):

0 1 0 0	0 0 1 0	0 0 0 1	0 1 0 1	1 0 0 0	1 0 0 1	0 1 1 1

| 1 nibble or 4 bits to indicate number of digits, i.e. 4 in our example. | 1 nibble to indicate position of binary point, the point is on the left of the second LSB in our case. | to indicate sign: minus in our case. | 5 | 8 | 9 | 7 |

4 nibbles (16 bits) for digits

2.15.2 Floating-point Numbers

Many microcomputers and virtually all mainframe computers utilise **floating-point number** representation. It has the advantage of being able to accommodate a much wider range of numbers for a given number of bits than fixed-point.

Floating-point numbers in decimal are very widely used, e.g.

Fixed-point	Floating-point representation
6 291 000	$6 \cdot 291 \times 10^6$ or $0 \cdot 6291 \times 10^7$
0·000 137	$1 \cdot 37 \times 10^{-4}$ or $0 \cdot 137 \times 10^{-3}$

Binary numbers can also be represented in this way, e.g.

Fixed-point	Floating-point representation
10110	$0 \cdot 10110 \times 2^5$
111001·11	$0 \cdot 11100111 \times 2^6$
0·001101	$0 \cdot 1101 \times 2^{-2}$

In general the floating-point representation of a number to any base may be written in the form:

$$n = \pm m b^{\pm e}$$

where e is known as the **exponent**

m is known as the **mantissa**

b is known as the **base**.

When the mantissa m is a fraction, with no zeros immediately after the point separating whole and fractional parts, the number is said to be in **normalized floating-point** form. This form is used in computers, where m lies within the range

$$0 \cdot 1_2 \leqslant m < 1 \quad (0 \cdot 5_{10} \leqslant m < 1)$$

A typical illustration of a floating-point number using 32 bits (4 bytes) is shown below:

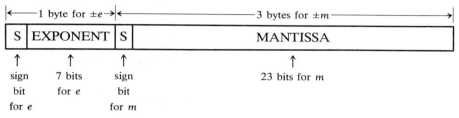

So for this example, the maximum value for the exponent e consisting of 1 sign bit and 7 magnitude bits is

$$e = \pm 1111111_2$$
$$= \pm 127_{10} \text{ (or } -128 \text{ to } +127 \text{ if twos complements used)}$$

whilst m consisting of 1 sign bit and 23 magnitude bits can vary between

$$m = \pm 0 \cdot 1000_2 \cdots = \pm 0 \cdot 5_{10} \quad \text{to}$$
$$m = \pm 0 \cdot 11111111 \cdots = \pm (1 - 2^{-23})_{10} = \pm 0 \cdot 999\,999\,88_{10}$$
$$= \pm 1 \cdot 0 \text{ to 7 decimal places}$$

Hence the maximum value number that can be stored in floating-point form using 4 bytes or 32 bits is

$$n_{max} = \pm 1 \cdot 0 \times 2^{127} \text{ (to 7 decimal places)} \approx \pm 1 \cdot 70 \times 10^{38}$$

and the minimum value number is

$$n_{min} = 0 \cdot 5_{10} \times 2^{-127} \approx 0 \cdot 3 \times 10^{-38}$$

i.e. with 4 bytes we can store numbers in the range 10^{38} to 10^{-38} to 7 decimal places of accuracy.

Note that with a mantissa of 23 bits we have an accuracy of 7 decimal places. If greater accuracy is required more bits must be used for the mantissa. For example, with 5 bytes to represent $\pm m$, an accuracy of 1 part in 10^{11} may be achieved; with 7 bytes (55 bits for m and 1 bit for sign), approximately 17 decimal places of accuracy is obtained. The use of extra bytes for m to obtain greater accuracy is known as **multiple precision**.

2.16 Floating-point Arithmetic

Here we give some brief guidelines to performing the basic arithmetic processes with floating-point numbers.

1 To add or subtract two floating-point numbers we must first make the exponent of the smaller number equal to the exponent of the larger number. This is accomplished by shifting the mantissa to the right, filling in with leading zeros, and incrementing the exponent one for each shift until the two exponents are equal. At this stage the mantissa can be added or subtracted as sign-and-magnitude numbers. For example,

a) To evaluate $(0.101100 \times 2^4) + (0.111100 \times 2^2)$

$$0.111100 \times 2^2 = 0.001111 \times 2^4$$
$$\underline{0.101100 \times 2^4} \quad \text{add}$$
$$\underline{0.111011 \times 2^4} \quad \text{answer}$$

b) To evaluate $(0.1101100 \times 2^{-3}) - (0.1010100 \times 2^{-4})$

$$0.1010100 \times 2^{-4} = 0.0101010 \times 2^{-3}$$
$$0.1101100 \times 2^{-3}$$
$$\underline{0.0101010 \times 2^{-3}} \quad \text{subtract}$$
$$\underline{0.1000010 \times 2^{-3}} \quad \text{answer}$$

2 To multiply and divide two floating-point numbers,

$$n_1 = m_1 2^{e_1} \quad \text{and} \quad n_2 = m_2 2^{e_2}$$

we apply the normal algebraic rules:

$$n_1 \times n_2 = m_1 \times m_2 2^{(e_1 + e_2)}$$
$$n_1 \div n_2 = \frac{m_1 2^{e_1}}{m_2 2^{e_2}} = (m_1/m_2) 2^{(e_1 - e_2)}$$

To multiply multiply mantissa as sign-and-magnitude numbers and add exponents.

To divide divide mantissa and subtract exponents.

Example 2.11 *a*) Evaluate $(0.1011 \times 2^4) \times (0.1110 \times 2^3)$
Multiply the mantissa

$$
\begin{array}{r}
.1011 \\
.111 \\
\hline
1011 \\
1011 \\
1011 \\
\hline
.1001101 \times 2^7
\end{array}
$$

Add the exponents: $4 + 3 = 7$

Answer

b) Evaluate $0.1110 \times 2^3 \div 0.1000 \times 2^{-2}$

Divide the mantissa

$$
\begin{array}{r}
1{\cdot}11 \\
100\,\overline{\smash{\big)}\,111{\cdot}00} \\
\underline{100} \\
110 \\
\underline{100} \\
100 \\
\underline{100} \\
\cdots
\end{array}
$$

Subtract the exponents $3-(-2)=5$

so the answer is $1{\cdot}11 \times 2^5 = 0{\cdot}111 \times 2^6$.

2.17 Alphanumeric Codes: Binary Codes for Numerical and Non-numerical Data

Digital systems work entirely with 1–0 digital signals. The binary data is represented by two-state electrical pulse trains where the voltage can take only one of two voltage levels: one level represents the binary 1 state, the other the binary 0 state. Many digital systems, and particularly digital computers, must be capable of handling alphabetical characters, and special characters such as $+ - * / \cdot) ($, in addition to numerical data and control information.

One of the most commonly used binary codes for information interchange between microprocessors, digital communication links and data processing systems is the **ASCII code**. The code employs 7 bits and therefore 2^7 or 128 different character codes may be defined. Table 2.7 summarizes the codes for decimal numbers, upper and lower case letters and some other useful symbols. Extra bits may be added to each of the 7-bit characters to indicate Start and Stop and for parity checking.

The **parity bit** is added to give an indication of whether or not an error has occurred in transmission. The basic idea is as follows. Either a 1 or a 0 bit—the parity bit—is appended to each 7-bit character so that the total number of 1s in a character is either even or odd.

When **odd parity** error detection is employed, the parity bit is 0 if the total number of 1s in the 7-bit character is odd. If the number of 1s is even, then the parity bit is a 1.

For **even parity**, the parity bit is such as to make the total number of 1s in all characters even.

Extra circuitry is, of course, required to add the parity bit at the sending end and to check the parity at the receiving end.

Table 2.7 The ASCII (American Standard Code for Information Interchange) codes for numbers, alphabet letters and other common symbols

Decimal numbers	ASCII code in binary	in hex	Alphabetical characters	ASCII code in binary	in hex
0	011 0000	30	@	100 0000	
1	011 0001	31	A (a)	100 0001	41 (61)
2	011 0010	32	B (b)	100 0010	42 (62)
3	011 0011	33	C (c)	100 0011	43 (63)
4	011 0100	34	D (d)	100 0100	44 (64)
5	011 0101	35	E (e)	100 0101	45 (65)
6	011 0110	36	F (f)	100 0110	46 (66)
7	011 0111	37	G (g)	100 0111	47 (67)
8	011 1000	38	H (h)	100 1000	48 (68)
9	011 1001	39	I (i)	100 1001	49 (69)
			J (j)	100 1010	4A (6A)
Other symbols			K (k)	100 1011	4B (6B)
:	011 1010	3A	L (l)	100 1100	4C (6C)
;	011 1011	3B	M (m)	100 1101	4D (6D)
<	011 1100	3C	N (n)	100 1110	4E (6E)
=	011 1101	3D	O (o)	100 1111	4F (6F)
>	011 1110	3E	P (p)	101 0000	50 (70)
?	011 1111	3F	Q (q)	101 0001	51 (71)
Space	010 0000	20	R (r)	101 0010	52 (72)
!	010 0001	21	S (s)	101 0011	53 (73)
"	010 0010	22	T (t)	101 0100	54 (74)
#	010 0011	23	U (u)	101 0101	55 (75)
$	010 0100	24	V (v)	101 0110	56 (76)
%	010 0101	25	W (w)	101 0111	57 (77)
&	010 0110	26	X (x)	101 1000	58 (78)
'	010 0111	27	Y (y)	101 1001	59 (79)
(	010 1000	28	Z (z)	101 1010	5A (7A)
)	010 1001	29			
*	010 1010	2A	[	101 1011	5B
+	010 1011	2B	\	101 1100	5C
,	010 1100	2C	]	101 1101	5D
-	010 1101	2D	↑	101 1110	5E
.	010 1110	2E	←	101 1111	5F
/	010 1111	2F			

In addition to the alphabetic, numerical and punctuation characters given in Table 2.7, the ASCII code also includes the following control signal codes:

Control signal meaning		ASCII code	Control signal meaning		ASCII code
NUL	Null	000 0000	DC2	Device control 2	001 0010
SOH	Start of heading	000 0001	DC3	Device control 3	001 0011
STX	Start of text	000 0010	DC4	Device control 4	001 0100
EOT	End of text	000 0011	NAK	Negative acknowl-	001 0101
EOT	End of transmission	000 0100		edge	
ENQ	Enquiry	000 0101	SYN	Synchronous idle	001 0110
ACK	Acknowledge	000 0110	ETB	End of transm.	001 0111
BEL	Bell (audio sound)	000 0111		block	
BS	Backspace	000 1000	CAN	Cancel	001 1000
HT	Horizontal tabulation	000 1001	EM	End of medium	001 1001
LF	Line feed	000 1010	SUB	Substitute	001 1010
VT	Vertical tabulation	000 1011	ESC	Escape	001 1011
FF	Form feed	000 1100	FS	File separator	001 1100
CR	Carriage return	000 1101	GS	Group separator	001 1101
SO	Shift out	000 1110	RS	Record separator	001 1110
SI	Shift in	000 1111	US	Unit separator	001 1111
DLE	Data link escape	001 0000	DEL	Delete	111 1111
DC1	Device control 1	001 0001			

The ASCII code is now very widely employed and is virtually the international standard for data communication and storage.

Another alphanumeric code developed by IBM and used on IBM computer systems is the **EBCDIC** code (Extended Binary Coded Decimal Interchange Code). This code uses 8 bits per character and control signal (excluding any parity bit), the four least significant bits defining a group of sixteen characters, whilst the four most significant bits qualify a particular group within the code, in a similar way to the 7-bit ASCII code. Some examples of the EBCDIC code are:

1	1111 0001	A	1100 0001	a	1000 0001
2	1111 0010	B	1100 0010	b	1000 0010
3	1111 0011	C	1100 0011	c	1000 0011

Problems 2: Computer Arithmetic

1 Convert the following decimal numbers to 4-bit binary numbers:
a) 7   *b*) 4   *c*) 15   *d*) 0

2 Convert the following 8-bit numbers to decimal numbers:
a) 1000 1000   *b*) 0101 1011   *c*) 1111 1111

3 Convert the following decimal numbers to binary numbers:
a) 100   *b*) 137   *c*) 12·125

4 Convert the following 8-bit binary patterns to octal number representations:
a) 1011 0011   *b*) 0011 0000   *c*) 1111 0111

5 Convert the following binary numbers into hexadecimal representation:
a) 0010 0001   *b*) 1011 0000   *c*) 1111 1101
d) 1100 0011 0110   *e*) 0101 1001 1101 0111

6 Convert the following hexadecimal numbers to binary numbers:
a) 2C9E   *b*) 33FB   *c*) A047   *d*) FDB8

7 Convert the following numbers into decimal numbers:
a) 781_8 *b*) EB_{hex} *c*) 1111_8 *d*) $FFEE_{hex}$

8 *a*) Code the decimal number 502 into 8421 BCD.
b) What decimal numbers do the following 8421 BCD codes represent:
  (i) 1001 0011   (ii) 0100 0101 0111   (iii) 1000 0110 0000 0001

9 A microcomputer requires 4 Kbytes of ROM and 256 bytes of RAM memory. Determine the start and end addresses of each memory block if the ROM and RAM memories occupy adjacent (contiguous) blocks of memory starting at 0000_{hex}.

10 An 8-bit microcomputer has the following memory blocks:

0000 to 0FFF of ROM memory

2000 to 41FF of RAM memory

6000 to 600F for I/O address ports

Determine *a*) the amount of ROM and RAM memory, *b*) the number of I/O ports.

11 Find, for the two 8-bit binary numbers:

$A = 0101\ 1011$ $B = 0110\ 1111$

a) $A + B$ and   *b*) $B - A$
expressing your result in both binary and hexadecimal.

12 Using binary shift add/subtract techniques throughout, find
a) 101×110 *b*) 1011×0111
c) $1001 \div 110$ *d*) $11101 \div 101$ (to 3 binary places)

13 Convert the following decimal numbers to 8-bit sign-and-magnitude binary numbers:
a) 55   *b*) −55   *c*) 11   *d*) 127   *e*) −127   *f*) 0

14 Convert the following decimal numbers to 8-bit twos complement binary numbers:
a) 43   *b*) −43   *c*) 80   *d*) 19   *e*) −19
and hence determine in twos complement form
f) $80 - 43$ *g*) $-43 - 19$ *h*) $19 - 43$

15   The general procedures for addition and subtraction of hexadecimal numbers are similar to decimal and binary except that it must be remembered that we are dealing with base 16 numbers. For example, a carry is generated when the sum of two or more hex numbers in any column exceeds 16; likewise any borrow required is of weight 16.

Determine   *a*) F9E+CCC   *b*) F9E−CCC

16   Two sign-and-magnitude numbers are represented in hex by

$$n_1 = 3\text{FFF} \quad \text{and} \quad n_2 = 2\text{FFF}$$

Determine   *a*) $n_1 - n_2$ and   *b*) $n_1 + n_2$

17   Express the following decimal numbers:
a) 16   *b*) 2·5   *c*) 0·1875   *d*) −100
in the normalized floating-point form $m2^e$.

If the following format is used for the binary representation:
exponent *e*   4-bits, twos complement representation
mantissa *m*   8-bits, sign-and-magnitude convention
write down the complete 12-bit binary pattern for each of the above numbers.

18   A 16-bit binary number AB56_{hex} is stored inside a computer. It is to be transmitted to a printer by the following means. A special program first converts the number to decimal and then codes each decimal digit in the number to its relevant ASCII code using *even* parity. The resulting 8-bit ASCII characters are stored in memory and thence transmitted to the printer in sequence. The printer decodes the binary patterns and prints out the decimal number. Determine
a) the decimal number
b) the ASCII codes for each character (using Table 2.7) assuming even parity.

3 Logic Devices, Circuits and Operations: the Building Blocks of Digital Electronics

3.1 Introduction to IC Logic Gates and Digital Systems

3.1.1 Digital Signals, Positive and Negative Logic

In digital systems, all numerical data, instructions, control-command infor-mation, etc. are communicated, processed and stored in binary form. The binary information is represented as two-state electrical signals consisting essentially of only two voltage levels, one of which is selected to indicate a binary 1 or logic 1 state and the other the binary 0 or logic 0 state.

Fig. 3.1 illustrates the idea of a **digital signal**. The 8-bit number 1101 0101 is represented as a series of eight pulses, the 1s being denoted by 5 V levels, the 0s by 0 V.

Fig. 3.1 Digital signal representation of the binary number 11010101

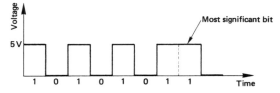

Fig. 3.2 Positive and negative logic

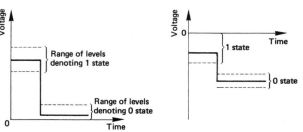

(a) POSITIVE LOGIC: the more positive (or less negative) voltage level is the 1 state

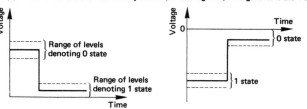

(b) NEGATIVE LOGIC: the more negative (or less positive) voltage level is the 1 state

When the logic 1 state is represented by a more positive voltage than the logic 0, then the logic system is referred to as working in **positive logic** (see fig. 3.2*a*).

Conversely, if the logic 1 state is a more negative voltage than the logic 0 state, we are dealing with a **negative logic** system (see fig. 3.2*b*).

The clear advantage of operating with digital 1–0 type signals is that the logic devices which process the digital information (i.e. that make logic decisions, do arithmetic operations, store results, output results to display devices, etc.) only need to handle *two* distinct voltage levels representing the 1–0 bits of information.

3.1.2   IC Logic Devices and Scales of Integration

Logic gates are the basic elements in all digital logic systems. There are various kinds of logic gate but each is a circuit consisting of transistors, diodes, resistors, interconnecting conductors, etc. A circuit for a single gate, or a digital logic circuit consisting of a combination of many gates, is manufactured as an **integrated circuit** (IC) on a tiny piece or *chip* of silicon. In fact, a single IC chip may contain many hundreds and even thousands of gates. This leads us to talk of various *scales of integration* for ICs. The following ranges are approximate but give a good guide to the number of gates that may be put down on a single chip and to the complexity of the various digital ICs:

SSI   (small-scale integration)   A single IC package containing up to 10 to 20 gates, e.g. ICs containing say 4 AND gates, 6 inverters (see fig. 3.5).

MSI   (medium-scale integration)   A single IC package containing approximately 20 to 100 logic gates or less than 1000 memory bits, e.g. counters, shift registers, input/output devices (I/O ports).

LSI   (large-scale integration)   A single IC package containing from 100 to 5000 logic gates or 1000 to 16 000 memory bits, e.g. memory chips, 8-bit microprocessors.

VLSI   (very-large-scale integration)   A single IC package containing more than 5000 gates and typically 100 000+ gates, e.g. high-density memory-storage chips, 16-bit microprocessor chips, microcomputer chips.

Diagrams of four types of IC packages are shown in fig. 3.3. The dual-in-line (DIL) is the most widely used and most microprocessor chips are packaged in DIL form with 40 pins for external connection. (Dual-in-line essentially refers to the double row of pins.)

It should be remembered that each individual gate may contain several transistors and other components so it is truly a technological miracle when one considers even SSI, let alone VSLI circuits where the complete working circuitry of a sophisticated digital computer-controller can be fabricated on a single silicon chip.

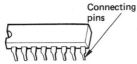

Connecting
pins

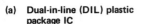

(a)   Dual-in-line (DIL) plastic   (b)   Dual-in-line ceramic   (c)   Flat-pack IC   (d)   Metal can (top-hat)
      package IC   package IC   package IC

Fig. 3.3 Integrated circuit packages

The two basic types of transistor, the bipolar and field-effect (fet) transistors, are used in integrated circuit fabrication. Both types lead to whole families of SSI, MSI and LSI chips. Two of the most important of these families are the bipolar-based transistor-transistor logic (TTL) family, which is very widely used for fast switching speed SSI, MSI and LSI units; and the fet-based metal-oxide-silicon (MOS) family, widely used for LSI and VLSI microprocessor and memory chips.

3.1.3   Combinational and Sequential Logic Elements

There are two distinct classes of logic elements used to construct digital electronic systems:

1   Decision-making gates—usually referred to as **combinational logic gates**. There are five fundamental gates: the AND, OR, INVERTER, NAND and NOR gates. We will be reviewing their logic properties immediately, in the next section.
2   Memory elements—usually referred to as **sequential logic gates**. These consist essentially of **bistable elements** or **flip-flops**. They, together with the combinational logic gates, are used extensively in registers, counters, arithmetic logic units, and provide the memory-storage properties normally required in control and computing applications.

We will be considering the properties and applications of these sequential elements in the later sections of this chapter.

3.2   The Basic Combinational Logic Gates: AND, OR, NOT, NAND, NOR and Exclusive-OR Gates

It is the purpose of this section to review the properties of the decision-making or combinational logic gates.

All combinational logic gates have at least one input line and a single output line. The output can take only a 0 or 1 state and this is controlled by 0–1 states present on the input lines. If the inputs are changed, the new output is completely determined by the new inputs. Logic circuits consisting only of combinational logic element have no memory, although, as we shall soon see, memory elements can also be synthesized from the basic gates.

First, however, let us review the properties of the basic gates, whose symbols and truth tables are given in fig. 3.4.

Fig. 3.4 Logic gate
symbols and their
truth tables
(two-input gates
are shown)

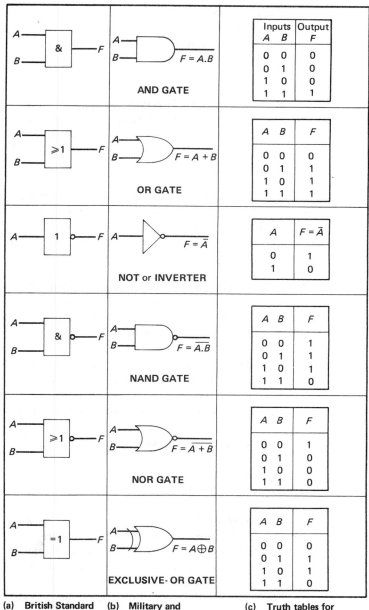

Inputs		Output
A	B	F
0	0	0
0	1	0
1	0	0
1	1	1

AND GATE

$F = A.B$

A	B	F
0	0	0
0	1	1
1	0	1
1	1	1

OR GATE

$F = A + B$

A	$F = \bar{A}$
0	1
1	0

NOT or INVERTER

$F = \bar{A}$

A	B	F
0	0	1
0	1	1
1	0	1
1	1	0

NAND GATE

$F = \overline{A.B}$

A	B	F
0	0	1
0	1	0
1	0	0
1	1	0

NOR GATE

$F = \overline{A + B}$

A	B	F
0	0	0
0	1	1
1	0	1
1	1	0

EXCLUSIVE-OR GATE

$F = A \oplus B$

(a) British Standard
     logic gate symbols:
     BS 3939

(b) Military and
     American Standards:
     MS 806B

(c) Truth tables for
     logic gates

1 The **AND gate** can have two or more inputs, and its output is at a logic 1 only if all inputs are at logic 1. If any of the inputs is taken to logic 0, then the output of the AND gate will also become a logic 0.

An example of an SSI AND IC containing four 2-input AND gates on a single chip is shown in fig. 3.5*a*.

2 The **OR gate** can also have two or more inputs. Its output takes the logic 1 state if any one of its inputs is taken to the 1 state. Its output is only in the 0 state when all inputs are in the 0 state.

An example of a TTL OR IC containing four 2-input OR gates is shown in fig. 3.5*b*.

3 The **NOT gate** or **Inverter** has only one input. Its output is always the complement or logical inverse of the state at the input. Thus if the input is held at a logic 0, the output is a logic 1, and vice-versa.

An example of a TTL inverter chip containing six NOT gates is shown in fig. 3.5*c*.

The AND, OR and NOT gates form the basic design blocks for all digital logic systems. By suitably interconnecting appropriate combinations, any required logic operation may be obtained. In the early evolution of logic circuit design, two very important universal gates were developed: the NAND and NOR gates.

4 The **NAND gate** is a combination of an AND gate followed by a NOT gate, i.e. NOT AND which is abbreviated to NAND. The output of a NAND gate is therefore a logic 0 only if all its inputs are held at logic 1; otherwise its output is a logic 1.

5 The **NOR gate** is a combination of an OR gate followed by a NOT gate, i.e. NOT OR which abbreviates to NOR. The output of a NOR gate is therefore a 0 state if any one of its inputs takes the 1 state; only when all inputs are held at logic 0 is the output a 1 state.

The importance of these two gates is that any logic circuit function can be implemented using either solely NAND gates or solely NOR gates. Examples of quadrupole 2-input TTL NAND and NOR gates are shown in figs. 3.5*d* and *e*, respectively.

6 The **exclusive-OR gate** is an example of a logic device which can be constructed by suitably combining AND, OR and NOT gates or it may be implemented entirely with NAND or NOR gates.

The output of an exclusive-OR gate takes the 1 state if either, but not both, of its two inputs are 1 states.

The exclusive-OR forms the basic element in the half-adder circuits which we will be considering later in section 3.17. An example of a quadrupole TTL exclusive-OR gate chip is shown in fig. 3.5*f*.

Fig. 3.5 7400 TTL digital integrated circuits: example of SSI where several gates are put down on an individual IC chip

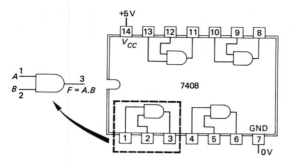

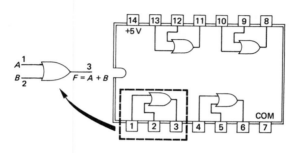

(a) A quadrupole 2-input AND gate IC

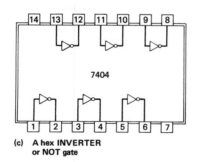

(b) A quadrupole 2-input OR gate IC

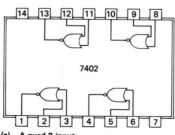

(c) A hex INVERTER or NOT gate

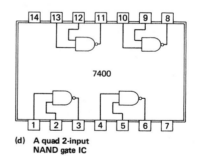

(d) A quad 2-input NAND gate IC

(e) A quad 2-input NOR gate IC

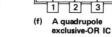

(f) A quadrupole exclusive-OR IC

Logic algebra symbols Logic function operations AND, OR, NOT are known as Boolean after the nineteenth century mathematician Boole who developed an algebra* to handle logic operations. The **Boolean symbols** given below are very useful in expressing the outputs from gates and logic circuits in concise form.

The AND operation is denoted by a dot .

The OR operation is denoted by a +

(*Note*: this does not mean plus as in normal algebra.)

The NOT or logical inversion is denoted by a bar over the input or output variables.

$F = A . B$ expresses the output of a 2-input AND gate

$F = A + B$ expresses the output of a 2-input OR gate

$\bar{A}$ denotes NOT A

$F = A \oplus B$ is used to denote the exclusive-OR function.

---

* Boolean algebra with applications to logic gates and circuits is considered in *Electrical and Engineering Mathematics* Volume 2 by R. G. Meadows, published by Pitman (1981).

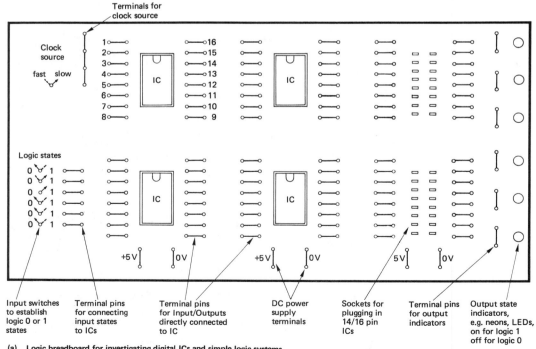

(a) **Logic breadboard for investigating digital ICs and simple logic systems**

3.3 Investigation of Logic Gates and Circuits Using a Logic Tutor Breadboard

There are now several kits available for investigating the properties of digital ICs and building up simple digital-logic circuits. Fig. 3.6*a* shows a typical example for TTL ICs. The breadboad contains a bank of switches to set logic 0–1 inputs, a clock source for sequential systems investigations, its own 5 V power supplies for the ICs, sockets for plugging in the ICs, and lamp indicators for output display.

Fig. 3.6*b* shows the standard DIL IC package and pin numbers for SSI and MSI devices, whilst fig. 3.6*c* shows a magnified section of the board with the push-on wire lead connections for investigating the properties of one of 2-input AND gates in a TTL 7408 IC.

Fig. 3.6 Investigation of logic circuits

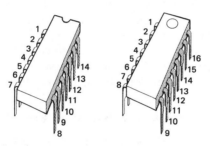

(b) **Standard 14 and 16 pin configuration for 7400 series digital ICs**

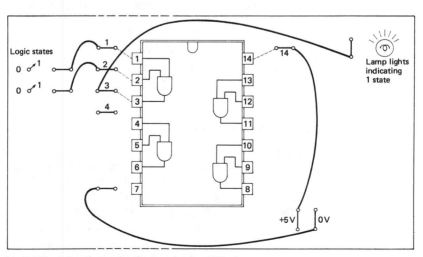

(c) **Patching to investigate action, for example, of an AND gate**

3.4 Some Examples of Combinational Logic Systems

3.4.1 A Simple Control System

This example illustrates the use of logic gates to implement the starting-up process of, for example, a processing plant. Suppose the process is to start when

the start button A is pressed, i.e. when $A = 1$

AND   when a safety condition B is pressed, e.g. $B = 1$ indicates that a safety guard is in place

AND   when two physical conditions C AND D are satisfied, e.g.
   $C = 1$ indicates material present
   $D = 1$ temperature at correct level

The process is to stop when any of the above conditions is not met AND if an emergency or stop button E is pressed.

In logic terms we define our start conditions by the logic function

$$F = A \text{ AND } B \text{ AND } C \text{ AND } D \text{ AND } (\text{NOT } E)$$
$$= A \cdot B \cdot C \cdot D \cdot \bar{E}$$

so we could implement F by the logic circuit of fig. 3.7, i.e. a 5-input AND gate plus an inverter for the E input.

When $A = 1$, $B = 1$, $C = 1$, $D = 1$, $E = 0$ (i.e. $\bar{E} = 1$) then $F = 1$, and this output state could be used to activate the drive to start the process. If any of the A, B, C, D inputs were zero, or if $E = 1$, then $F = 0$ and this output state would be used to disengage the drive.

3.4.2 Implementation of an Exclusive-OR Circuit

Fig. 3.8a shows how an **exclusive-OR circuit** can be implemented entirely with NAND gates; b shows its implementation using AND, OR and NOT gates. Check that both circuits do indeed implement the function, by making

$A = 0$, $B = 0$ and showing $F = 0$

$A = 0$, $B = 1$ and showing $F = 1$

$A = 1$, $B = 0$ and showing $F = 1$

$A = 1$, $B = 1$ and showing $F = 0$

3.4.3 A Simple Decoder

A **decoder** is a logic circuit which can select a given output line or a device according to the 1–0 states (i.e. the binary number) impressed on its input line. Fig. 3.9 shows an example of a simple 2-input to 4-output decoder, which illustrates the basic decoding idea.

The two input lines A_0 and A_1 can take $2^2 = 4$ different 0–1 combinations, each one of which may be used to select one of the four output lines F_0, F_1, F_2, F_3. For example, if $A_0 = 0$ and $A_1 = 0$, the inputs to the top-most AND gate in fig. 3.9b are $\bar{A}_0 = \bar{0} = 1$, $\bar{A}_1 = \bar{0} = 1$, so $F_0 = 1$, i.e. $A_0 = A_1 = 0$ inputs

Fig. 3.7 Logic circuits diagram for start-up control

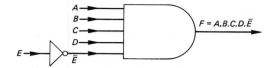

$F = A.B.C.D.\bar{E}$

Fig. 3.8 Implementation of exclusive-OR circuit by interconnection of the basic logic gates

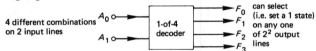

$F = A \oplus B$

(a)   NAND gate implementation of the exclusive-OR

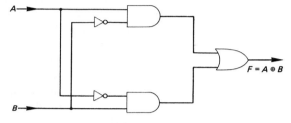

$F = A \oplus B$

(b)   Exclusive-OR constructed using AND, NOT and OR gates

Fig. 3.9 Implementation of a simple decoder using basic logic gates

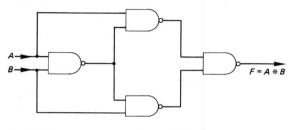

4 different combinations on 2 input lines

A_0 ○ → 1-of-4 decoder → F_0 can select
→ F_1 (i.e. set a 1 state)
A_1 ○ → → F_2 on any one
of 2^2 output
→ F_3 lines

Inputs		Outputs			
A_0	A_1	F_0	F_1	F_2	F_3
0	0	1	0	0	0
0	1	0	1	0	0
1	0	0	0	1	0
1	1	0	0	0	1

(a)   A 1-of-4 decoder and its truth table

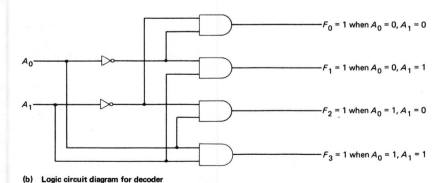

$F_0 = 1$ when $A_0 = 0, A_1 = 0$

A_0

$F_1 = 1$ when $A_0 = 0, A_1 = 1$

A_1

$F_2 = 1$ when $A_0 = 1, A_1 = 0$

$F_3 = 1$ when $A_0 = 1, A_1 = 1$

(b)   Logic circuit diagram for decoder

select the F_0 output line. The output of all the other AND gates remain in the 0 state. Check the selection for the three other sets of input.

3.5 Tri-state Gates

Tri-state gates, also known as 3-state drivers and 3-state buffers, play an important role in allowing the transmission of data to and from various units in a complete logic system to share common lines or a common bus.

Fig. 3.10a shows a tri-state gate which passes its data input A to the output F when the control signal state, known as the **enable**, is set at a 1 state. When the enable is a 0 state, the gate is disabled or inhibited and transmission is blocked. The output is effectively disconnected and is said to float.

Fig. 3.10b shows the complementary version in which the gate is enabled when the enable is set to a 0 state; note the ○ at the end of the enable line which indicates the negation or complementation. Thus in this case, when $\overline{\text{enable}} = 0$, then $F = A$, whilst if $\overline{\text{enable}} = 1$, transmission is blocked and the output floats.

The ability of tri-state gates to be disabled and have floating outputs allows us to connect their outputs together. This would not be possible with the normal logic gates, since if one or more gate outputs were at logical 1s whilst others were at 0s, then circulating currents would flow and burn out the devices.

The practice of using a common line or **bus** to transmit data to and from more than one different source or unit is known as **multiplexing**. In logic systems the common line is shared on a time basis.

Fig. 3.11 shows a simple multiplexing system using tri-state gates to transmit data $A, B, C, \cdots$ from an input port along a common line to an output port. When the input data A is to be transmitted, tri-state gates AI and AO are enabled by $E_A = 1$, and all other gates are disabled whilst the A data transmission takes place. When the input data B is to be transmitted, $E_B = 1$ and all other gates are disabled, and so on.

3.6 Introduction to Memory Elements

The decision-making or combinational logic gates we have so far considered are not, without modification, able to "remember" or "store" any past information. In most digital systems and in all computer-type applications, elements capable of storing binary information are also required. For example, the arithmetic logic circuits of a computer must be able to hold results during the processing of a problem. It is therefore of fundamental importance to provide logic elements which have a memory and are capable of storing 1–0 binary data for a given time so that this may be subsequently used when required.

This leads us to the subject of *sequential logic circuits*—circuits constructed from both combinational and memory-type elements. The basic memory elements are collectively known as **bistables** and commonly referred to as **flip-flops** or **latches**. The term flip-flop arises from the way the bistable operates. The bistable (the flip-flop) can exist with its output taking only one of two stable states: either the 0 or 1 state. When used to store a 1

Fig. 3.10 Tri-state gates

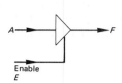

Input A	Enable E	Output F
0	1	0
1	1	1
0	0	} output disconnected
1	0	} i.e. floating

(a) Gate enabled when $E = 1$ so $F = A$

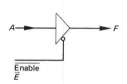

Input A	Enable $\bar{E}$	Output F
0	0	0
1	0	1
0	1	} output disconnected
1	1	} i.e. floating

(b) Gate enabled when $E = 0$

Fig. 3.11 A simple unidirectional multiplexing system using tri-state gates

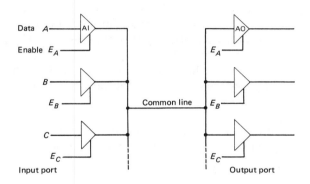

bit, the 1 bit input "flips" the bistable so the output takes (and therefore stores) the 1 state. It will then hold this state indefinitely or until it is reset or "flopped" back to its other stable state (the 0 state) by a subsequent input. The term latch arises because the bistable is often used to temporarily hold or "latch" a binary level.

Flip-flops may be designed to work in either positive or negative logic and are made in IC form using bipolar and MOS technologies. Respective flip-flop families are, of course, compatible with the combination logic gate families and indeed most digital IC chips inevitably contain a large number of circuits made up of combinational gates interconnected with memory elements.

Fig. 3.12 illustrates the simplest possible type of memory element, formed by feeding back the output of a 2-input OR gate to one of its input lines. When a 1 bit is fed to the other input, the output becomes a 1. If the input is subsequently removed and returns to the 0 state, the output is still held in the 1 state by virtue of the 1 state output being fed back to the second input line. Thus the output effectively "remembers" and stores the input bit even

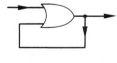

Input	Output
0	0
1	1

Fig. 3.12 An OR gate with feedback which acts as a simple memory element

when this is removed. Unfortunately this simple circuit can only remember one event. It can only be reset by turning off the power. However, this circuit does provide us with a useful lead-in to the basic flip-flop memory element.

3.7 The R-S (reset-set) Flip-flop

There are many different versions of flip-flops available, of which the following ones are mainly used: the R-S, the D-type, the T-type, and the J-K. We start with perhaps the simplest and most basic, the **R-S flip-flop**. All other flip-flop types are essentially derivatives of this element.

R stands for **Reset** which means that the output is established at a 0 state.

S stands for **Set** which means that the output is set to a 1 state.

The symbol and truth table for the R-S flip-flop are given in fig. 3.13.

Let us explain carefully its properties and the notation used in the truth table. We are now dealing with systems which work on a *sequential* basis and we therefore need a definite convention regarding the states of inputs and outputs as successive changes in input data are made. We denote the output states *after* the nth input conditions R_n and S_n have been applied as Q_n and P_n. Thus after the $(n+1)$th input states R_{n+1} and S_{n+1} have been applied, we denote the new output states as Q_{n+1} and P_{n+1}.

When $S_{n+1} = 0$ and $R_{n+1} = 0$, the outputs are unchanged:

$$Q_{n+1} = Q_n \qquad P_{n+1} = P_n = \bar{Q}_n$$

Note that the outputs are complements, e.g. if $Q_n = 1$, then $Q_{n+1} = 1$, $P_n = 0$.

If $S_{n+1} = 0$ and $R_{n+1} = 1$, the circuit is *Reset*:

$$Q_{n+1} = 0 \qquad P_{n+1} = 1$$

If $S_{n+1} = 1$ and $R_{n+1} = 0$, the circuit is *Set*:

$$Q_{n+1} = 1 \qquad P_{n+1} = 0$$

The simultaneous application of 1 states to the R and S inputs must always be avoided since it gives rise to non-predictable output states. We thus write X in the output column of the truth table where X is described as a **"don't-know" condition**. We explain at the end of this section why we "don't know".

The R-S flip-flop can be constructed using cross-coupled NOR gates or NAND gates as shown in fig. 3.14. Consider the operation of the NOR gate version. Suppose we first set the flip-flop by making $S = 1$ whilst holding $R = 0$. The output from the lower NOR gate Q should be a 1 state. This 1 state is fed back to the upper NOR gate which, with $S = 1$, has two 1-state inputs and therefore its output $P = \bar{Q} = 0$. The output from the upper NOR gate is fed back to the lower NOR gate input, thus making the second 0 state input with $R = 0$. This is consistent with its output $Q = 1$.

If we now reset the flip-flop by making $R = 1$ and $S = 0$, you can check by similar reasoning that the circuit changes state to $Q = 0$, $P = \bar{Q} = 1$.

Fig. 3.13 Symbol and truth table for an R-S flip-flop

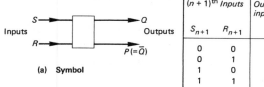

(a) Symbol

$(n+1)^{th}$ Inputs		Outputs after $(n+1)^{th}$ input applied		
S_{n+1}	R_{n+1}	Q_{n+1}	P_{n+1}	
0	0	Q_n	$\bar{Q}_n$	memory state
0	1	0	1	... reset
1	0	1	0	... set
1	1	X	X	... "don't know"

(b) Truth table for R-S flip-flop

Fig. 3.14 Implementation of an R-S flip-flop using cross-coupled NOR and NAND gates

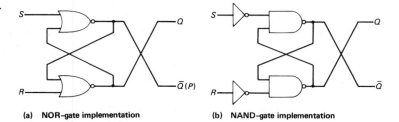

(a) NOR–gate implementation   (b) NAND–gate implementation

Now assume that both inputs $R = S = 1$, the condition that is always avoided in practice. On applying the NOR gate property, it is plausible to assume that we can obtain a stable state with $Q = P = 0$. Check that this is so. Suppose the $R = S = 1$ inputs are then followed by the simultaneous application of $R = S = 0$ inputs. Both NOR gates now have two logic 0 inputs so they must change their output state from 0 to 1. These outputs immediately create two 0 state inputs to each of the NOR gates and hence both outputs switch back to 1 states—at least theoretically—and the whole cycle continually repeats itself.

If the two gates were absolutely identical with equal delays and exactly equal switching speeds so that they changed state at the same instant, the sequence would continue indefinitely. However, in practice such perfect symmetry never occurs and one of the gates switches state faster. This will cause the flip-flop output to latch with the faster gate determining whether $Q = 0$ or 1. The two gates literally **race** each other to reach a 1 state. Whichever gate reaches the 1 state first, forces, via the feedback link, the other gate output to be a 0 state. Thus we really "don't know" what the output will be and hence the input condition $R = S = 1$ is always avoided in the R-S flip-flop.

Finally, to summarize the properties of an R-S flip-flop:

R-S flip-flop
   The flip-flop is **set** when $S = 1$, $R = 0$, so $Q = 1$ and remains in this state when S is returned to 0.
   The flip-flop is **reset** when $R = 1$, $S = 0$, so $Q = 0$.
   Note that the flip-flop provides complementary outputs Q and $\bar{Q}$.
   The condition $R = S = 1$ must always be avoided as it leads to a **race hazard** with don't-know outputs.

3.8 Clock, Preset and Clear Signals

Before introducing the other practically used types of flip-flop and the reasons they are needed, we will first consider three basic control signals commonly employed in sequential logic circuits. These are the *clock, preset* and *clear* signals.

In most digital systems, a **clock signal** acts to synchronise the system so that all flip-flops can work together in an orderly controlled manner. The clock signal is a continuous wavetrain of rectangular pulses of very stable frequency generated by a crystal-controlled oscillator. The clock pulses are normally fed to all units in the logic system so that the various flip-flops, counters, shift registers, etc. operate in a defined sequence. The clock signal, as well as synchronising the circuits, determines the speed at which the system operates. It is used, for example, to trigger flip-flops and thus determines how frequently they are clocked and hence how long a complete operation—such as addition, data transfer, etc.—takes to complete.

The system clock is known as the **master clock** and has a repetition frequency of typically 1 MHz, 2 MHz, 4 MHz and even higher for very fast systems. In addition, a sequential system may also have a number of subordinate clock signals. All subordinate clocks are derived from the master clock. For example, subordinate clocks may be obtained by dividing the master frequency by 2, 4, 6, 8, 10, etc. using divider circuits, or by altering the phase of the master clock signal using an inverter or delay network.

Some important terms associated with clock waveforms (see fig. 3.15) are

Repetition frequency f = number of clock pulses per second.
Period $T = 1/f$ = time interval between two successive pulses.
Leading edge   the edge associated with the pulse rising from
                   a 0 (low) state to a 1 (high) state.
Trailing edge   the edge associated with the pulse falling from
                   a 1 to a 0 state.
Rise-time t_r = time for pulse to rise from 10% to 90%
                   of its peak value (i.e. pulse height).
Fall-time t_f = time for pulse to fall from 90% to 10%
                   of its peak value.

In addition to the clock signals, two other signals are frequently used in flip-flop circuits. The **clear signal** may be used independently from the clock and any data signals and acts to reset the flip-flop so the output $Q = 0$. The **preset signal** acts to set flip-flops, i.e. make $Q = 1$, and again may be used independently from clock and data signals.

Fig. 3.15 Clock wave-
forms

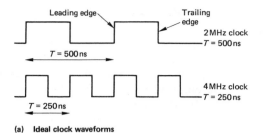

Leading edge

Trailing edge

2 MHz clock
T = 500 ns

T = 500 ns

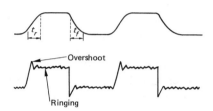

4 MHz clock
T = 250 ns

T = 250 ns

(a) **Ideal clock waveforms**

Overshoot

Ringing

(b) **Practical clock waveforms illustrating rise-time (t_r),
fall-time (t_f), ringing and overshoot**

3.9 Synchronous and Asynchronous Operation

Synchronous system operation occurs when the system acts under the control of the clock. The system will only respond to inputs in the presence of a clock pulse or, for edge-triggered devices (see p. 58), on either the leading or trailing edges of clock pulses.

Asynchronous system operation occurs when the system responds to inputs as soon as they are applied and requires no additional clock pulse for gating.

The basic R-S flip-flop is an example of an asynchronous device. It operates without clocking. Clear and preset signals are used to reset or set a flip-flop asynchronously. The clocked R-S flip-flop now to be considered illustrates the ideas of synchronous operation in which gating is effected by clock pulses, and also asynchronous operation with the addition of preset and clear inputs which may be used, respectively, to set and reset the flip-flop asynchronously.

3.10 The Clocked R-S Flip-flop

Fig. 3.16 shows the symbol, circuit and waveforms illustrating the action of a **clocked R-S flip-flop**. Data information contained on the S and R input lines are only "read in" and stored when the clock pulse is a 1 state or if, edge-triggering is employed, when the clock pulse changes from 0 to 1 (leading-edge) or 1 to 0 (trailing-edge).

For example, if $S = 1$, $R = 0$ and the clock pulse CLK is a 1, then the top AND gate of fig. 3.16b has two 1 inputs and hence its output takes the 1 state. This 1 output acts as the set input to the basic cross-coupled NOR R-S circuit, so the flip-flop output $Q = 1$. Only when the clock pulse is a 1 can the circuit be set or reset. When the clock pulse is a 0, the input AND gates inhibit any action taking place.

The initial state of the flip-flop can be preset independently by applying a 1 state at the preset input or cleared by applying a 1 state at the clear input, i.e. if $PS = 1$, then $Q = 1$, and if $C = 1$, then $Q = 0$. Normally after the initial setting, the preset and clear signals thereafter remain at logic 0.

Fig. 3.16 The clocked R-S flip-flop

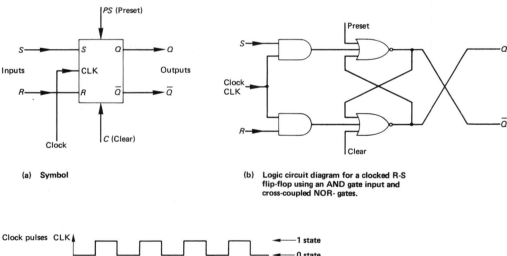

(a) Symbol

(b) Logic circuit diagram for a clocked R-S flip-flop using an AND gate input and cross-coupled NOR- gates.

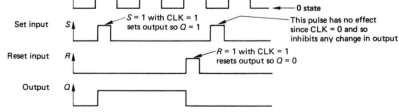

(c) Waveform diagrams illustrating action of the clocked R-S flip-flop

3.11 The D-type Flip-flop

The **D-type flip-flop** is used both to temporarily store one bit of binary data and also to act as a delay element, since the stored bit is essentially held or "delayed" for one clock cycle. Hence it is usually referred to as D-type, where D can be thought to stand for "data" and "delay".

The D-type flip-flop circuit of fig. 3.17b is essentially a simple adaptation of the clocked R-S flip-flop. An inverter is included in series with one of the inputs to the lower AND gate, thus ensuring that the inputs to the NOR gates of the flip-flop are always complementary. In this way the race hazards, which occur in the R-S flip-flops when $R = S = 1$, are avoided.

When $D = 1$ with CLK $= 1$ (or with edge-trigger), the output is set to $Q = 1$ and stores the 1 when the clock and data signals are removed.

If $D = 0$ with CLK $= 1$, the output is reset with $Q = 0$. The Q copies and stores D provided a clock pulse is present with the D input.

If CLK $= 0$, the flip-flop is inhibited and no output changes can occur.

Fig. 3.17 The D-type flip-flop

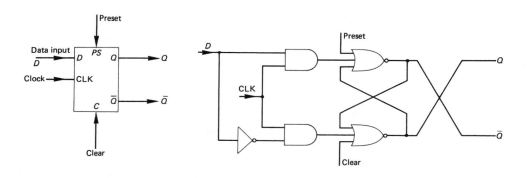

(a) Symbol

(b) Logic circuit diagram for a D-type flip-flop

Input before $(n + 1)^{\text{th}}$ clock pulse		Output after $(n + 1)^{\text{th}}$ clock pulse		
D_{n+1}	CLK	Q_{n+1}	$\bar{Q}_{n+1}$	
0	0	Q_n	$\bar{Q}_n$	Output unchanged in absence of clock pulse
1	0	Q_n	$\bar{Q}_n$	
0	1	0	1	Data applied at D transferred to output
1	1	1	0	

(c) Truth table for D-type flip-flop

3.12 Leading-edge and Trailing-edge Triggering of Flip-flops

In our discussions on the clocked R-S and D-type flip-flops, we stated that the flip-flops are enabled so as to transfer or copy binary data from input to the Q outputs, either during the presence of a clock pulse or on the leading or trailing edge of a clock pulse. Fig. 3.18 shows the notation used in circuit diagrams to distinguish between the so-called static and dynamic clock gating modes.

In fig. 3.18a we have *static inputs* in which the 1 state is defined by the presence of the 1 state voltage level. Thus if $S = 1$ and the clock pulse CLK = 1 with $R = 0$, then Q will be set. If CLK = 0, no change takes place.

In b(i), the arrowhead on the clock input indicates *dynamic input* triggering on the **leading-edge** of the clock pulse when it changes from the 0 to the 1 state.

In b(ii), the addition of the small circle plus the arrowhead indicates that the flip-flop is triggered on the **trailing-edge** of a clock pulse when it changes from 1 to 0.

Fig. 3.18 Notation used to distinguish between static and dynamic inputs, and leading and trailing edge clock triggering

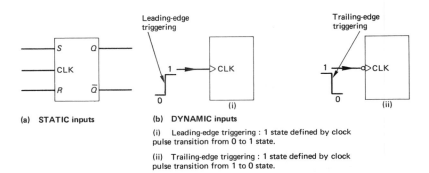

(a) STATIC inputs

(b) DYNAMIC inputs

(i)   Leading-edge triggering : 1 state defined by clock pulse transition from 0 to 1 state.

(ii)   Trailing-edge triggering : 1 state defined by clock pulse transition from 1 to 0 state.

The reasons for using **edge-triggering** follow from the importance of being able to effect changes as rapidly as possible. For example, in most storage-register applications, input 1–0 data should be transferred to the Q outputs as soon as possible so that the input lines can accept new values. This may present severe timing problems if static triggering is employed. The clock pulse duration must be long enough in its 1 state to ensure that the slowest flip-flop in the system is triggered, but should also be short enough to return to zero before the inputs change, thus ensuring that the Q states governed by the original inputs are not influenced by new inputs until the next clock pulse.

Edge-triggering is one of the methods used to overcome this problem by triggering the flip-flop at the instants the clock pulse changes either from 0 to 1 or 1 to 0. In such cases additional electronic circuitry is incorporated within the clock input. In **leading-edge triggering**, 0 to 1 triggering, the clock pulse is differentiated and rectified (see fig. 3.19) and the very short leading-edge pulse or "spike" so formed is used to enable the flip-flop. The data inputs are then copied to Q only on leading-edge changes of the clock

Fig. 3.19 Formation of pulse for leading-edge and trailing-edge triggering

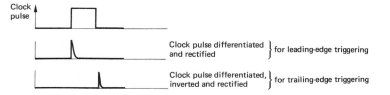

pulse. In **trailing-edge triggering**, the clock pulse is differentiated, inverted, and rectified, and the trailing-edge spike is used to clock the flip-flop.

3.13 The Master-Slave

In addition to edge-triggering, the **master-slave** principle of operation is extensively used to overcome the problem of isolating input changes in order to prevent them from affecting flip-flop output changes until we require them to do so.

The master-slave concept may be applied to all types of flip-flop. Fig. 3.20 shows the idea for the R-S flip-flop. We can explain the actions of these two flip-flop circuits (the master and slave flip-flops) as follows.

Fig. 3.20 Master-slave R-S flip-flop

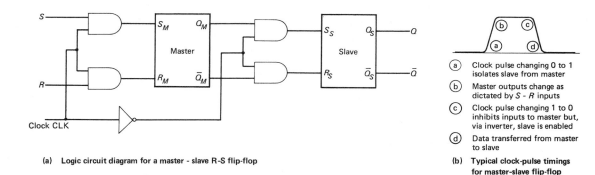

(a) Logic circuit diagram for a master - slave R-S flip-flop

(b) Typical clock-pulse timings for master-slave flip-flop

As the clock pulse changes from 0 to 1, the first flip-flop (known as the master) will be, by the action of the input AND gates, set to 1 if $S = 1$, reset if $R = 1$, or remain unchanged if $R = S = 0$, exactly as one would expect for a clocked S-R flip-flop. The master's outputs Q_M and $\bar{Q}_M$, however, are isolated from the second flip-flop during this time, since the clock pulse is also sent, but via an inverter, to the input AND gates of the slave. The slave is thus disabled while the master accepts the input data.

When the clock pulse subsequently changes from 1 to 0, the master is now disabled and thus its inputs, S_M and R_M, will be isolated from any new set of data fed to the S and R inputs. At the same time the slave is enabled, and thus the master's outputs Q_M and $\bar{Q}_M$ are transmitted to the slave flip-flop and this data is then copied to the outputs Q and $\bar{Q}$. A typical timing diagram showing the sequence of events is drawn in fig. 3.20b.

Master-slave action is extensively used in D, J-K as well as in R-S flip-flops. Master-slave flip-flops always employ two clocked flip-flops in cascade. The outputs of the first, the master, are coupled to the second, the slave, and a common clock pulse is used, except that it is inverted before being applied to the slave input. The master takes on the input data values when the clock pulse changes from 0 to 1, the slave at this time being isolated from the master. The data values stored in the master are transmitted to the slave and therefore to the output when the clock pulse changes from 1 to 0. At this time any new inputs are inhibited from affecting the master until the next clock pulse is received. It should be noted that many master-slave flip-flops operate in an inverse manner, and thus for these cases the master is enabled on 1 to 0 and the slave on 0 to 1 clock pulse changes.

3.14 The J-K Flip-flop

The avoidance of the condition $R = S = 1$ in S-R flip-flops can often impose severe restrictions on the design of sequential circuits and for this reason the **J-K flip-flop** has been developed and is very widely used.

The truth table of the J-K flip-flop, given in fig. 3.21c, shows that the flip-flop acts exactly as the S-R version, except that the input condition $J = K = 1$ is now permitted and results in the outputs simply changing state. They are complemented, i.e. when inputs are $J = K = 1$, then if Q were in a 1 state it changes to 0; if it were a 1, it changes to a 0.

Fig. 3.21 The J-K flip-flop

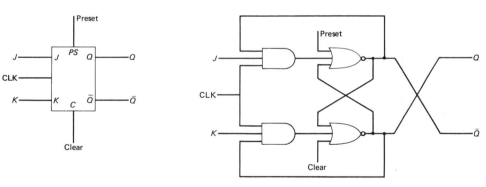

(a) **Symbol**

(b) **Logic circuit diagram for a J-K flip-flop**

Inputs before $(n+1)$ clock pulse			Outputs after $(n+1)^{th}$ clock pulse		
J_{n+1}	K_{n+1}	CLK	Q_{n+1}	$\bar{Q}_{n+1}$	
0	0	1	Q_n	$\bar{Q}_n$	previous data stored
0	1	1	0	1	output reset by $K = 1$
1	0	1	1	0	output set by $J = 1$
1	1	1	$\bar{Q}_n$	Q_n	output complemented when $J = K = 1$

(c) **Truth table for J-K flip-flop with flip-flop enabled by clock pulse**

Fig. 3.21*b* shows a circuit diagram of a simple *J-K* flip-flop. The circuit is similar to a clocked *S-R* flip-flop but has, in addition, feedback from the Q output to K input AND gate and feedback from the $\bar{Q}$ output to the J input AND gate. You can easily check that, in the clock enable condition, i.e. when CLK = 1, for this circuit,

$J = 1, K = 0$ sets the flip-flop so $Q = 1, \bar{Q} = 0$

$J = 0, K = 1$ resets the flip-flop so $Q = 0, \bar{Q} = 1$

so the *J-K* flip-flop acts identically to a clocked *S-R* flip-flop with $J \equiv S$ and $K \equiv R$.

Fig. 3.22 A master-slave J-K flip-flop

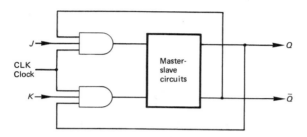

The basic difference occurs when $J = K = 1$. A short clock pulse is timed to be in the 1 state so that it, together with the feedback signals, initiates only a single transition in the output states of the cross-coupled NOR gates but falls back to zero before any further transitions can occur (thereby inhibiting the input AND gates). Thus, with this pulse, we will obtain complementation with

$$Q_{n+1} = 1 \text{ if } Q_n = 0 \quad \text{or} \quad Q_{n+1} = 1 \text{ if } Q_n = 1$$

Normally, edge-triggering circuitry and/or master-slave circuits (see fig. 3.22) are employed to ensure reliable operation.

3.15 The T-type Flip-flop or Toggle

T-type flip-flops, commonly referred to as **toggles**, are used exclusively for complementing. They change their output state on receipt of each clock pulse. Various versions are available, which toggle on either leading or trailing-edges of the clock pulse (see fig. 3.23*a* and *b*). A *T*-type flip-flop can be regarded as a simplified version of the *J-K* with *J*, *K* and clock inputs joined together to produce the single *T* input, as indicated in *c*.

T-type action can also be produced by feeding back the outputs of an *S-R* circuit as shown in *d*.

From the truth table in *e*, if $T = 1$ or changes 0 to 1 or 1 to 0 for edge-triggered versions, the output is complemented.

Fig. 3.23 T-type
flip-flops or toggles

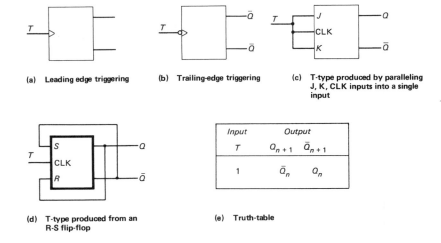

(a) Leading edge triggering

(b) Trailing-edge triggering

(c) T-type produced by paralleling J, K, CLK inputs into a single input

(d) T-type produced from an R-S flip-flop

(e) Truth-table

Input	Output	
T	Q_{n+1}	$\bar{Q}_{n+1}$
1	$\bar{Q}_n$	Q_n

3.16 Introduction to Digital Counters

An extremely important and very widely used application of flip-flops is in counting. The basic function of a counter is to measure the total number of input pulses, say from the clock or a pulse generator, that occur in a selected time interval.

A **digital counter** produces a digital output in a required code, which indicates the number of pulses in a selected time interval. Its type, e.g. binary, BCD, modulus-N, is defined by the code used to perform the counting and the mode of operation, whether synchronous or asynchronous.

Counters are the basic building blocks of many other logic circuits. They are used in direct counting; in time and frequency measurement; in frequency division (e.g. dividing the frequency of a master oscillator or clock by n where n is a multiple of 2); in the generation of pulse-type waveforms; and in the sequencing of operations (e.g. in a digital computer where counters are used to count operations and control the fetching of the next program instruction from memory when the preceding one has been completed).

3.17 Examples of Asynchronous Counting Circuits

3.17.1 An Asynchronous 4-bit Binary Up-counter

Fig. 3.24a shows an example of an **asynchronous counter** consisting of four T-type flip-flops connected in cascade. The flip-flops employ trailing-edge triggering action and the circuit provides a binary output count of the input pulses applied. The outputs Q_0, Q_1, Q_2, Q_3 are weighted respectively 1, 2, 4, 8. Thus this 4-bit counter is able to count from zero (0000) to 15 (1111). On receipt of a 16th pulse the counter is reset to 0000.

Fig. 3.24 An asynchronous 4-bit binary counter

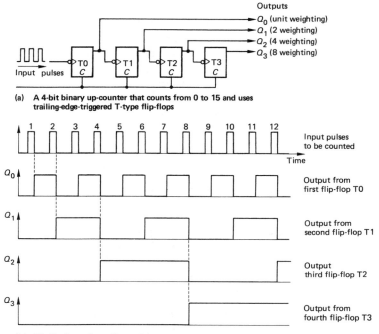

(a) A 4-bit binary up-counter that counts from 0 to 15 and uses trailing-edge-triggered T-type flip-flops

(b) Idealized waveforms illustrating action of counter

Number of input pulses	Output states after input pulses received			
	Q_0	Q_1	Q_2	Q_3
0	0	0	0	0
1	1	0	0	0
2	0	1	0	0
3	1	1	0	0
4	0	0	1	0
5	1	0	1	0
6	0	1	1	0
7	1	1	1	0
8	0	0	0	1
9	1	0	0	1
⋮				
14	0	1	1	1
15	1	1	1	1
16	0	0	0	0

(c) State diagram for counter

The operation of the counter is as follows. A clear pulse is initially applied to all flip-flops so they are all initially in the 0 state. The train of pulses to be counted is applied to the input of the first flip-flop T0. On the trailing-edge of the first input pulse, the output Q_0 of T0 switches from 0 to 1. Q_0 forms the input to the second flip-flop T1 and, although Q_0 now equals 1, it will not trigger T1 until the second input pulse is received, and T1 falls from 1 to 0, i.e. on the trailing-edge. At this instant, T0 is again triggered, changing Q_0 from 1 to 0, and this change causes trailing-edge triggering of T1 and toggles Q_1 from 0 to 1.

The waveform diagrams of fig. 3.24b illustrate the overall operation of the counter with successive flip-flops only being triggered on the trailing-edges of their inputs. In this way the counter can count up to 15 before all flip-flop outputs are again all 0 states, and then the whole procedure is repeated. The output states Q_0, Q_1, Q_2, Q_3 represent, in binary form, the total number of input pulses (up to 15), since the counter was initially set to zero by the clear pulse. Fig. 3.24c summarises the output state diagram for the counter. For counting beyond 15 pulses, further counter stages are required with additional circuitry to generate a 1 carry bit to the next counter stage input on receipt of the 16th, 32nd, 48th, etc. pulses.

3.17.2 A BCD Up-counter Stage

Fig. 3.25a shows the adaptation that can be made to the 4-bit binary counter just described to produce an 8421 **BCD decade counter**.

After receipt of the 10th input pulse, the output Q states of the four flip-flops must be reset to zero and a carry 1 bit must be generated, i.e. $Q_4 = 1$, to be fed to the next higher-order decade stage. This means that, at every sequence in the count that Q_1 and Q_3 would become 1 states, i.e. if

$$Q_3Q_2Q_1Q_0 \text{ were to become equal to } 1010 = \text{decimal } 10$$

a carry bit $Q_4 = 1$ should be generated to be fed to the input of the next stage, and at the same time all the four flip-flops in the first stage should be cleared. This is achieved in a by feeding Q_1 and Q_3 to an AND gate, the output of which, Q_4, provides the carry and also effects the clear operation.

The action of the counter is illustrated in the waveform diagrams of fig. 3.25b. Note that, on the receipt of the 10th pulse (and subsequently, on multiples of 10 pulses), Q_1 rises for a very short time to a 1 state (the spike), whilst Q_3 is still a 1 state. This generates $Q_4 = 1$ for a sufficient time to activate the input to the next counter and also clears all four flip-flops of the first stage. A table of output states for the counter for the first twelve input pulses is given in fig. 3.25c.

3.17.3 A 4-bit Binary Down-counter Stage

The two counters just considered operate as up-counters, measuring in the "up" or increasing count direction. Counters that operate in the "down" sense are also sometimes required.

The 4-bit **binary counter** of fig. 3.24 can be made to operate a down-counter, as shown in fig. 3.26a, by connecting the T-inputs of second, third and fourth flip-flops to the $\bar{Q}$ outputs instead of Q of their predecessors. The waveform diagrams and table of output states for this mode of operation are given in fig. 3.26b and c, assuming that the four flip-flops are initially set in 1 states using an initial preset pulse.

We could, of course, use the counter of fig. 3.24 to provide both up and down count records, using the outputs $\bar{Q}_3$, $\bar{Q}_2$, $\bar{Q}_1$, $\bar{Q}_0$ for the latter.

Fig. 3.25 An asynchronous BCD decade counter stage

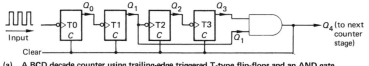

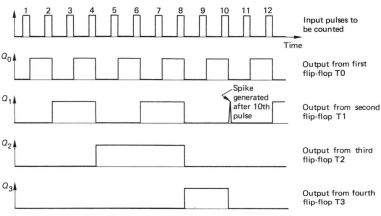

(a) A BCD decade counter using trailing-edge triggered T-type flip-flops and an AND gate

(b) Idealized waveforms illustrating action of counter

Number of input pulses	Flip-flop outputs				Carry to next stage
	Q_0	Q_1	Q_2	Q_3	Q_4
0	0	0	0	0	0
1	1	0	0	0	0
2	0	1	0	0	0
3	1	1	0	0	0
4	0	0	1	0	0
5	1	0	1	0	0
6	0	1	1	0	0
7	1	1	1	0	0
8	0	0	0	1	0
9	1	0	0	1	0
10	0	0	0	0	1
11	1	0	0	0	1
12	0	1	0	0	1

(c) State diagram for counter

3.18 Asynchronous and Synchronous Operation: Hazards and Relative Advantages

Asynchronous system operation has the advantage of speed since all flip-flops begin to respond immediately their input states change. However, there is a serious limitation caused primarily by the inherent delays as changes propagate through the various circuits and devices making up the complete system. Different parts of an asynchronous system are changing

Fig. 3.26 An example of a 4-bit binary down-counter

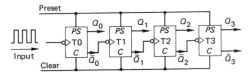

(a) A 4-bit trailing-edge triggered down-counter

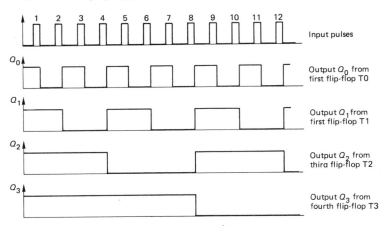

(b) Idealised waveforms illustrating down-counter action.
Note Q_0, Q_1, Q_2, Q_3 are initially preset to 1 state

Number of input pulses	Output states				Decimal equivalent
	Q_0	Q_1	Q_2	Q_3	
0	1	1	1	1	15
1	0	1	1	1	14
2	1	0	1	1	13
3	0	0	1	1	12
4	1	1	0	1	11
5	0	1	0	1	10
⋮	⋮	⋮	⋮		⋮
12	1	1	0	0	3
13	0	1	0	0	2
14	1	0	0	0	1
15	0	0	0	0	0

(c) State diagram for counter

states at different times and this may give rise to spurious instantaneous values, which may result in the system malfunctioning. For example, in asynchronous counters, each input pulse essentially "ripples" through a chain of flip-flops. The time taken will be the sum of the delay times of all flip-flops through which it passes and, if the chain is long, the propagation time may well be longer than the time interval between successive input pulses, and thus false counts are recorded. Also, when two or more signals which have travelled along paths of different delay and are combined, then the result can depend on which arrives first, i.e. which one wins the **race**. The race can lead to a false output state and system malfunction. These problems are known as **hazards** and impose severe restrictions in asynchronous circuit design.

Synchronous systems, on the other hand, are provided with circuits which govern the timing of all elements in the entire system. All storage devices are constrained to change state under the action of clock pulses or, in the case of counters, under the action of the input signal to be counted. Synchronous operation largely overcomes timing and delay difficulties, and the possibility of hazards and races is eliminated. Synchronous systems, however, are slower, since time must be allowed between successive clock pulses for the slowest elements in the system to respond. In the case of a synchronous counter, the maximum repetition rate of the input signal is limited by the delay of a single flip-flop plus the propagation time of any control gates required.

3.19 Examples of Synchronous Counting Circuits

3.19.1 A Synchronous 4-bit Binary Counter Stage

Fig. 3.27 shows an example of a 4-bit **synchronous counter** circuit employing trailing-edge triggered J-K flip-flops with the J-K inputs joined together so they act as toggles.

The input pulses to be counted are applied to the clock inputs of all four flip-flops simultaneously so as to effect synchronous operation. The J-K input to the first flip-flop is held continuously at a 1 state. A clear pulse is applied so the Q outputs of all four flip-flops are initially 0 states.

The operation of the flip-flop may be explained as follows. The output Q_0 of the first flip-flop changes state from 0 to 1 on the trailing-edge of the first input pulse to be counted. Its inputs are $J_0 = K_0 = 1$, and are always held in this state. Hence it will always be triggered and change state on the trailing-edge of each pulse received. The other three flip-flops, although in receipt of the same input trigger pulse, remain at 0 since their J-K inputs are zero.

On the trailing-edge of the second input pulse, Q_0 is toggled from 1 to 0, whilst at the same time the second flip-flop, whose J_1-K_1 inputs are 1 states, toggles from $Q_1 = 0$ to $Q_1 = 1$. The outputs are then

$$Q_0 Q_1 Q_2 Q_3 = 0100 \quad \text{(i.e. decimal 2)}$$

On the trailing-edge of the third pulse, Q_0 toggles from 0 to 1, whilst Q_1 stays at 1, since $J_1 = K_1 = 0$ prior to the trigger being received. Note that, after receipt of the third pulse, the inputs Q_0 and Q_1 to the AND gate feeding the third flip-flop are 1 and hence the AND gate output provides $J_2 = K_2 = 1$.

Thus on the trailing-edge of the fourth pulse the third flip-flop is triggered so Q_2 changes 0 to 1, whilst Q_0 and Q_1 then drop back to 0. Q_0, Q_1 and Q_2 form the inputs to the second AND gate feeding the fourth flip-flop. Thus the fourth flip-flop is only triggered to change state when $Q_0 = Q_1 = Q_2 = 1$ which sets the output of the AND gate to 1 and hence $J_3 = K_3 = 1$ on the trailing-edge of the 8th (or multiple of 8) pulse.

Thus to summarise: all flip-flops are triggered directly from the input pulses—this ensures synchronous operation. The J-K input to any given flip-flop in the counter chain consists of the ANDed outputs of all previous flip-flops. This prevents the flip-flops changing state on every clock pulse trigger and enables the counter to count in a binary sequence.

The waveform diagrams illustrate the counter action, but make no allowance for flip-flop delay. In practice the output changes will be delayed with respect to the trailing-edge by only one flip-flop delay (unlike the cases of asynchronous counters where the delays are cumulative). The state diagram for the counter is summarized in fig. 3.27c showing that the counter operates as a 4-bit binary counter and is reset to 0000 after the trailing edge of the 16th pulse.

3.19.2   A Synchronous BCD Decade Counter Stage

The counter of fig. 3.28a operates in a similar manner to the 4-bit binary counter just described from the count 0 to 9 (0000 to 1001). On receipt of the 10th pulse, however, all flip-flops are reset to zero. It thus acts as a decade counter stage providing an 8421 BCD output $Q_0 Q_1 Q_2 Q_3$ as shown in the state diagram of fig. 3.28b. As a useful exercise to reinforce your understanding of flip-flop operation and counting circuits, check this state table.

3.20   Shift Registers

Shift registers are used to store strings of binary digits, where the string may represent a binary number, a machine code instruction, etc. They are extremely useful building blocks and widely used in digital systems, e.g. as storage registers; in arithmetic logic units, where its "shift property" is used to feed data in and out and in the processes of multiplication and division; in multiphase clock-pulse generators; and, in general, in any application involving the transfer or "shifting" of data (typically one or two byte, 8 or 16 bit, words).

A single flip-flop can store one bit of information. A series of n flip-flops can therefore act to store an n-bit word and, when used in this manner, the n-flip-flop block is known as a **register**. A register which is designed to allow the individual bits making up the data word to be fed in (and out) of the register serially, under the action of clock-pulses, is known as a **shift register**.

A shift register is constructed basically by joining n flip-flops in series, with the output of the preceding one feeding the input of the next. Data is applied to the first and clocked in by successive clock-pulses: the basic property of the shift register is that after each clock pulse the $(r+1)$th flip-flop takes on the previous value of the rth. This applies to all flip-flops except the first—thus data is **shifted** from one flip-flop to the next.

Fig. 3.29a shows a simple 4-bit shift register, constructed by joining four D-type flip-flops in series. The bits of data making up a word are applied in

Fig. 3.27 A synchronous 4-bit binary counter

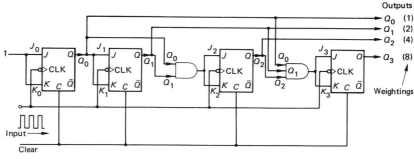

(a)   A 4-bit synchronous counter using J-K flip-flops connected as toggles and trailing-edge triggering

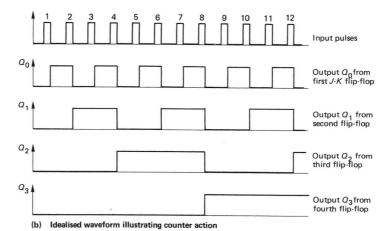

(b)   Idealised waveform illustrating counter action

Number of input pulses	Output States Q_0 Q_1 Q_2 Q_3			
0	0	0	0	0
1	1	0	0	0
2	0	1	0	0
3	1	1	0	0
4	0	0	1	0
⋮				
13	1	0	1	1
14	0	1	1	1
15	1	1	1	1
16	0	0	0	0

(c)   State diagram for counter

sequence to D input of the first flip-flop. Each bit is transferred in turn, left to right, one flip-flop to the next by a common clock pulse. Thus the rate at which the data bits are fed in is related to the clock pulse frequency, and in our case takes 4 clock pulses. The clock must, of course, cease its input to the register as soon as the word is loaded.

Consider briefly the mechanism of how data is fed and stored in the register. All four of the flip-flops are first cleared by means of a clear pulse, so all the four outputs Q_0, Q_1, Q_2, Q_3 are initially zero. The 4-bit word is

Fig. 3.28 A BCD synchronous counter stage

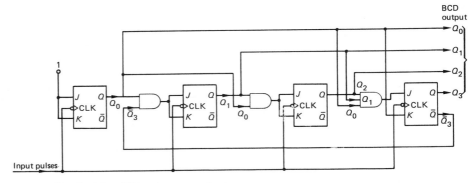

(a) Circuit for a BCD synchronous counter stage

Number of input pulses	Output states after input pulse received Q_0 Q_1 Q_2 Q_3			
0	0	0	0	0
1	1	0	0	0
2	0	1	0	0
3	1	1	0	0
4	0	0	1	0
5	1	0	1	0
6	0	1	1	0
7	1	1	1	0
8	0	0	0	1
9	1	0	0	1
10	0	0	0	0

(b) State table for counter

now fed to the input of the first flip-flop. Edge-triggered or master-slave type flip-flops must be used since all flip-flops will be receiving new data whilst using their existing outputs as inputs to the next stage.

Suppose our data input is 1011. The least significant bit, a 1 in this case, is entered into the first flip-flop D3 when triggered by the leading-edge, say, of the first clock-pulse, so Q_3 changes to a 1 state with all other outputs remaining 0 states. On triggering by the second clock pulse, the existing Q_3 state is transferred to flip-flop D2 and just afterwards the second input bit, again a 1 in our example, enters and is stored by D3.

On triggering by the third clock pulse, the third input bit, the 0, enters and is then stored by D3; all other data is shifted to the right by one flip-flop, with D2 and D1 storing the first two 1 bits of the word. Finally on receipt of the fourth pulse, loading is completed and $Q_3Q_2Q_1Q_0 = 1011$. The loading sequence is summarised in the table of fig. 3.29b.

The outputs each have their own output line and therefore may be read simultaneously or in parallel. When data is fed in serially and read out in parallel, the register is often referred to as a series-to-parallel converter or more explicitly as a *series-in parallel-out register*. Various combinations of inputting and outputting data in shift registers are available. Fig. 3.30 shows an example of a *parallel-in parallel-out* register. Data may be loaded-in in parallel using the preset inputs and read-out in parallel by simultaneously sampling the $Q_3Q_2Q_1Q_0$ output lines. The figure also indicates the other

Fig. 3.29 A 4-bit shift register (serially loaded)

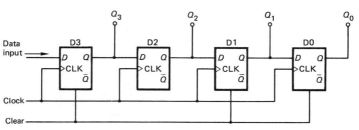

(a) A basic 4-bit shift register constructed from D-type flip-flops and loaded serially.

Clock pulse	Data bit	Outputs of shift register after each successive clock pulse
		Q_3 Q_2 Q_1 Q_0
1	1 ⟶	1 0 0 0
2	1 ⟶	1 1 0 0
3	0 ⟶	0 1 1 0
4	1 ⟶	1 0 1 1

(b) Table showing outputs of shift register flip-flops after each clock pulse

Fig. 3.30 An example of a parallel-in/ parallel-out shift register

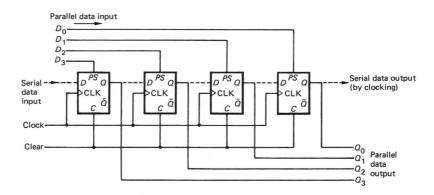

combinations: *parallel-in series-out* registers; series-in parallel-out registers; *series-in series-out* registers.

When data is transferred out of shift register, the original contents are normally lost. If this is to be avoided, arrangements for recycling of the data can be made so a copy can be retained. Fig. 3.31, for example, shows a circuit in which an *n*-bit data word can be loaded serially into one shift register, register X, by enabling AND gate ① and the flip-flops of X for *n* clock pulses. The word stored in X may then be transferred serially to Y by enabling AND gate ② for the next *n* clock pulses. If a copy is required to be retained in X, AND gate ③ should also be simultaneously enabled. This will allow data to be recycled via the OR gate to register X whilst the transfer X to Y is being made.

Fig. 3.32 shows another example, illustrating the application of a shift register and appropriate control gates in "reading" and storing data from a data bus and also in "writing" stored data from register to the bus. When

Fig. 3.31 An example of data transfer (serial mode) between two shift registers

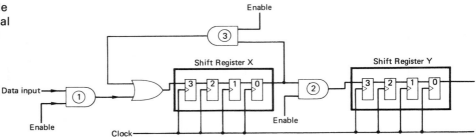

Fig. 3.32 An example of reading data in from a data bus and storing in a register, and writing data from the register to the bus

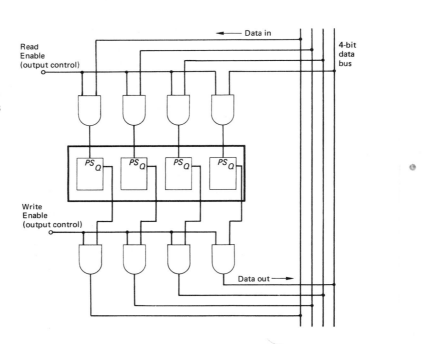

the read enable control lines to the top AND gates are set 1, data on the individual wires making up the bus are transferred via these gates to the preset inputs of the register and in this way stored in the register. When the write enable control lines are enabled, the data stored in the register are effectively parallel-outputted to the data bus lines.

3.21 Introduction to Arithmetic Units: the Half-adder and Full-adder Circuits

An **arithmetic logic unit** (ALU) is basically a digital circuit which can perform the arithmetic processes ($+ - \times \div$) and make logical comparisons with binary numbers.

The fundamental circuit in all ALUs is the full-adder circuit. This circuit simply adds two one-bit numbers and generates their sum and, where

Fig. 3.33 Half and full adders

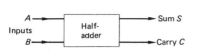

Inputs		Outputs	
A	B	S	C
0	0	0	0
0	1	1	0
1	0	1	0
1	1	1	1

(a) Schematic diagram of a half-adder and its truth table

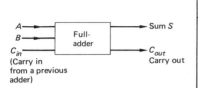

	Inputs			Outputs	
A	B	C_{in}		S	C_{out}
0	0	0		0	0
0	0	1		1	0
0	1	0		1	0
1	0	0		1	0
0	1	1		0	1
1	0	1		0	1
1	1	0		0	1
1	1	1		1	1

(b) Full-adder and truth table

Fig. 3.34 Implementation of half-adder circuits

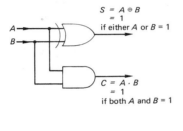

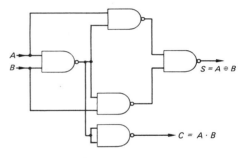

(a) Implementation of a half-adder using an exclusive-OR and an AND gate

(b) Implementation using NAND gates

necessary, a carry bit. However, it can readily be adapted with additional gates and logic blocks to subtract, multiply, divide and perform many other basic functions—hence its fundamental importance and the reason why we begin our discussions on ALUs by considering half- and full-adder circuits.

A **full-adder** is a logic circuit which generates two outputs (the sum and carry) for three 1-bit binary number inputs, two of which are the bits to be added and the third a possible carry bit from a preceding lower-level addition. The full-adder consists of an additional OR gate and two simpler "adder" devices—half-adders. A **half-adder** is a logic circuit which adds two 1-bit inputs to produce their sum and carry bits. Block schematic diagrams and the truth tables for the half- and full-adders are shown in fig. 3.33.

The sum output S for a half-adder may be produced using an exclusive-OR element, i.e. $S = 1$ if and only if A or $B = 1$. The carry output C can easily be generated using an AND gate, i.e. $C = 1$ only if A and $B = 1$. Thus we obtain the half-adder circuit of fig. 3.34a. We may use NAND gates entirely to generate S and C; this leads to the implementation shown in b.

Fig. 3.35 Construction of a full-adder using two half-adders and an OR gate

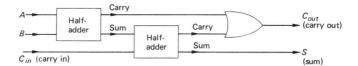

By using two half-adders, we can implement, as shown in fig. 3.35, the full-adder circuit. The full-adder adds two single-bit number inputs A and B plus any carry-in bit C_{in} from a previous addition and generates the sum output S plus a carry-out C_{out} bit.

3.22 Parallel and Serial Adder Circuits

In general, we are, of course, interested in adding multi-bit binary numbers. Two n-bit numbers may be added using full-adders by either parallel or serial techniques. A parallel adder requires n full-adder circuits; a serial adder only one, but additional register-memory circuits.

3.22.1 A Parallel Adder

Fig. 3.36 shows an example of a 4-bit **parallel adder**: the circuit is designed to add two 4-bit numbers, $A = A_3A_2A_1A_0$ and $B = B_3B_2B_1B_0$, fed in in parallel to the adder inputs together with the carry-in bit C_{in}, and produce the sum $S = S_3S_2S_1S_0$ plus the carry-out bit C_{out}. The action of the circuit may be explained as follows.

Fig. 3.36 Block diagram of action of a parallel 4-bit adder

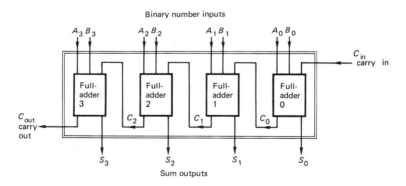

The individual pairs of bits making up A and B are applied to the respective full-adder inputs, LSBs A_0 and B_0 at right, MSBs A_3 and B_3 at left. The far-right full-adder, labelled 0, adds A_0 and B_0 and C_{in}. The carry-out bit C_0 generated is applied to the next adder 1 together with the next most significant bits A_1 and B_1. The carry-out bit C_1 from this adder is applied to adder 2 together with A_2 and B_2, and so on.

Note that the carry bits are passed sequentially through all adder stages and thus the individual sum outputs are only correct when the preceding stage carry has been generated. Hence the entire addition is only effected after the last carry has been generated and acted upon. Even though the inputs A and B to the adder block are in parallel, the circuit acts in a sequential manner and sufficient time must elapse for the propagation of all carry bit pulses before reading out the result. For this reason, parallel adders usually have output gates incorporated that are disabled until all carrys have propagated through the entire chain of adder circuits.

3.22.2 A Serial Adder

The addition of two n-bit number may be accomplished using a single full-adder circuit plus shift registers for storing the numbers and the inter-mediate and final results. Fig. 3.37 shows an example of a **serial adder** utilising two shift registers for storing and feeding in two numbers, A and B, bit by bit to a single full-adder. A third shift register, the sum register, stores the results; and a simple D-type flip-flop is used to store the carry bits as they are generated in the serial sequence of additions. The action of the circuit may be explained as follows.

Fig. 3.37 An example of a serial adder

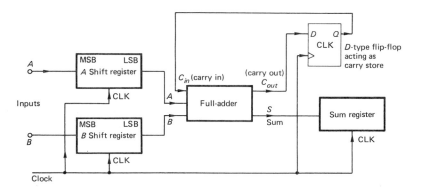

Each pair of bits in the numbers A and B to be added is presented to the full-adder sequentially from the two shift registers used to initially store the numbers. The addition will therefore take n clock cycles for two n-bit numbers. In the first clock cycle, the LSBs A_0 and B_0 are applied to the full-adder together with $C_{in} = 0$. The sum output S_0 is saved in the sum register. The carry-out bit C_{out} is also saved in the carry storage register (which could consist of a D-type flip-flop) and in the next clock cycle it is presented to the adder together with the next two bits, A_1 and B_1. The outputs S_1 and the new C_{out} are again saved. The serial process continues and, after n clock pulses, the full n-bit sum, $S_{n-1}S_{n-2} \cdots S_1 S_0$, will have been effected and stored in the sum register. Any final carry from the nth addition is also stored and available for addition in a higher-order adder block.

3.23 Accumulators: their Use in Serial and Parallel Adder Circuits

An **accumulator** is a fundamental register used in ALUs for the storage of both intermediate and final results of arithmetic operations. It is normally involved in all operations on data and in transfers of data. The contents of the accumulator are continually updated to hold the "accumulated" result of the operations so far executed—hence its name: the accumulator.

1 Fig. 3.38a shows an example of a *serial adder* circuit using the accumulator principle. The A shift register in this circuit becomes the accumulator and the circuit is capable of any number of additions. Its action can be summarised as follows.

The first two numbers, say A and B each of n bits, are fed serially, one to the accumulator, the other to the B register, and then added bit by bit in the full-adder block. The sum bits are fed back to the accumulator input and so, after the n clock pulses used to send the bits to the adder, the accumulator will hold the sum bits comprising $A + B$. The third number to be added, say C, is now clocked into the B register and then the contents of the accumulator and the B register added bit by bit in the full adder. At each stage the sum bit is fed back to the accumulator, so after a further n clock pulses the accumulator holds the sum $A + B + C$, whilst the B register is cleared and ready for the next number input. The sequence can be repeated for any number of additions with the results of each step in the addition being returned to the accumulator overwriting the previous contents.

2 Fig. 3.38b shows a simplified version of a *parallel adder* circuit using the accumulator principle. The inputs to the parallel adder block consist of the number to be added and the contents of the accumulator holding the previous sum. The new sum is returned to the accumulator and overwrites the original contents on the next clock pulse. A typical sequence is as follows:

1 Accumulator set to zero. First number, A say, from a storage register applied to parallel adder.
2 After receipt of clock pulse, accumulator enabled to receive sum fed back from adder—in this case A, since original contents of the accumulator were zero. Second number, B say, fed to adder.
3 After next clock pulse, resulting sum $A + B$ fed back and overwrites contents of accumulator. Third number, C say, fed to adder.
4 After next clock pulse resulting sum $A + B + C$ fed back to accumulator, and so on.

3.24 Subtraction Using Adders and Complement Circuits

Although direct binary subtraction may be accomplished using full subtractor type logic circuits, these circuits are now seldom used. Virtually all ALUs perform subtraction by the addition of a complement. In this way the

Fig. 3.38 Adder circuits using an accumulator

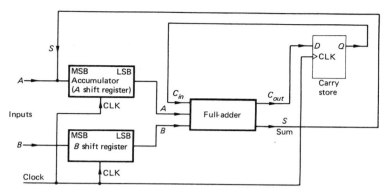

(a) An example of a serial adder using an accumulator

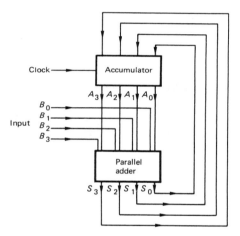

(b) An example of a parallel adder using an accumulator

need for separate subtractor circuits is eliminated. Only full-adder circuits are required, plus, of course, auxiliary logic chips to complement numbers when the subtraction operation is undertaken.

Fig. 3.39 shows the block schematic of an **adder/twos-complement subtractor circuit**. When used as a subtractor, the control signal X to the true/complement chip is set at 0. This chip is then configured to generate the ones complement of the number, B say, to be subtracted, e.g. if $B = 0101$ the chip output generated is 1010. The inverter provides a $C_{in} = 1$ to the parallel adder block which, when combined with the ones complement of B, forms the twos complement of B, e.g. twos complement of $B = 0101$ is $1010 + 0001$.

The subtraction $A - B$ is then performed by adding $A + (-B)$ in the parallel adder block. The output provides the result in twos complement form. If the control signal X is set at 1, the true/complement chip outputs B directly and the adder outputs the sum $A + B$.

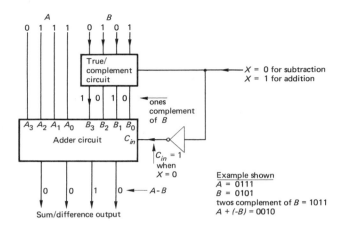

Fig. 3.39 Example of an adder/twos-complement subtractor circuit

3.25 Binary Multiplier Circuits

In section 2.11 we explained that binary multiplication could be effectively accomplished using the add-shift principle. This principle forms the basis of multiplication in ALUs where repeated additions, controlled by an add-shift logic unit, are performed in an adder block with successive accumulated results being used to up-date an accumulator.

Before considering the operation of a practical circuit let us briefly review the add-shift technique used in binary multiplication by evaluating $A \times B$ where

the multiplicand $A = 0111$

the multiplier $B = 1011$

$$
\begin{array}{r}
0111 \\
1011 \\
\hline
0111 \\
0111 \\
0000 \\
0111 \\
\hline
1001101
\end{array}
$$

$0111 \leftarrow \times$ by LSB of multiplier
$0111 \leftarrow$ shift one place and multiply by next significant bit
$0000 \leftarrow$ shift one place and $\times$ by next significant bit
$0111 \leftarrow$ shift one place and $\times$ by MSB

$1001101 =$ product $=$ sum of partial products

Using this example we can deduce some general results:

1   Each partial product equals multiplicand if multiplier bit is a 1, otherwise it is zero.
2   After obtaining each partial product, we shift one place.
3   The resulting product is the sum of all partial products.

Fig. 3.40 Example of a binary multiplier circuit

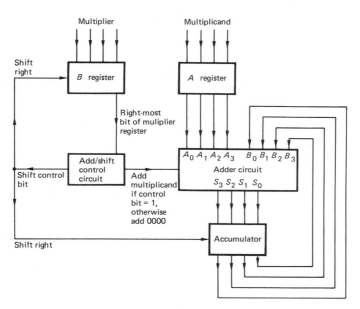

These observations with slight modifications are used in the practical **multiplier circuit** of fig. 3.40. We will consider the action of the circuit using the above example and assume the A, B and accumulator registers have, respectively n, n, $2n$ bit storage capacity to accommodate the two numbers and their resulting product. In our case, $n = 4$ since we are dealing with 4-bit numbers and a product which will contain up to 8 bits.

Step 1   The multiplicand $A = 0111$ and the multiplier $B = 1011$ are entered into the A and B registers. The accumulator is cleared.

B register				A register				Accumulator							
1	0	1	1	0	1	1	1								
Multiplier B				Multiplicand A				(contents actually all 0s but left blank for clarity)							

Step 2   The add/shift logic circuits examines the right-most digit of the multiplier in the B register. If it is a 1, it instructs the adder to add contents of the A register, the multiplicand, to the contents of the accumulator. If it is 0, add 0000, i.e. in this case contents of accumulator are unchanged. In our example the right-hand bit in B is a 1 so 0111 is added to accumulator. Hence we obtain

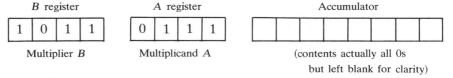

B				A				Accumulator							
1	0	1	1	0	1	1	1	0	1	1	1				

Step 3   After step 2 has been executed, the add/shift logic control shifts the contents of both the B register and the accumulator one place to the right.

Hence we obtain (note LSB of *B* is "lost"):

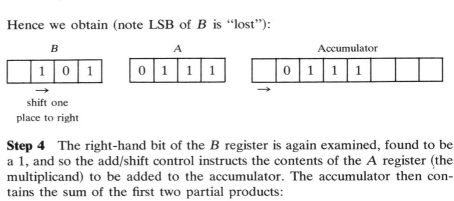

shift one
place to right

Step 4 The right-hand bit of the *B* register is again examined, found to be a 1, and so the add/shift control instructs the contents of the *A* register (the multiplicand) to be added to the accumulator. The accumulator then contains the sum of the first two partial products:

sum of first two partial products.

Step 5 The add/shift control now shifts contents of the *B* register and the accumulator one place to the right:

Step 6 The right-hand bit in the *B* register is examined, found to be a 0, so 0000 is added to shift register contents:

Step 7 The add/shift controls once again shifts contents of the *B* register and accumulator one place to right:

Step 8 The right-hand bit in the *B* register (the only one left now) is a 1 so the add/shift control instructs the contents of *A* to be added to the accumulator. The accumulator now contains the sums of all partial products, that is the final product result.

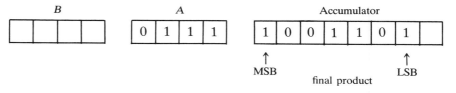

MSB

LSB

final product

Thus we see that the action of this multiplier circuit is very similar to the "long-hand" add-shift operations performed manually, except for two minor differences. At each step the partial product terms are added to the accumulated sum rather than waiting to the end; and the partial products are shifted right rather than the functionally equivalent "long-hand" manual method of starting our repeated multiplication each time one place to the left.

3.26 Binary Division

Multiplication may be accomplished by a series of repeated additions plus appropriate shifting. Since division is essentially the "opposite" process it can be accomplished by a series of repeated subtractions of the divisor from the dividend plus appropriate shifting. This subtract-shift principle is used in many ALUs to perform **binary division**. The following outlines one form of approach, known as the restoring method.

1. Subtract divisor from dividend.
2. *a*) If result is positive, a 1 is placed in the right-most position of the quotient register.

    b) If the result is negative, the divisor is added back to the dividend and the right-most bit in the quotient register remains a 0.
3. Shift contents of quotient register to left one place and shift divisor to right one place.
4. Repeat steps 1, 2 and 3 until a subtract yields a zero difference or until required accuracy is obtained, when in practice all available bit positions in quotient register will be filled.

The following example illustrates the basic procedure:

to evaluate $99 \div 11$, i.e. in binary

$$1100011 \div 1011 = \text{answer}$$

dividend   divisor   quotient

Description		Contents of quotient register (QR)
	1011	
	1011 ‾‾‾‾‾‾1100011	
Subtract divisor from dividend. →	1011↓	
Result +ve, place 1 in right of QR. →	00010	1
Shift divisor left, QR right; subtract. →	1011	1
Negative difference.	0111	1 0
Add divisor back, i.e. **restore**.	1011↓	
	00101	
Shift divisor left, QR right; subtract. →	1011	1 0 0
Negative difference	1010	
Add divisor back (restore).	1011↓	
	01011	
Shift divisor left, QR right; subtract. →	1011	1 0 0
Zero difference, add 1 to right-most bit of QR and stop.	0000	1 0 0 1
		Answer

Problems 3: Logic devices, circuits and operations

1 Determine for the gates shown in fig. 3.41a to f the logic output F for the input states indicated.

2 Determine the logic output F for the quadrupole 2-input gate combinations shown in the circuits of fig. 3.42a and b when
(i) all input states are 0 (ii) all input states are 1,
(iii) $A = 1, B = C = D = E = 0$ (iv) $A = 0, B = C = D = E = 1$
State also the logic function of each circuit.

3 Show by drawing up the truth tables for the NOR gate circuits of fig. 3.43a and b that they, respectively, implement the AND and OR logic functions.

4 Draw up the truth table for the logic circuit of fig. 3.44 and hence determine its logic output F when the input signals $A = 101011$ and $B = 110101$ are applied at the input lines.

5 The starting control for a particular industrial process is to be governed by the following conditions:
the process starts when
$\quad\quad\quad\quad A$ the start button is pressed
AND when B the material present exceeds 1000 kg
AND when C the quantity of reagent material exceeds 100 kg
AND when D the temperature is cooled to below 0 °C
AND when E the pressure exceeds 5×10^5 N/m^2
Define the conditions in logic form and draw the logic circuit diagram for a circuit designed to produce a 1 state when all start conditions are satisfied assuming that you have available, either
$\quad a$) a quadrupole 2-input AND gate chip or
$\quad b$) only 2 input NAND gates.

6 a) Determine the output state F on the common line of the tri-state gate multiplexer circuit of fig. 3.45a for input states $A = 1, B = 0, C = 1$ when
(i) $E_A = 1, E_B = 0, E_C = 1$
(ii) $E_A = 0, E_B = 1, E_C = 1$
(iii) $E_A = E_B = E_C = 1$
b) Determine the output state F in the data routing circuit of fig. 3.45b for input states $A = 0, B = 1$ when
(i) $C_A = 1, C_B = 0$ (ii) $C_A = 0, C_B = 1$

Fig. 3.41

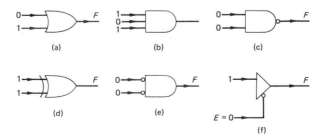

Fig. 3.42

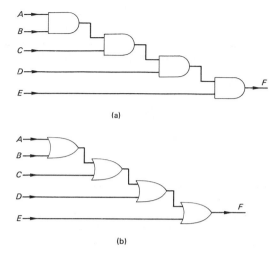

(a)

(b)

Fig. 3.43 NOR gate circuits

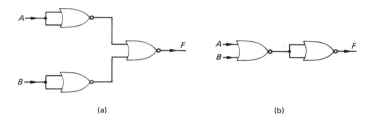

(a)   (b)

Fig. 3.44 Logic circuit

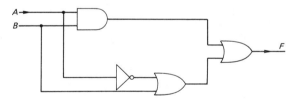

Fig. 3.45 Multiplexer circuit

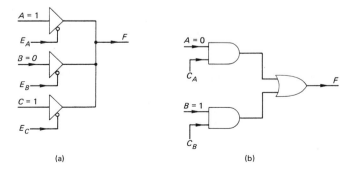

(a)   (b)

7 Fig. 3.46 shows the logic circuit of an 8-channel multiplexer chip in which binary data on any one of the inputs D_0 to D_7 may be selected by appropriate bits on the address inputs A_0, A_1, A_2 and transmitted to the common line output at F.

Determine which data input line is selected when the inhibit signal is a 0 state and
a) $A_0 = 0$, $A_1 = 0$, $A_2 = 0$
b) $A_0 = 0$, $A_1 = 1$, $A_2 = 1$
c) $A_0 = 1$, $A_1 = 1$, $A_2 = 1$
What happens if the inhibit signal is a 1 state?

8 Complete the truth tables shown in fig. 3.47a and b, respectively for the S-R and J-K flip-flops. Explain why the state $S = R = 1$ must be avoided in the case of an S-R flip-flop.

9 Explain with reference to the following changes the action of the cross-coupled NOR circuit of fig. 3.48, when
a) Initially $Q = 0$, $P = 1$, $A = B = 0$ and then A changes to a 1 state with B remaining at 0, and finally A returns to 0.
b) Initially $Q = 1$, $P = 0$, $A = B = 0$ and then B changes to 1 with $A = 0$, and finally B returns to 0.
c) Both A and B are made 1 and then return to 0 states.

Fig. 3.46 8-channel multiplexer circuit

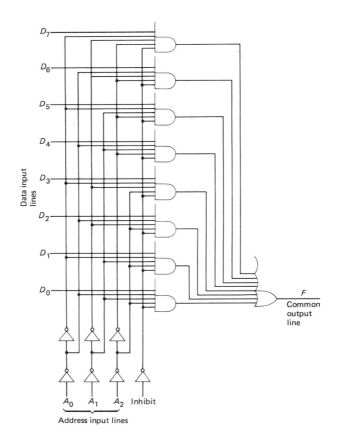

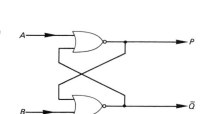

Fig. 3.47

(a)

S_{n+1}	R_{n+1}	Q_n	Q_{n+1} $\bar{Q}_{n+1}$
0	0	0	
0	0	1	
0	1	1	
1	0	0	
1	0	1	

J_{n+1}	K_{n+1}	Q_n	Q_{n+1} $\bar{Q}_{n+1}$
0	0	1	
0	1	1	
1	0	0	
1	0	1	
1	1	0	
1	1	1	

(b)

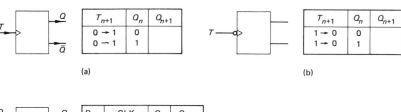

Fig. 3.48

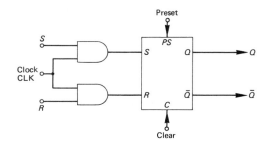

Fig. 3.49

T_{n+1}	Q_n	Q_{n+1}
$0 \rightarrow 1$	0	
$0 \rightarrow 1$	1	

(a)

T_{n+1}	Q_n	Q_{n+1}
$1 \rightarrow 0$	0	
$1 \rightarrow 0$	1	

(b)

D_{n+1}	CLK	Q_n	Q_{n+1}
0	$0 \rightarrow 1$	1	
1	$0 \rightarrow 1$	0	

(c)

Fig. 3.50

10 Explain the action of the clocked S-R flip-flop circuit shown in fig. 3.49 and
determine the output state Q when
a) CLK $= 0$, $S = 0$, $R = 0$, $PS = 1$, $C = 0$
b) CLK $= 0$, $S = 0$, $R = 0$, $PS = 0$, $C = 1$
c) CLK $= 1$, $S = 0$, $R = 1$
d) CLK $= 1$, $S = 1$, $R = 0$ followed by
e) CLK $= 0$, $S = 0$, $R = 0$

11 State the advantages of edge triggering and distinguish between leading-edge and
trailing-edge triggered flip-flops. Complete the truth tables for the T and D type
flip-flops shown in fig. 3.50.

12 Explain the reasons why master-slave flip-flops are used in many sequential logic circuit applications. Describe briefly the action of the master-slave circuit of fig. 3.51.

13 Explain the action of the D-type flip-flop circuit shown in fig. 3.52a. Complete also the waveform diagram for the Q output given in b.

14 Fig. 3.53 shows the circuit of a J-K flip-flop plus two input gates. Assume the flip-flop is initially set so $Q = 1$, $\bar{Q} = 0$. Determine the subsequent output states for the following input conditions.
a) $J_1 = 1$, $J_2 = 0$, $K_1 = 1$, $K_2 = 0$ after first clock pulse.
b) New input conditions then established with $J_1 = J_2 = 0$, $K_1 = K_2 = 0$, followed by second clock pulse.
c) New conditions $J_1 = J_2 = 1$, $K_1 = 0$, $K_2 = 0$, followed by third clock pulse.
d) New conditions $J_1 = 1$, $J_2 = 0$, $K_1 = K_2 = 0$, followed by fourth clock pulse.
e) New conditions $J_1 = 1$, $J_2 = 1$, $K_1 = 0$, $K_2 = 1$, followed by fifth clock pulse.
f) New conditions $J_1 = 1$, $J_2 = 1$, $K_1 = 1$, $K_2 = 0$, followed by sixth clock pulse.

15 The input to the cascaded T-type flip-flop circuit of fig. 3.54 is a square wave of 1 MHz frequency. Sketch the input waveform and outputs Q_0, Q_1, Q_2, Q_3, Q_4 and determine their repetition frequencies.

16 Distinguish between synchronous and asynchronous system operation and state one advantage of each.
Fig. 3.55 show a 4-bit J-K flip-flop counter. Describe briefly its mode of operation and sketch, for the input waveform shown, the waveforms obtained at Q_0, Q_1, Q_2 and Q_3. Assume initially that all outputs are 0 states.

17 Draw up the output state table for Q_0, Q_1, Q_2 in the synchronous counter circuit shown in fig. 3.56 for a sequence of 10 input pulses. Sketch also the waveforms at Q_0, Q_1, Q_2 for the first 6 input pulses. What property can you deduce about the counter's characteristics.

18 The shift register of fig. 3.57 is first cleared and a 5-bit data word 10011 fed in serially in 5 successive clock pulses. Explain the action of the circuit and complete the state table also shown in the figure. Assume all flip-flops are of the master-slave type.

Fig. 3.51

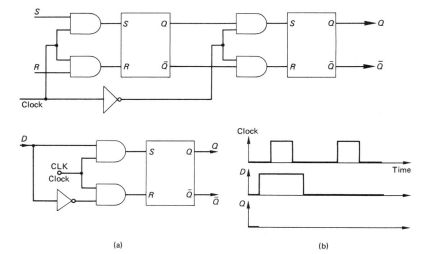

Fig. 3.52

(a)   (b)

Fig. 3.53

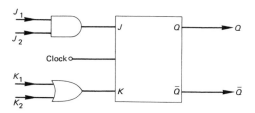

Fig. 3.54

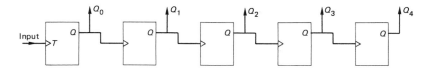

Fig. 3.55

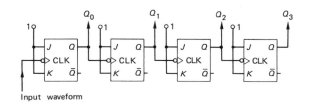

Fig. 3.56

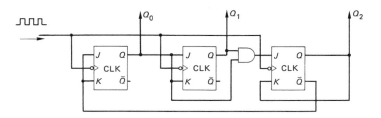

Fig. 3.57 Shift register and state table

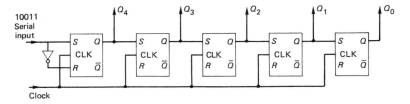

Time	Q_4	Q_3	Q_2	Q_1	Q_0
0	0	0	0	0	0
after 1st clock pulse					
after 2nd clock pulse					
after 3rd clock pulse					
after 4th clock pulse					
after 5th clock pulse					

Fig. 3.58

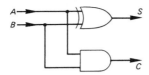

Fig. 3.59

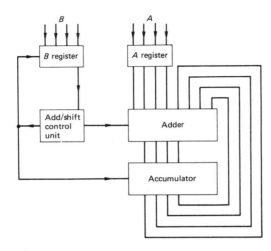

19 Construct the truth table for the half-adder circuit shown in fig. 3.58. Draw the circuit diagram showing how two half adders can be used to construct a full-adder and construct the truth table for your circuit.

20 Draw labelled circuit diagrams of *a*) serial and *b*) adder circuits which are capable of adding a sequence of 4-bit numbers. Explain the circuit action for the addition:

$A + B + C$ where $A = 1010$, $B = 1111$, $C = 0101$

21 The circuit of fig. 3.59 is used to multiply the numbers $A = 1010$ and $B = 1011$. Explain the step-by-step operation of the circuit showing the contents of registers A and B and the accumulator after each step.

4 Microprocessor Architecture and System Operation

4.1 Introduction: the Emergence of the Microprocessor

The microprocessor is a natural development of the integration of the basic digital logic circuits described in the previous chapter. It is difficult to select one particular device as being the "first" microprocessor, particularly as the early development work was intended for military applications. However, it is, without doubt, the Intel 8008 microprocessor which first found widespread application in the commercial market, and which set the trend for future development.

Prior to the arrival of the Intel 8008, Datapoint, a firm based in San Antonio, Texas, USA, were (and still are) the manufactures of *intelligent* computer peripherals. Intelligent peripherals are devices which contain a small, dedicated computer to control the peripheral operation (see sections 7.3.5 and 7.5.1). During the period 1968-69 the Datapoint engineers designed a very simple computer and contracted with Intel and Texas Instruments to implement their design on a single chip. The objective of the Datapoint engineers was to produce a controller circuit, for use in a wide variety of intelligent peripherals, where the different peripheral requirements could be accommodated by using different control instructions (*software control*). This approach is to be compared with the then-existing technology, in which a new circuit control board had to be produced for each new peripheral (*hardware control*).

The integrated circuit, which was subsequently produced, worked extremely well. Unfortunately, it executed instructions far too slowly to be of use in the Datapoint systems. As a consequence Datapoint declined to purchase the chips, and continued using existing technology to meet their production needs. Intel, on the other hand, in an attempt to recover some of the development costs, renamed the device the INTEL 8008 and marketed it as a programmable logic controller.

Despite its slow operating speed, the Intel 8008 was of immediate use in many applications, which served as a test bed for engineers to evaluate, what was then, an entirely new philosophy in solutions to logic control. The subsequent success of the Intel 8008 paved the way for the development of more sophisticated devices by both Intel, and other manufacturers, who realised that a new market now existed where the rewards for a successful device could be very great indeed—they have been proved right!

It is interesting at this stage to review briefly the development of microelectronics technology and indicate the economic factors as well as the engineering ones, which led to the emergence of the microprocessor as a fundamental chip in modern digital electronic systems.

Prior to 1947, when the transistor was invented, the electronic industry had been totally dependent on the vacuum tube or **valve**. Valves were relatively large, fragile and high power-consuming devices, and dependence on these as the primary active device would have severely restricted the growth and applications of digital computers and control systems.

After the invention of the **transistor**, the electronics industry was able, in the early 1950s, to develop many new markets, notably transistor radios and digital computers. However, it soon became apparent that the ability to design increasingly complex electronic equipment was outpacing technological progress, particularly where size, weight, power consumption and reliability were at a premium.

Thus in the early 1950s development began in the integration of circuit components—transistors, diodes, resistors, capacitors—within a single silicon chip, to reduce both size and weight and to increase reliability by removing soldered interconnections. This heralded the beginning of **integrated circuits**.

By the early 1960s integrated circuits were being made on a silicon chip measuring only 1 to 2 mm square and about 0·2 mm thick, containing several tens of components. By 1980 the most complex LSI and VLSI silicon chips—microprocessor and memory chips—containing tens to several hundred thousand components on a chip approximately 10 mm square were not only possible but were in mass production.

The ability to put down more and more devices into a given chip size has led, over the past two decades, to drastic cost reductions. Fig. 4.1 illustrates very vividly the increasing scale of integration and the decline in cost per gate: a factor of the order of 100 000 in improvement! These cost reductions coupled with compactness and increased reliability are the prime reasons for the creation of major new developments and markets—and in particular to the emergence of the **microprocessor**.

The microprocessor's virtue is that it is a programmable device. It can be used in a wide variety of applications, each application determined by the program instructions that the user can write into the microprocessor or its

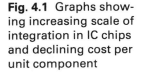 **Fig. 4.1** Graphs showing increasing scale of integration in IC chips and declining cost per unit component

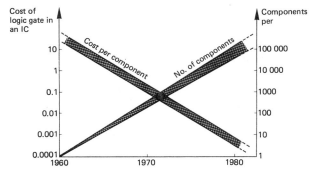

associated memory chips. It is, however, misleading to assume that all electronic products will be based entirely on microprocessors with circuit design skills solely replaced by the ability to write software. An understanding of the hardware and system operation is fundamental.

Furthermore many digital functions are incompatible with microprocessors and can be best implemented using other digital building blocks. Moreover we live in an analogue world so that much electronics including that associated with microprocessor systems will remain in analogue form. These last comments are in no way meant to diminish the importance of the microprocessor—it is here to stay—they are included to put its role in perspective.

4.2   The Architecture of a Basic Microcomputer

The combination of a microprocessor, memory and input and output ports to form a microprocessor-based computer system is known as a **microcomputer**. The term **architecture**, as applied in computer systems, is used to denote the logical structure or organisation of the hardware making up the system. A simplified architecture showing a typical organisation of the basic hardware units and their interconnections for a microcomputer is shown in fig. 4.2a. The function of the units is as follows.

1   The MICROPROCESSOR

The microprocessor, often referred to as the microprocessor unit or MPU, is a large-scale or very-large-scale integrated circuit which acts as the central processor of the microcomputer. It contains on a single IC chip all the logic circuits necessary to interpret and execute the individual machine instructions which make up our programs. Microprocessors are generally mounted as a 40-pin dual-in-line package as shown in fig. 4.2b.

The internal architecture of a microprocessor is, as you might expect, complex and will be considered in detail in later sections of this chapter. However, as far as the user is concerned, it may be considered to comprise the following:

a) A number of **registers** (temporary storage elements) which can each hold a number of bits of binary information, typically 8 bits (1 byte) and 16 bits (2 bytes) representing machine instructions, data, addresses.
b) The **arithmetic logic unit** (**ALU**) which performs the arithmetic and logical decisions.
c) The **timing and control circuits** which control both the internal operation of the microprocessor and the external operation of the complete microcomputer system. These circuits control the operation of the ALU and registers, coordinate input and output transfers to and from memory and the I/O ports, and ensure that the desired action specified by the program instructions is performed.

2 The MEMORY

The central memory units are used to store the programs currently being executed by the computer, and also the firmware—those permanently stored programs which are necessary for the user to operate the computer system. In a microcomputer two types of memory devices are employed: ROMs and RAMs.

ROM (read only memory) Read only memory, universally known as ROM, is memory which is permanently programmed and can only be **read**, i.e. program instructions, data, etc. can only be copied from ROM memory. No information can be written into ROM.

ROM has program instructions "burnt" into its store during manufacture or possibly by the user. ROM is employed to store permanently required programs, the firmware. For example: *monitor programs*, which are programs that control the operation of a microcomputer system and allow the user to run application programs, to input and output data, to examine and modify memory, etc.; and *dedicated programs*, each of which is specially devised to fulfil one particular function, like the control of an industrial process for instance.

ROM memory is *non-volatile*. This means that when the power supplies are switched off, the information stored in ROM is not lost.

RAM (random access memory) Random access memory, universally known as RAM, but more realistically defined as **read/write** memory, is designed to have information both written into it and also read out of it.

The term random access is used to define memory in which each stored word can be accessed or retrieved in a given amount of time—the memory locations storing the words making up a program instruction, data, etc. can be accessed in any (i.e. random) order in the same amount of time. The access time is independent of the position of the word. In this sense ROMs are also random access devices but programs stored on magnetic tape must be accessed sequentially and are therefore not "randomly" accessible.

RAM is used for storing applications programs, fed in, for example, from a tape, disc, or printer. They are also used for storing intermediate results during a program execution. Information stored in RAM can readily be modified.

RAM memory is normally volatile in that data stored in RAM is lost when the main power supplies to the system are switched off. RAM can, however, be made non-volatile by providing back-up power supplies to maintain power when the mains supplies are turned off.

3 The I/O unit, INPUT and OUTPUT PORTS

An input port is an IC that connects signals from external devices to the microprocessor. An output port is an IC that allows the microprocessor to output signals to external devices.

The function of input and output ports is often combined into a single unit, the I/O unit. This unit is a single IC, similar in size to the microprocessor IC package, and is controlled by the microprocessor to input information

Fig. 4.2 Simplified architecture of a microprocessor-based computer system

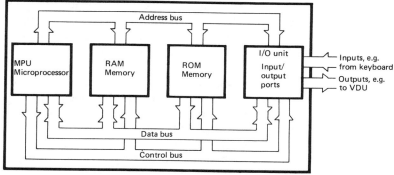

(a)   A basic microcomputer system

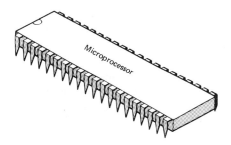

(b)   A typical microprocessor
Integrated circuit dual in line (DTL) package, with 40 pins for external connection to data, control and address buses.
(Drawn to scale: approx 52 x 13 x 3mm)

when required from a data source and output data as instructed by the program being executed.

In general, I/O units form the **interface** between the microprocessor and the input and output devices.

4   The BUSES

The microprocessor, memory and I/O integrated circuits are interconnected by three buses. The term *bus* is used to denote a group of wires or conduction tracks which act as paths for digital signals that have a common function. There are three main buses used in microprocessor systems: the control bus, the data bus, and the address bus.

a) The **control bus**   This bus is used to send control signals generated in the timing-control circuits of the microprocessor to the memory and I/O units. For example, it carries read/write signals to memory and the input and output ports.

b) The **data bus**   This bus is used to transfer machine instructions and data from memory to the microprocessor and data associated with input/output transfers. The data bus, as distinct from the control and address buses, is **bidirectional**. Data can travel in both directions, either to or from the microprocessor. The data bus in most microprocessor systems consists of 8 tracks so it can carry simultaneously 8 bits or 1 byte words.

c) The **address bus** The address bus is used to transmit the address of the location in memory or the input/output port involved in a data transfer.

Every instruction, each piece of data stored in ROM and RAM memory, has its location identified by an *address*—a binary number, usually 16 bits long. When the contents of a given location are required in program execution, the microprocessor places its address on the address bus. The address bus transports the address bits which are used to access the required storage location. The contents of the accessed location are then placed on the data bus which reads the contents to the microprocessor. Alternatively if data is to be stored in RAM, the microprocessor places the address code on the address bus which selects the location specified. A write control signal to the device will then allow a copy of the data on the data bus to be written into the location.

Most address buses consist of 16 tracks and thus, as each address line can carry either a 1 or 0 address bit, there are $2^{16} = 65\,536$ different possible combinations and hence addresses, i.e. a 16-line address bus can access up to 65 536 different storage locations and input/output devices.

4.3 Some General Microprocessor System Concepts: Memory, I/O Ports and Buses

In the last section we considered the basic architecture of a simple micro-computer and explained briefly the functions of the MPU, the ROM and RAM memory chips, the I/O ports and the bus system linking the units. Here we focus our attention in more detail on the memory and I/O chips—what basic logic circuits are inside them and how they operate—together with some fundamental concepts concerning the flow of data, control and address signals along the buses.

4.3.1 Memory and Address Space Concepts

The memory elements in both ROM and RAM chips consist essentially of a large number of storage cells with each cell capable of storing either a 1 or 0 bit of binary information. These storage cells are organised in groups known as **locations**, where each location is capable of holding one word of binary information. In an 8-bit microprocessor system the wordlength employed is 8 bits or 1 byte, so for these systems each location comprises 8 single-bit cells.

In order to access the program instructions and data words stored in these memory locations, each location must be individually identifiable by a unique **address**. The binary word stored at a given address is known as the

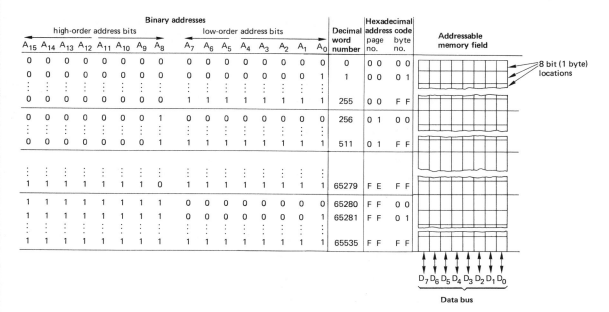

Fig. 4.3 Address bus and its relation to the memory field. A 16-line address bus can access 65 536 memory locations (i.e. **64 Kbytes of information for an 8-bit microprocessor)**

contents of that address. I/O ports are also specified by means of an unique address in the same way as memory locations.

The accessing of memory locations or an I/O port to both read or write data on to the data bus is made by means of the address bus. At each stage in the execution of a program, when the microprocessor has to fetch an instruction or transfer data, the MPU places a binary signal—the address—on the address bus and this signal selects the memory location or I/O port required. The address specifies the source or destination of the data word required, which will be subsequently placed in and propagated along the data bus.

This brings us to the concepts of address and memory space. **Address space** refers to the total set of addresses which the microprocessor can employ. The maximum number of addresses available is determined by the number of lines making up the address bus. As each line can take either a 0 or 1 state, the total number of different combinations for an n-line address bus is 2^n. For example, if a microprocessor had only 4 address lines, it could generate only $2^4 = 16$ addresses, i.e. binary 0000, 0001, 0010, $\cdots$ to 1111. This number would not be adequate for all but the very simplest of applications and consequently typical microprocessors have between 12 and 16 address lines. A 12-line bus can address $2^{12} = 4096$ separate addresses; a 16-line bus, $2^{16} = 65\,536$ separate addresses.

Fig. 4.3 shows a pictorial representation of the address space available in an 8-bit microcomputer with a 16-line address bus. This figure also serves to introduce the concepts of **memory space** or *field* and pages in memory.

The concept of a **page** in memory is very important in 8-bit microcomputers. The internal organisation of an 8-bit MPU is based on 8-bit registers and 8-bit parallel data paths. Most arithmetic and logic operations take place on 8 bits of data at a time. Likewise, the 16-bit program counter, which determines which instruction is to be executed, is normally divided into two 8-bit buses. One contains bits 0 to 7, the lower-order address bits; the other contains bits 8 to 15, the high-order address bits. With this in mind we can think of the address space shown in fig. 4.3 as consisting of 256 blocks, each consisting of 256 specific address locations. Each one of these blocks is referred to as a page of memory. The high-order bits of the address indicate in which page the address is located; the low-order bits indicate a specific address on that page.

The size of a computer memory is normally quoted in terms of the number of storage locations available in its ROM and RAM chips using the binary kilo, symbol K, as the unit:

$$1K = 2^{10} = 1024$$

Thus a typical microprocessor with a 16-line address bus can address up to

$$2^{16} = 2^6 \times 2^{10} = 64K \text{ or } 65\,536 \text{ locations}$$

and for an 8-bit system where each location can store an 8-bit or 1 byte word, it is possible to have a maximum memory of

$$64K \times 8 \text{ bits} = 64 \text{ Kbytes}$$

IC manufacturers supply ROM and RAM chips with individual memory cells organised in groups of 1, 4 and 8 bits. Thus, for example,

A $1K \times 1$-bit RAM chip has 1024 storage cells and hence 8 such chips would be required to store 1 Kbytes.

Two $1K \times 4$-bit RAM chips could provide $1K \times 8$-bit locations, i.e. 1024 locations each storing 1 byte.

A $2K \times 8$-bit ROM chip stores 2 Kbytes of binary information.

The range of addresses employed and the type of memory used is often indicated pictorially by a diagram known as a **memory map**. An example of a typical memory map for a microcomputer is shown in fig. 4.4. The map shows that the computer has 2 Kbytes of ROM allocated to firmware (the monitor program), 8 Kbytes of RAM for application programs, whilst addresses 2000 to 2007 (hex) are allocated to address 8 I/O ports.

4.3.2 ROM and RAM Chips: Accessing Memory, Read and Write

1 Fig. 4.5 shows schematic diagrams of the pin connections to the bus lines and typical logic circuits within a $1K \times 8$-bit **ROM chip** (a read only memory chip capable of storing 1024 words of 8-bit length).

The **ten address lines** labelled $A_0, A_1, \cdots A_9$ can access $2^{10} = 1024$ locations within the chip. The binary signal on these lines is decoded by the internal decoder logic circuits to select the required location.

The **chip select line** labelled CS is a higher-order address line, e.g. A_{10}, which is used to select the chip itself.

The **read control line** labelled MR is a line from the control bus with a read signal, which together with the chip select signal enables the tri-state gate driving the eight **data lines** $D_0, D_1, \cdots D_7$ of the data bus.

Fig. 4.4 A typical memory map for an 8-bit microcomputer

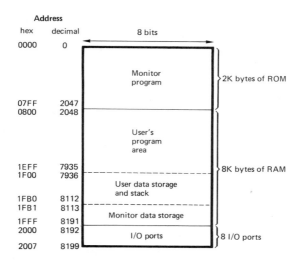

Address

hex	decimal	
0000	0	

8 bits

Monitor program — 2K bytes of ROM

| 07FF | 2047 |
| 0800 | 2048 |

User's program area

| 1EFF | 7935 |
| 1F00 | 7936 |

8K bytes of RAM

User data storage and stack

| 1FB0 | 8112 |
| 1FB1 | 8113 |

Monitor data storage

| 1FFF | 8191 |
| 2000 | 8192 |

I/O ports — 8 I/O ports

| 2007 | 8199 |

Fig. 4.5 Pin connections and internal organisation of a typical ROM chip capable of storing 1K × 8 bits of binary data

Memory location 0 in this chip is addressed by the MPU sending out the address signal

$$A_0 A_1 \cdots A_9 = 0000000000$$

with $CS = A_{10}$ (say) = 1 (to select the required chip) and the read control signal $MR = 1$ to enable the data bus drivers. This will place the contents of location 0 on the data bus, i.e. data is read from location 0. Likewise any of the other 1023 locations may be accessed by the appropriate address. The chip select and memory read signals in our example and for the chip of fig.

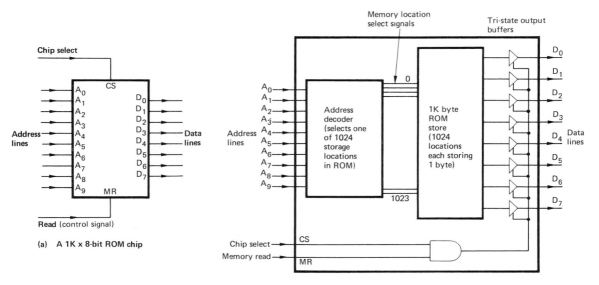

(a) A 1K × 8-bit ROM chip

(b) Functional block diagram of the inside of the ROM chip

4.5 have been taken as active high, i.e. CS = 1, MR = 1. In many cases these may be active low; the pins are then labelled $\overline{CS}$ and $\overline{MR}$ and a read operation is obtained when $\overline{CS} = 0$, $\overline{MR} = 0$.

2   Fig. 4.6 shows the bus connections and typical circuits within a $1K \times 8$-bit **RAM chip**. Any one of 1024 memory locations can be accessed in a similar manner to that described for the ROM above: the required location by the address bits on lines A_0, A_1, $\cdots A_9$, the chip by using a higher-order line $A_{11} = CS$, say.

In the read mode, the read signal MR = 1 (assuming active high) and this together with CS = 1 enables the tri-state data bus drivers, placing the contents of the addressed location on the data bus to be read.

In the write mode, the write signal MW = 1, sent from the MPU along one of the control lines, together with CS = 1 enables the input data control logic within the RAM chip. A copy of the word on the data lines D_0, D_1, $\cdots D_7$ is then written into the RAM store location specified by the address on lines A_0, A_1, $\cdots A_9$.

The read-write control is very often combined on a single line and this has the advantage that only one control line and only one pin on the chip is then required, as indicated in fig. 4.6*b* where the line is labelled **read/$\overline{\text{write}}$**. In this case, to write data into the RAM, the read/write signal should be a 0 state, i.e. $\overline{\text{write}} = 0$. To read data from the RAM, this signal should be a 1 state, i.e. read = 1.

3   Fig. 4.7 illustrates how several chips making up the required memory for a microprocessor system are connected and how any individual chip and memory location within this chip may be addressed. This example refers to an 8 Kbyte total memory built up from eight $1K \times 8$-bit ROM and RAM chips. Fig. 4.8 gives in detail the addresses assigned to the 8K available locations.

4.3.3   Parallel I/O Ports

The ideas of addressing and read and write to I/O ports are very similar to those used for memory. Thus to complete this section, the action of a simple parallel input/output port is explained. It has been implicitly assumed in our previous discussion that the MPU and memory chips operate as a parallel system in which words of data and addresses are handled simultaneously, i.e. the 8-bit words or 16-bit addresses propagate in parallel along the data and address buses. Some input devices generate binary data in serial form and, where this occurs, serial inputs must be converted to parallel form before being passed to the processor system. IC chips, known as UARTs (Universal Asynchronous Receiver Transmitter), are available for series-to-parallel and parallel-to-series conversion. In the present discussion we consider only the **parallel input/output** chips.

1   Fig. 4.9 illustrates how data can be read from an input port and written to

Fig. 4.6 Pin connections and internal organisation of a typical RAM chip capable of storing **1 Kbyte**

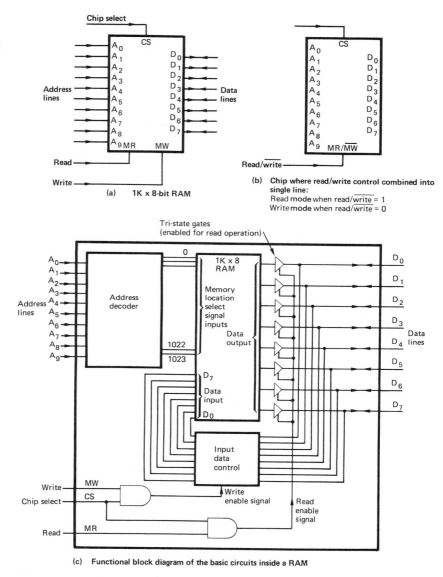

(a)   1K x 8-bit RAM

(b)   **Chip where read/write control combined into single line:**
Read mode when read/$\overline{\text{write}}$ = 1
Write mode when read/$\overline{\text{write}}$ = 0

(c)   **Functional block diagram of the basic circuits inside a RAM**

an output port. The internal circuits within the I/O ports are represented for simplicity as two banks of eight switches. When data is required or fed in from an input port, the given port is addressed by the MPU via the address bus using, for example, a higher-order address line to carry the *chip select* signal. This signal acts to effectively close one bank of switches. The *read* signal sent from MPU along a control bus line closes the second bank of switches, thus connecting the data on the eight parallel input device lines to the data bus.

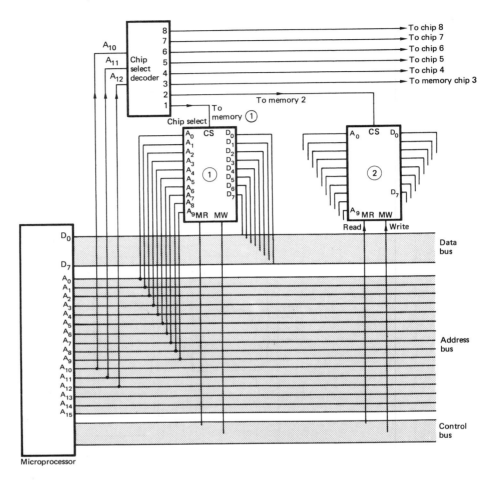

Fig. 4.7 An example of accessing memory locations: the microprocessor places the address of the required location on the 16 address lines of the address bus; the address lines indicate which memory chip should be selected and which location in that chip should be addressed.

In the example we are to address any one of 8K memory locations contained in **eight individual 1 Kbytes memory chips. Address lines A_{10}, A_{11}, A_{12} are sent** to the chip-select decoder which enables the given 1K memory chip. Lines A_0 to A_9 are used to access the required location—any one of 1024—in the device. When the location is accessed, a control signal memory read or write is activated and the contents of the location are either "copied" onto the data lines (for a Read command) or the bits on the data bus are copied into the location (for a Write command), the latter only being permissible for RAM chips

Address		Address line states		Address line numbers
		Chip-select bits	Locations within individual devices	
decimal	hex	A_{15} A_{14} A_{13} $\quad$ A_{12} A_{11} A_{10}	A_9 A_8 A_7 A_6 A_5 A_4 A_3 A_2 A_1 A_0	
0	0 0 0 0	0 0 0 $\quad$ 0 0 0	0 0 0 0 0 0 0 0 0 0	
1	0 0 0 1	0 0 0 $\quad$ 0 0 0	0 0 0 0 0 0 0 0 0 1	Memory chip 1
2	0 0 0 2	0 0 0 $\quad$ 0 0 0	0 0 0 0 0 0 0 0 1 0	addresses
⋮				0 to 1023
1022	0 3 F E	0 0 0 $\quad$ 0 0 0	1 1 1 1 1 1 1 1 1 0	
1023	0 3 F F	0 0 0 $\quad$ 0 0 0	1 1 1 1 1 1 1 1 1 1	
1024	0 4 0 0	0 0 0 $\quad$ 0 0 1	0 0 0 0 0 0 0 0 0 0	
1025	0 4 0 1	0 0 0 $\quad$ 0 0 1	0 0 0 0 0 0 0 0 0 1	Memory chip 2 addresses
⋮				1024 to 2047
2047	0 7 F F	0 0 0 $\quad$ 0 0 1	1 1 1 1 1 1 1 1 1 1	
2048	0 8 0 0	0 0 0 $\quad$ 0 1 0	0 0 0 0 0 0 0 0 0 0	Memory chip 3
⋮				addresses
3071	0 B F F	0 0 0 $\quad$ 0 1 0	1 1 1 1 1 1 1 1 1 1	2048 to 3071
3072	0 C 0 0	0 0 0 $\quad$ 0 1 1	0 0 0 0 0 0 0 0 0 0	Memory chip 4
⋮				addresses
4095	0 F F F	0 0 0 $\quad$ 0 1 1	1 1 1 1 1 1 1 1 1 1	3072 to 4095
4096	1 0 0 0	0 0 0 $\quad$ 1 0 0	0 0 0 0 0 0 0 0 0 0	Memory chip 5
⋮				addresses
5119	1 3 F F	0 0 0 $\quad$ 1 0 0	1 1 1 1 1 1 1 1 1 1	4096 to 5119
5120	1 4 0 0	0 0 0 $\quad$ 1 0 1	0 0 0 0 0 0 0 0 0 0	Memory chip 6
⋮				addresses
6143	1 7 F F	0 0 0 $\quad$ 1 0 1	1 1 1 1 1 1 1 1 1 1	5120 to 6143
6144	1 8 0 0	0 0 0 $\quad$ 1 1 0	0 0 0 0 0 0 0 0 0 0	Memory chip 7
⋮				addresses
7167	1 B F F	0 0 0 $\quad$ 1 1 0	1 1 1 1 1 1 1 1 1 1	6144 to 7167
7168	1 C 0 0	0 0 0 $\quad$ 1 1 1	0 0 0 0 0 0 0 0 0 0	Memory chip 8
⋮				addresses
8191	1 F F F	0 0 0 $\quad$ 1 1 1	1 1 1 1 1 1 1 1 1 1	7168 to 8191

Fig. 4.8 Addresses assigned to **8 Kbytes** of memory comprised of 8 individual **1 Kbyte** memory chips.

Note that lines A_{10}, A_{11}, A_{12} are used via a decoder to select particular memory device; lines A_0 to A_9 are used to access individual location within each memory chip; lines A_{13}, A_{14}, A_{15} are held at 0 since, although a 16-line address bus has the capability of addressing up to 64K locations, only 8K locations are required in the example

When a copy of the data placed on the data bus by the MPU is to be outputted to a given output port, the port is first accessed by its address being placed on the address bus (the chip select signal) and then followed by the write control signal. These signals effectively close both banks of switches, thereby connecting the 8-bit word on the data bus to the lines feeding the parallel output device.

2 Fig. 4.10 shows the connections and the typical logic circuits within a chip which can be used both as an input and an output port. Consider its action when, for example, an 8-bit word is to be read from a parallel input device. The input device supplies the word on eight data input lines labelled DI_0, DI_1, $\cdots DI_7$. This information is latched into the D-type flip-flops on

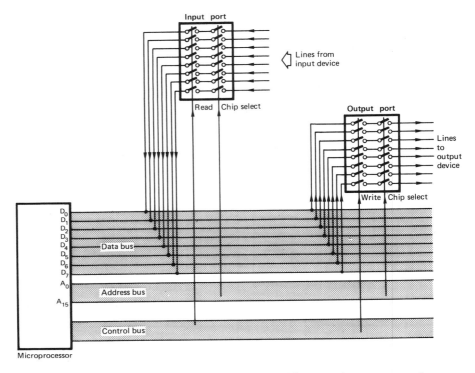

Fig. 4.9 Diagram showing how data can be read from an **input port and** written to an **output port.**

For a read instruction, the input port is accessed by the appropriate address on the address bus; a read signal is then sent from MPU along the control bus to the input device; data from the input device is then placed on the 8 lines of the data bus.

For a write instruction, the output port is accessed by the address bus and a write signal from the control bus effectively connects the 8 data bus lines to the output port.

receiving a clock pulse via a control bus line from the MPU. The input signal—and in the case of an output port, the word on the data bus—may only be present for a microsecond or less, so it is necessary to have a temporary store to catch the data whilst present and "lock" the bits into a latch until such time as the information is required. On receiving the chip select signal, the tri-state gates are enabled and the data stored in the D-type flip-flop latch are then connected direct to the data bus lines D_0, $D_1, \cdots D_7$.

The same type of chip can be used as an output port. As an output port the chip's input data lines are connected in parallel with the data bus. For a write-to-output operation, the word on the data bus is latched into the D-type flip-flops by a clock control signal, and then copied to the output when the tri-state gates are enabled by the chip-select signal.

Fig. 4.10 I/O chips: typical external connections and basic internal organisation of chips which can be used as either an input or an output port

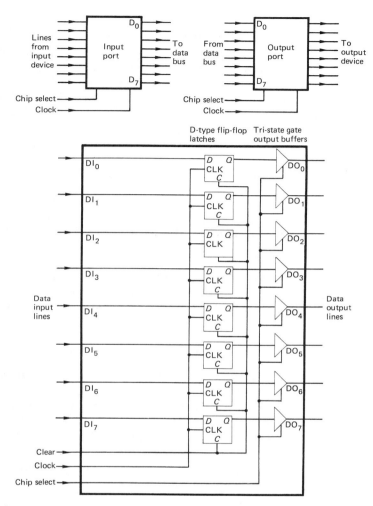

4.4 Introduction to Microprocessor Internal Architecture

In the context of the present discussion, and as already noted, the term *architecture* refers to the internal structure of a microprocessor, i.e. the number, type and function of the various internal registers, control-timing circuits, etc. In this section the architecture of two different microprocessors will be discussed. These are the **Rockwell 6502** and the **Zilog Z80** microprocessors, which have been selected for the following three reasons. First, these two microprocessors are among the most popular devices currently available, being used extensively as the central processing unit (CPU) in most microcomputing systems. Consequently the reader with access to a minicomputer or microprocessor system will, in all probability, have access to at least one, if not both, of these microprocessors. Second, whilst neither the 6502 nor the Z80 can be described as an ideal microprocessor, they do possess between them most of the features of such an ideal device. Finally, by discussing two different microprocessors, together with their instruction sets and addressing modes (see Chapter 5), the reader is encouraged to constructively compare microprocessor characteristics and features. This is an important exercise for anyone contemplating microprocessor applications where inevitably the first question to be asked is: "which microprocessor do we use?"

Since it is the simpler of the two microprocessors we will first examine the Rockwell 6502.

4.5 Architecture of the Rockwell 6502 Microprocessor

Fig. 4.11 illustrates the basic architecture of the 6502, with fig. 4.12 showing the corresponding pin-out connections. As with all microprocessors the internal components may be classified as being either *registers*, which hold data or instructions, or *control circuits*, which control the microprocessor operation.

4.5.1 6502 Registers

At the heart of the microprocessor is the **arithmetic logic unit** or ALU. The function of the ALU is to perform arithmetic (addition or subtraction) or logical (AND, OR, E-OR, etc.) operations on bytes of data which are fed in via the two inputs. In almost all operations, one byte of the input data will originate from the **Accumulator** or A-register, whilst the other bytes will usually originate from the external memory. The result of the ALU operation is an output and this output is usually stored back in the accumulator. For example, the instruction

ADC $4000   [$ indicates that a hex number follows]

will add (ADC $\equiv$ Add with Carry—see section 5.4) the number stored in memory at address 4000_{16} to the number currently stored in the accumulator. The result of the addition will be returned to the accumulator. Thus if the accumulator contains the number 12_{16} and the number 26_{16} is stored at 4000_{16}, the instruction ADC $4000 will result in the number 38_{16} ($38_{16} = 12_{16} + 26_{16}$) being returned from the ALU and stored in the accumulator.

As the above discussion implies, the accumulator (which *accumulates* results) is the main 6502 register capable of holding one byte of data. The ALU–accumulator combination is a "classic" CPU design which allows short single-byte instructions to specify both arithmetic and logical operations.

The X and Y (index) registers are both one-byte registers which can serve three functions. First they can be used as **scratch pad registers** to store

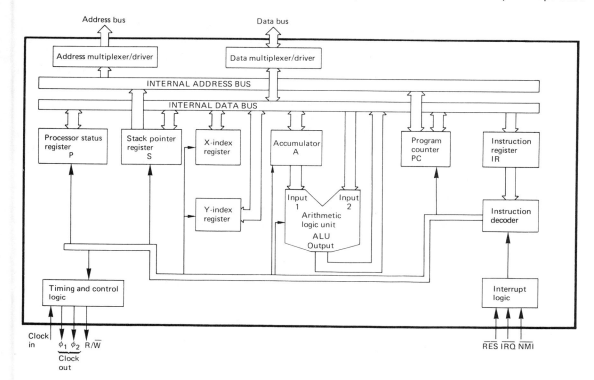

Fig. 4.11 Internal
architecture 6502

Fig. 4.12 Pin-out
connections 6502

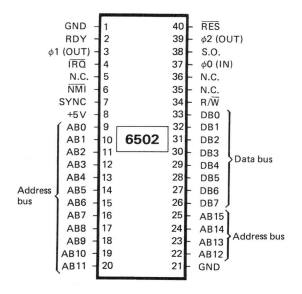

N.C. = NOT CONNECTED

temporary data such as the intermediate results, e.g. partial products, of calculations. Second, they can be used as counters for program loops and timing applications. Finally, they can be used as **index registers** to allow operations to be performed on tables of data stored in memory (see 5.17.1).

Although the X and Y index registers can be used for the temporary storage of data, difficulties arise if more than two bytes of data require storage or if the X and Y registers are already being used, e.g. as counters, when the need for temporary storage arises. To overcome these problems the 6502 is equipped, like most microprocessors, with a portion of memory space located in one of the system's RAM chips. This memory is known as the **stack memory** and is accessed by the microprocessor by the **stack pointer register** (SP).

The stack memory, or to give it its proper name of LIFO (last-in/first-out) memory, is a very convenient way of providing temporary storage, for a large number of bytes of data, using a simple single-byte instruction. The LIFO stack is analogous to the plate-stacking devices used in some canteens and restaurants (fig. 4.13). With such an arrangement the last plate *pushed* onto the top of the stack is the first plate to be *pulled* off by the next customer.

Fig. 4.13 A canteen "Lowerator"

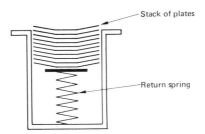

Stack of plates

Return spring

Operation of the stack in the 6502 is as follows. The stack is allocated a specific area in memory which, in the 6502, is page 1 or the 256 locations from 100_{16} to $1FF_{16}$. The stack pointer register is a nine-bit register which holds the address of the next available memory location in the stack. When the microprocessor is first switched on, and the system reset, the SP register is set to $1FF_{16}$, which is the address of the start of the stack. To store data on the stack, an instruction of the form PHA (push accumulator to stack) is used which results in the contents of the accumulator being stored at $1FF_{16}$ and the SP register decremented, by one, to $1FE_{16}$. If a second PHA instruction is executed, the contents of the accumulator are stored at $1FE_{16}$ and the SP register decremented to $1FD_{16}$. To retrieve data from the stack, an instruction of the form PLA (pull accumulator from the stack) is used in which the SP register is **first incremented** and the contents of the location addressed by the SP loaded into the accumulator.

The **program counter** PC is a 16-bit register which holds the address in memory of the next instruction to be executed. Thus when the microprocessor finishes executing the current instruction, the PC register indicates where the next instruction is to be found.

The **status register** P is an 8-bit register which contains information as to the present status of the microprocessor, in particular the accumulator. Seven of the P register bits (one is not used) act as **flags** which are set to binary 1 if, for example, the result of a calculation is zero or negative or if a carry occurred during an addition. A full description of the flags register is given in section 5.7.

The 8-bit **instruction register** IR holds the instruction to be executed. During operation, the microprocessor first fetches the instruction from memory and stores it in the IR register prior to the execution.

4.5.2 6502 Control Circuits

If the ALU is the heart of the microprocessor then the **instruction decoder** circuit is its brain. As its name implies, the instruction decoder decodes the current instruction held in the instruction register (i.e. determines what action is to be taken), and, together with the timing and control logic, manipulates the internal registers, address and data bus, such that the instruction is executed (see 4.7).

The three **interrupt lines** provide a means of gaining the attention of the microprocessor when it is executing a program. This may be necessary, for example, to inform the microprocessor that an external device has data available or that an alarm condition has occurred which must be dealt with immediately. The $\overline{\text{RES}}$ (reset, active low) line is used to reset the microprocessor and as such is only used when the microprocessor is switched on or a program has "crashed". The $\overline{\text{IRQ}}$ (interrupt request) and $\overline{\text{NMI}}$ (non-maskable interrupt) are true interrupt lines. The difference between them is that the microprocessor must always obey an NMI, whilst the IRQ may be masked (i.e. turned off or disabled) by the programmer. Since they are invariably associated with input/output devices, the interrupt lines will be discussed under this heading (see 4.9.2).

Interfacing the microprocessor to the system, or external, data and address buses is accomplished using the address and data multiplexer/driver circuits which are controlled by the instruction decoder and the timing and control logic.

The $R/\overline{W}$ (READ/$\overline{\text{WRITE}}$) line is used by the microprocessor to signal that it is either reading data from, or writing data to, an external device or memory. If the $R/\overline{W}$ line is at logical 1, the microprocessor is in the read mode, whilst if at logical 0 the microprocessor is in the write mode.

The ϕ_1 and ϕ_2 clock signals are generated by the microprocessor in response to an external clock signal ϕ which is usually a crystal-controlled oscillator. ϕ_1 and ϕ_2 are used to synchronise operations during the microprocessor fetch-decode-execute cycle discussed later (4.7).

Three of the pins shown in fig. 4.12 are unaccounted for in the microprocessor architecture shown in fig. 4.11. This omission is quite deliberate since these three pins, the RDY (or READY, pin 2), SYNC (or SYNCHRONISE, pin 7) and S.O. (SET OVERFLOW FLAG, pin 38) are associated with functions which are beyond the scope of the present text. For present purposes it is sufficient to note that the RDY and SYNC lines enable the microprocessor to be used with slow-responding memories (see 6.8.1) whilst the S.O. line was intended as a form of interrupt, which has never been fully implemented in the 6502 system design.

4.6 Architecture of the Zilog Z80 microprocessor

Fig. 4.14 illustrates the architecture of the Z80 microprocessor with fig. 4.15 showing the corresponding pin-out connections. As with the 6502, fig. 4.14 represents a simplified architecture since the more complex features of the Z80 are beyond the scope of the present discussion. Like the 6502 the Z80 architecture may be divided into register and control circuits which will be discussed separately.

4.6.1 Z80 Registers

The one striking feature of the Z80 is the large number of 8-bit duplicated registers which can be used for data handling. The duplicated registers are the accumulator A, the general-purpose registers B, C, D, E, H and L, and the flags register F. The duplicate registers are denoted with a prime (e.g. A'). At any particular instant the microprocessor may only operate on one set of registers. Special instructions allow the contents of one set of registers to be exchanged with the other, thus allowing one set of data to be conveniently stored whilst the data in the second set is manipulated.

Apart from their use as general-purpose registers, the register pairs, BC, DE and HL, may be used to hold a 16-bit absolute address. For example the instruction:

LD   A,(HL)

in Z80 assembly code will load the accumulator with the data stored at the absolute address contained in the H (high-order byte) and L (low-order byte) registers. Thus if the H register contained $D2_{16}$ and the L register contained $3F_{16}$, the above instruction would result in the accumulator being loaded with the data stored at the absolute address $D23F_{16}$.

The **arithmetic logic unit**, or ALU, functions in exactly the same way as the ALU in the 6502 and requires no further comment.

The two **flags registers** F and F' contain the microprocessor status information. Their operation is similar to the 6502 P register and full details are given in section 5.7.

The Z80 **stack pointer register** SP fulfils the same rôle as the 6502 stack pointer. There are, however, differences. First, the Z80 stack pointer register is a 16-bit register, thus allowing the stack to address any section of the 64K memory. Second, the base address of the stack may be fixed *anywhere* in memory (in the 6502 the base of the stack was set at $1FF_{16}$). The Z80 stack grows downwards from the base address, as with the 6502.

Like the 6502, the Z80 possesses two **index registers** IX and IY. These are both 16-bit registers which allow indexed addressing over the full 64K of memory (see 5.15.2).

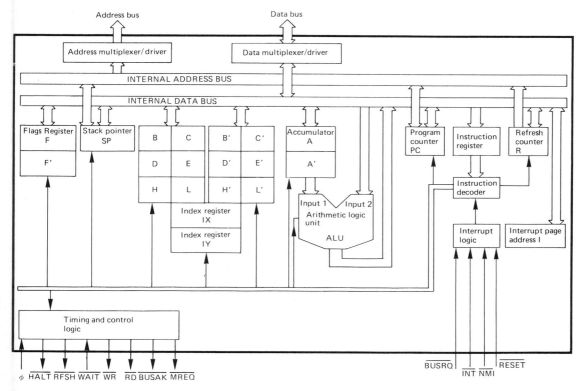

Fig. 4.14 Internal
architecture Z80

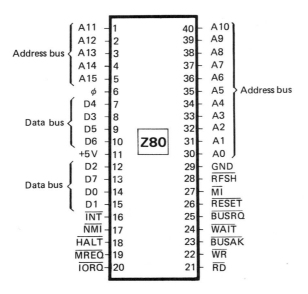

Fig. 4.15 Pin-out
connections Z80

The Z80 **program counter** PC and the **instruction register** operate in an identical fashion to the 6502.

The **refresh counter** or **register** R is incremented during each microprocessor cycle (see 4.7). The purpose of the R register is to allow the automatic refresh of *dynamic memories* (see 6.9.2).

Finally, the **interrupt page address register** I is used to form an absolute address to which program control may be passed when an interrupt occurs (see 4.9.2).

4.6.2 Z80 Control Circuits

The Z80 **instruction decoder** functions in a similar fashion to the 6502 instruction decoder and thus requires no further explanation at this stage. The same is true of the Z80 address and data bus multiplexers and drivers.

The Z80 has, effectively, four **interrupt lines**. These are the RESET, NMI, INT and BUSRQ, which are all active low (for the first three, see 4.9.1).

The Z80 **clock signals** may be derived from either an internal (i.e. contained within the Z80) or an external oscillator. To use the internal clock, a pull-up resistance of approximately 330 Ω is connected between pin 6 and the +5 volt supply rail. If an external clock is to be used—essential if the clock frequency is above 4 MHz—the external clock signal is fed in via the ϕ input and ground.

The HALT is an acknowledge signal generated by the Z80 after it has executed a HALT instruction.

The RFSH (refresh) line is activated when the Z80 has a valid refresh address on the address bus (see 6.9.2).

The WAIT state is a signal used to synchronise the Z80 with a slow memory or external device. When activated, the Z80 executes a special wait routine until the line is deactivated, when the Z80 continues with the normal sequence.

The WR (write) and RD (read) lines are used to indicate to external devices that the Z80 is in the write or read mode, respectively.

The BUSAK is an acknowledge signal supplied by the Z80 in response to a BUSRQ interrupt.

Finally, the MREQ (memory request) signal is used by the Z80 to indicate that it is transferring data to or from memory (as opposed to data transfer to or from an input/output port).

4.7 The Microprocessor Fetch–Decode–Execute Cycle

Fig. 4.16 illustrates the format in which a Z80 or 6502 machine code program is stored in memory. Each instruction comprises a "generalised" operation code, usually referred to as the **Op code**, followed by either none, one or two bytes of data which the Op code, when executed, will manipulate. Consequently instructions are described as being *one byte* (no data specified), *two byte* (one byte of data specified), or *three byte* (two bytes of

Fig. 4.16 Format of machine code program

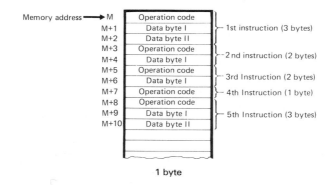

data specified). Examples of one, two and three byte instructions are given in Chapter 5.

As might be expected, instructions are stored sequentially in memory with successive instructions occupying the higher memory addresses. The location in memory of the first instruction depends, to a great extent, upon the system designer and programmer, although the position of the reset and interrupt vectors (see below) will be an influencing factor.

The basic microprocessor operational cycle consists of three phases. These are

1 FETCH instruction
2 DECODE instruction
3 EXECUTE instruction.

4.7.1 Fetch Instruction

In this, the first phase, the instruction to be executed is **fetched** from memory and placed in the instruction register. The contents of the program counter—which, it will be recalled, contains the address of the next instruction to be executed—are placed on the address bus and a *read from memory* signal placed on the control bus. (Pin 34 set to logical 1 [6502]; pin 21 reset to logical 0 [Z80].) A short time later, depending upon the access time of the memory (see 6.1), the memory will place the instruction Op code on the data bus, following which the microprocessor reads the data bus and places the Op code in the instruction register. The microprocessor then increments the program counter by one, two or three, depending upon the Op code just read into the instruction register, such that the program counter points to the next instruction. At this stage the fetch cycle is complete.

The fetch cycle, like the subsequent decode and execute cycles, is synchronised with the microprocessor clock.

Fig. 4.17 Timing sequence for a 6502 fetch cycle

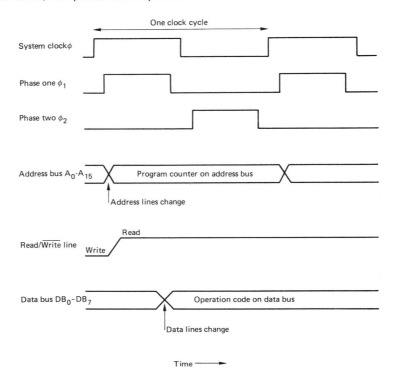

1 Fig. 4.17 illustrates the timing sequence of the 6502 fetch cycle. The 6502 produces two non-overlapping clock signals called ϕ_1 and ϕ_2 from the system clock ϕ. During the ϕ_1 cycle, the microprocessor places the contents of the program counter on the address bus and sets the read/write line to read. The external memory responds by placing the data, stored at the PC address, onto the data bus. During the ϕ_2 cycle, the 6502 reads the data bus and places the data (or Op code) into the instruction register. The system designer ensures that the frequency of ϕ, ϕ_1 and ϕ_2 are such that the data bus has sufficient time to stabilise before the ϕ_2-read operation occurs.

2 Fig. 4.18 illustrates the same timing sequence for the Z80. The fetch cycle, which is also known as machine cycle 1 or MC1, requires four clock cycles or T-states. During the first T-state T1, the contents of the program counter are placed on the address bus and the memory request and read lines activated. The external memory responds by placing the data, stored at the PC address, on the data bus. The data, which is the instruction Op code, is read into the Z80 instruction register on the rising edge of the third T-state T3. The second T-state T2 is used, amongst other purposes, to provide a delay such that the data bus has sufficient time to stabilise before the data is read in during T3. During the last two T-states, the Z80 generates a refresh address, which is placed on the address bus, and the RFSH line activated (see 6.9.2).

Fig. 4.18 Timing sequence for a Z80 fetch cycle

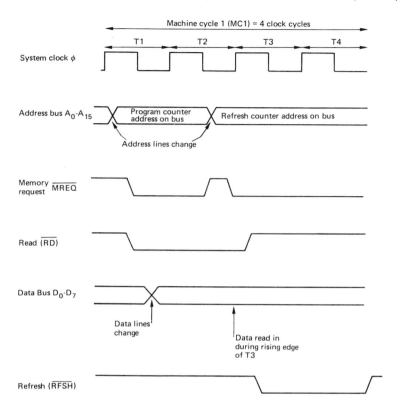

4.7.2 Decode and Execute

Once the Op code is placed in the instruction register, the instruction decoder generates the correct sequence of internal and external signals such that the instruction is executed correctly. The timing sequences of the decode and execute phases are similar to the fetch phase. However, the number of clock cycles, or T-states, required depends purely upon the particular instruction. For example, single-byte instructions are faster (require less clock cycles) than two-byte instructions which, in turn, are faster than three-byte instructions. The instruction sets of the Z80 and 6502, listed in the appendixes, give the total number of clock cycles or T-states which each instruction requires.

Following the execution of an instruction, the microprocessor enters the fetch phase of the next fetch-decode-execute cycle.

4.7.3 The First Instruction—the Action of the Reset Lines

A question which frequently arises is: given the fetch-decode-execute cycle, how does the microprocessor "know" where the first instruction is located in memory? The answer to this question is to be found in the *reset operation*.

In most systems the reset line (pin 40 [6502] and pin 26 [Z80]) is activated by the user who presses a key which, temporarily, shorts the reset pin to ground. Once the reset line is activated, the microprocessor performs a sequence of initialisation operations, such as clearing all of its internal registers, following which it loads the program counter with a specific address to obtain the first instruction.

1   For the Z80, following reset, the program counter is loaded with 0000_{16} (an obvious choice!) and consequently the first instruction must be stored at 0000_{16}. Note, however, that this first instruction can be used to make the microprocessor jump to another part of memory where the main program may be stored.

2   The 6502 uses addresses $FFFC_{16}$ and $FFFD_{16}$ as *vectors* which point to the location which contains the first instruction. For example, if the first instruction of the program occurs at 0200_{16}, the programmer must ensure that the address $FFFC_{16}$ contains 00 (low-order byte of the address 0200_{16}) and $FFFD_{16}$ contains 02_{16} (the high-order byte of the address 0200_{16}). Thus, following the activation of the reset line, the 6502 will use the data stored in $FFFC_{16}$ and $FFFD_{16}$ to form the address 0200_{16}, which is then deposited in the program counter.

4.8   Input and Output Techniques: Memory Mapped and I/O Mapped Ports

Microprocessor input and output ports may be classified as either:
 a) Memory mapped, or
 b) Input/output mapped—usually referred to as I/O mapped.
All microprocessor systems may be designed with memory mapped ports. However, only those microprocessors equipped with the appropriate hardware and I/O instructions may operate with I/O mapped ports.

4.8.1   Memory Mapped Ports

A **memory mapped** I/O port is, as far as the microprocessor is concerned, identical to a RAM location. To output data from a memory mapped port, the microprocessor simply writes the data to the port address as though the port address were a RAM location. To input data from a memory mapped port, the microprocessor reads from the port address in the same way in which it would read from a RAM location.

Fig. 4.19 illustrates the circuitry, or hardware, of a memory mapped I/O port which, for this example, is located at address $D000_{16}$ in memory. IC1 and IC2 are both 4-bit bus-transceivers comprising eight tri-state drivers coupled back-to-back. When the write enable (WE) line is set to logical 1, the four drivers on the left-hand side of both ICs are enabled, allowing the transfer of data from the data bus of the microprocessor to the I/O data lines (i.e. $D_0 - D_7$ to $IO_0 - IO_7$).

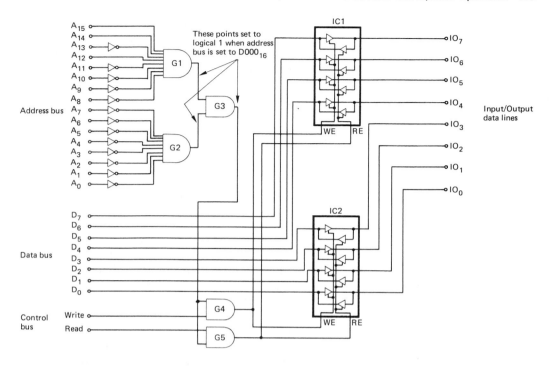

Fig. 4.19 A memory-mapped I/O port

If the read enable RE line is set to logical 1, the four drivers on the right-hand side of both ICs are enabled, allowing the transfer of data from the I/O lines to the microprocessor data bus ($IO_0 - IO_7$ to $D_0 - D_7$). Note that the WE and RE lines (fig. 4.19) must not be set to logical 1 simultaneously (see Problem 1 at the end of the Chapter).

Operation of the memory mapped I/O port is as follows. To output data which, typically, is stored in the accumulator, the microprocessor is instructed to write the contents of the accumulator to memory address $D000_{16}$. For the 6502 and Z80 microprocessors this would be accomplished using the instructions:

STA $D000   [6502]

i.e. store accumulator (STA) at address D000, with $ indicating that a hex number *follows* it.

LD   D000H,A   [Z80]

i.e. load (LD) address D000 from accumulator A, with H indicating that the number *preceding* it is in hex.

As a consequence the microprocessor places the address $D000_{16}$ on the address bus, the contents of the accumulator on the data bus, and, with additional logic circuitry (not shown in fig. 4.19, see Problem 11), sets the write and read lines in fig. 4.19 to logical 1 and 0 respectively.

When the address bus is set to $D000_{16}$, all inputs to the two-input AND gates, G1 and G2, are at logical 1. As a result the outputs from G1, G2 and G3 are also at logical 1. Since the Write line is also at logical 1, the output from G4 is high, enabling the WE inputs of IC1 and IC2 and resulting in the transfer of data on the microprocessor bus to the I/O data bus.

To input data from the port, the microprocessor is instructed to "read from memory location $D000_{16}$". The appropriate read instructions for the 6502 and Z80 are:

LDA $D000   [6502]

LD   A,D000H   [Z80]

i.e. load (LD) accumulator (A) from address $D000_{16}$.

As a consequence the microprocessor places the address $D000_{16}$ on the address bus, sets the Read and Write lines in fig. 4.19 to logical 1 and 0, respectively, and reads the data on the data bus into the accumulator. The combination of $D000_{16}$ on the address bus and the logical levels of the Read and Write lines results in the output from G5 being set to logical 1. The RE line is thus enabled, permitting the transfer of data from the port lines $IO_0 - IO_7$ to the microprocessor data bus $D_0 - D_7$.

The main advantage of the memory mapped I/O port is that it may be placed at any location in memory, thus allowing the programmer "one degree of freedom" when developing software. Its main disadvantage is that it requires more hardware than the I/O mapped port described below. In addition the instructions to input and output data from a memory mapped system take longer to execute than the special instructions used in I/O mapped systems. Generally, however, this does not represent a problem.

It should be noted that the Z80 and 6502 instructions, used in the above example, are the same instructions used to store and retrieve data from RAM or ROM (retrieve data only).

4.8.2   I/O Mapped Input/Output Ports

In a microprocessor which is designed to operate with **I/O mapped input/output**, Page 0 (the first 256 locations in memory, i.e. 0000_{16} to $00FF_{16}$) is used to address up to 256 input/output ports. In order to differentiate between memory and I/O operations, the microprocessor is equipped with special input/output instructions and control lines. For the Z80 microprocessor, the input and output instructions are

IN   (C),A

i.e. input data from port C and store it in the accumulator,

OUT   (C),A

i.e. output the data in the accumulator to port C,
where C is an address in Page 0 usually called the *port number*. The Z80 I/O control line is the MREQ (pin 19) line which, as already described, is set to logical 0 when the microprocessor is transferring data to or from memory and which is set to logical 1 when the data transfer is to or from an I/O port.

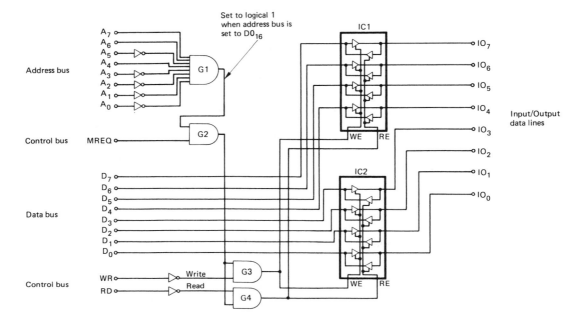

Fig. 4.20 An I/O-mapped I/O port for the Z80

(Note: the 6502 is not equipped for I/O mapped input/output.)

Fig. 4.20 illustrates the circuitry of an I/O mapped port situated at $D0_{16}$, in Page 0 (i.e. $00D0_{16}$), on a Z80 system. To output data, stored in the accumulator, from this port, the instruction

OUT D0H,A

is used. As a consequence the Z80 places the address $D0_{16}$ on the first eight address lines $(A_0 - A_7)$, the contents of the accumulator on the data bus, and then sets the MREQ and WR (Write) control lines to logical 1 and 0 respectively.

When the address $D0_{16}$ is placed on $A_0 - A_7$, all eight inputs of the 8-input AND gate G1 are set to logical 1. Since the MREQ is at logical 1 and WR at logical 0, the outputs from gate G2, and hence G3, are high, thus enabling the write enable pins (WE) of the two 4-bit bus transceivers IC1 and IC2. Consequently the data on the microprocessor data bus is transmitted to the port output lines $IO_0 - IO_7$.

To input data from this port the instruction

IN D0H,A

is used. In response the Z80 places the address $D0_{16}$ on lines $A_0–A_7$, sets the MREQ and RD control lines to logical 1 and 0 respectively, and reads the data on the data bus into the accumulator. During this operation, the read enable (RE) pins of IC1 and IC2 are activated, allowing the transfer of data from the I/O data bus to the Z80 data bus.

The main advantages of I/O mapped input/output ports, when compared with memory mapped ports, are that they require less hardware and allow a faster transfer of data. In the two examples given, the I/O port requires one less 8-input AND gate and transfers data 18% faster (Z80 instruction set) than the memory mapped port. An additional advantage is that RAM, also controlled by the MREQ line, may occupy the same addresses as the I/O ports, thus allowing the full 64K memory space for RAM and ROM usage.

A disadvantage of I/O mapped ports is that only 256 such ports may be addressed. However, it should be noted that, if necessary, additional memory mapped ports may be added. Furthermore, situating the I/O ports in Page 0 does, theoretically, reduce the flexibility of programming during software development. In practice neither of these disadvantages represents a limitation.

4.9 Input/Output Techniques: I/O Control

In a typical application a microprocessor is likely to be receiving data from, and transmitting data to, several peripherals connected to the I/O ports described in the previous section. Most peripherals require at least two I/O ports, one of which is used for the transfer of data and the other(s) to transmit control or handshake signals. **Control signals** are used to help organise the flow of data, whilst **handshake signals**, which permit the microprocessor or peripheral to acknowledge the successful receipt of data, regulate the flow of data.

In order that information is not lost, or ignored, careful control of the data flow is necessary. This may be achieved using one of the following:
  a) Software control
  b) Interrupt control.

4.9.1 Software Control

Software control is the simplest form of I/O control both in concept and implementation. As the name suggests the microprocessor program exercises total control over the I/O data. Under software control, the microprocessor **polls** (or looks at in turn) each of the I/O ports to see if input data is available, or whether the peripheral attached to the I/O port is ready to receive output data.

As an example, consider an input peripheral which is found on almost all microprocessor systems—the keyboard. (Keyboards are discussed in Chapter 7 to which the reader should refer for more detailed information.) In the simplest case, each key on the keyboard—which is just a switch that is closed when the key is pressed—is connected to one input line of an I/O port. This arrangement requires one input port for every eight keys on the keyboard. To input data, under software control, the microprocessor polls each key to see if that particular key is pressed. The important point to note is that, having pressed a key, the user must wait until the microprocessor polls the keyboard before the information enters the system.

Fig. 4.21 8-key keyboard with interrupt control

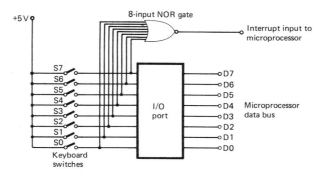

Software control has the advantage of requiring minimal hardware and provides for easy programming. Its main disadvantage is that it is very inefficient in its usage of microprocessor time. For example in the case of the simple keyboard just described, the microprocessor will spend most of its time polling keys which are not pressed. During this time the microprocessor could be more gainfully employed performing calculations, transferring data, etc. More important, under software control a peripheral cannot attract the attention of the microprocessor to, for example, notify it that data is available or that an "alarm" condition exists which needs to be dealt with immediately.

4.9.2   Interrupt Control

Under **interrupt control** a peripheral is able to gain the attention of the microprocessor at any instant during the program execution if, for example, it has input data available or is ready to accept more output data.

Interrupts are accomplished with hardware which activates one of the various interrupt pins on the microprocessor. As an example fig. 4.21 illustrates the circuit of a simple 8-key keyboard designed for interrupt control input. When a key is pressed, the key data is presented to the input port and the interrupt line is set to logical 0. The interrupt line, which may be connected directly to one of the microprocessor interrupt pins, "informs" the microprocessor that input data is available. In response the microprocessor halts its current activity, at a suitable point, and reads the input port to see which key has been pressed.

Since the 6502 (fig. 4.11) and the Z80 (fig. 4.14) have different interrupt facilities these two microprocessors will be discussed separately.

1   6502 Interrupts   As described, the 6502 has two interrupt lines. These are the NMI *non-maskable interrupt* and the IRQ *interrupt request*. Their action is as follows.

When the NMI line is set to logical 0, the 6502 finishes executing the current instruction and then stores the program counter and status register onto the stack. This action is necessary since the microprocessor will be required to continue with the present operation when it has finished dealing with the interrupt. The 6502 then loads the program counter with the absolute address which is stored at $FFFA_{16}$ (low-order byte of address) and $FFFB_{16}$ (high-order byte of address).

Thus in response to an NMI the 6502 jumps to the program whose *address vectors* are stored at $FFFA_{16}$ and $FFFB_{16}$. This program—called the interrupt subroutine—is designed by the user to respond, in the appropriate manner, to whatever generated the interrupt. When the microprocessor finishes the interrupt subroutine, it continues with the original main program by retrieving the status register and program counter from the stack and returning them to their respective positions.

The NMI is a high-order priority interrupt which cannot be masked out (hence *non-maskable*) and to which the 6502 must respond at all times. Consequently its use is reserved for fairly "catastrophic" events such as power failure in part of the system.

The IRQ interrupt operates in a similar fashion to the NMI but with two differences. First, the IRQ vectors are stored at $FFFE_{16}$ and $FFFF_{16}$ in memory. Second, the IRQ may be disabled or masked out (i.e. "switched off") by the program. Disabling the IRQ may become necessary if several peripherals, which can each generate an interrupt, are connected to the system. Since the microprocessor can only deal with one interrupt at a time, disabling the IRQ is a convenient way of allowing the microprocessor to ignore a second interrupt whilst attending to a first. Since this interrupt can be disabled, the IRQ is referred to as a low-priority interrupt.

The control of multi-interrupt systems is beyond the scope of the present text. However, it should be noted that, if several peripherals are connected to an interrupt line, one of the first tasks of the interrupt subroutine must be to determine which peripheral generated the interrupt. In the 6502 this can only be achieved by polling each peripheral.

2 Z80 Interrupts The Z80 has two interrupt inputs. These are the NMI *non-maskable input* and the INT *interrupt.*

The response of the Z80 to an NMI is identical to the 6502 with the exception that the Z80 jumps directly to an interrupt routine starting at 0066_{16} in memory.

The Z80 INT, like the 6502 IRQ, is a maskable interrupt which may be disabled by the software. However, the Z80 INT is a very flexible and powerful interrupt having three operating modes, each of which may be selected by software. These three modes are as follows.

1 *Mode* 0 In this mode the peripheral which generates the interrupt places a single instruction, for the microprocessor to execute, on the data bus. This instruction usually calls a subroutine specifically designed to handle an interrupt from a particular peripheral. It should be noted that with this arrangement each peripheral, by referencing a different subroutine, may identify itself as the originator of the interrupt. Thus, unlike the 6502, the Z80 has no need to poll each peripheral to discover the origin of the interrupt.

2 *Mode* 1 This mode is identical with the simple 6502 IRQ except that the Z80 jumps directly to the subroutine stored at 0038_{16} in memory.

Fig. 4.22 Z80 mode-2
vectored interrupt

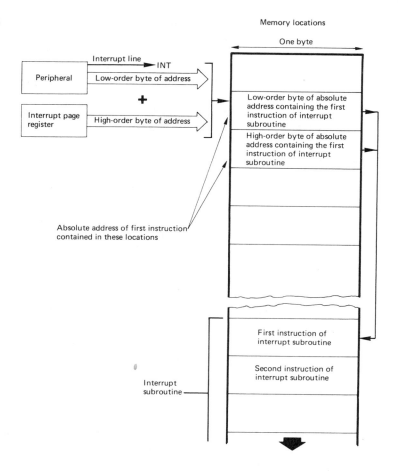

3 *Mode* 2 In this mode the peripheral generating the interrupt places an 8-bit address on the data bus. The Z80 uses this address as the low-order byte of an absolute address which contains the vector of the interrupt subroutine. The high-order byte of the address is obtained from interrupt page address register—the I register (fig. 4.14)—and is set by the programmer. The operation of the mode 2 interrupt is shown, schematically, in fig. 4.22.

As with the mode 0 interrupt, the mode 2 interrupt enables each peripheral to reference a different subroutine. Not only does this make for easier programming, it also obviates the need for polling each peripheral to discover the origin of the interrupt.

4.10   Input/Output Techniques: the Dedicated PIO Chip

Whilst the two circuits shown in fig. 4.19 and 4.20 illustrate the principle of the I/O port, they are, nevertheless, inefficient both in terms of the hardware and the software needed to control them. Consequently these circuits do not find widespread usage.

Most I/O ports are designed around a single programmable I/O chip—the **PIO**—which, typically, contains all the hardware for two I/O ports and associated interrupt and control lines. In addition the PIO also contains circuits for parallel-to-serial and serial-to-parallel conversion as well as timing circuits for producing pulses, pulse trains, pulse counting, etc.

Fig. 4.23 illustrates the architecture of a typical PIO chip. Port A and port B are two 8-bit I/O ports. Each of the I/O lines (PA0–PA7 and PB0–PB7) may be used for input or output. If necessary the data may be entered into input or output latches and thus the PIO may act as a temporary storage area. The control lines, CA1, CA2, CB1 and CB2, may be used for control, handshake or interrupt signals.

The parallel-to-serial and serial-to-parallel data convertors allows the PIO—and hence the microprocessor—to be connected directly to peripherals which operate on data in a serial format (e.g. printers, RS 232 interface, see 7.9.2). Serial data is synchronously clocked in or out of the serial registers using an external clock (supplied by a peripheral), the microprocessor clock or a timing signal generated by one of the timing circuits.

The internal timers may be used to produce single, multiple or square-wave pulses whose period and width may be varied under software control. Alternatively they can be used to count, measure the period and duration of input pulses.

The PIO interfaces directly with the microprocessor via the address, data and control buses. Some additional logic circuits (not shown in fig. 4.23 and usually just one chip) are used to provide the appropriate address decoding.

In any application the microprocessor program which controls the PIO begins with a short routine which programs the PIO for its functional rôle. This process is known as *configuring* the PIO and consists of entering the appropriate instructions and data into the PIO internal registers.

In addition to the features outlined above, the PIO may be constructed with up to several thousand bytes of RAM and ROM. For many simple applications (e.g. dishwashers, engine control, basic workshop equipment control), the PIO memory more than meets the system requirements. This can result in a microprocessor control system whose digital components are solely the microprocessor and PIO.

4.11   Test and Fault-finding Devices for Digital Systems

Introduction With the advent of digital systems and in particular microprocessor-based ones, new tools and techniques have had to be developed for testing and to carry out trouble-shooting. Although digital electronic products have led to improved reliability and performance, this

Fig. 4.23 Architecture of a PIO

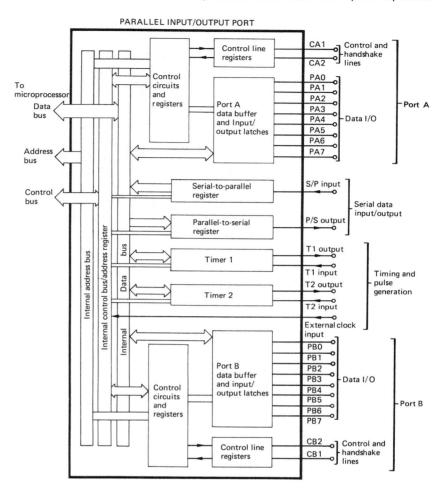

has been accompanied by a greater and greater degree of information handling. Vast amounts of digital information flow, for example, over the buses of a microcomputer system and even a single faulty chip or a single incorrect bit can lead to a total system mal-function. It has been estimated that even with an average component failure rate of less than 0.1% per year, several tens of millions of ICs in digital equipment go faulty every year. Thus the ensuing maintenance/repair costs can actually exceed the initial selling price of some products over their predicted lifetime. It is therefore of paramount importance to establish highly efficient testing and servicing techniques in order to minimise maintenance costs. Industry has recognised this need and many new testing methods and instruments have now been developed.

In this final section we introduce some of the basic tools used to test and trouble-shoot in digital circuits and systems. We include the simpler hand-held devices—the logic probe, clip, pulser and current tracer—and also provide some initial, but basic, ideas underlying the use of the more powerful system test equipment—the signature and logic analyzers.

1 The logic probe

The logic probe is a hand-held instrument designed to detect the logic state at a point (normally referred to as a *node*) in a digital circuit. Fig. 4.24*a* shows a sketch of a typical probe, which can be used to detect high, low and "bad" logic levels and also the presence of digital pulse trains for both TTL and CMOS digital ICs.

TTL/CMOS selection is made by a switch which sets the respective input logic threshold levels. In the TTL position these levels are approximately constant and independent of power supply voltage, as indicated in fig. 4.24*b*, i.e.

A logic high (1 state) corresponds to a level over 2 V.

A "bad" level (e.g. fault or "flashing" output in the case of a tri-state gate) corresponds to a level greater than 0·8 V but less than 2 V.

A logic low (0 state) corresponds to a level below 0·8 V.

With the switch in the CMOS position these thresholds vary with power supply as indicated in fig. 4.24*c*.

The probe can be powered by an external supply but is normally and preferably connected to use the power supply of the system under test. To test the logic state or activity at any given node in a circuit, place probe tip to make contact with the node. The indicator lamp on the probe povides one of the following observations:

1 *Lamp off* indicates that node is below logic 0 threshold.

2 *Lamp "dim"* indicates a logic state between 0 and 1 state thresholds, e.g. a "bad" level such as a fault or the "correct" level for a flashing output at a tri-state or wired-or gate.

3 *Lamp bright* indicates that node is above logic 1 threshold.

4 *Lamp flashing* indicates dynamic changes at node, e.g. pulse trains passing through node. Pulses of width down to 10 ns and repetition rates up to 40+ MHz can normally be detected by most quality probe units; the circuitry within the probe "slows" down the blink rate so that the flashing can be seen.

2 The logic clip

Fig. 4.25 shows a sketch of a logic clip, which may be used to test the logic states present at each pin of a digital IC. When clipped onto the IC, the LEDs or indicator lamps on the clip's display show the state at each pin: lamp off indicates logic 0, lamp on indicates a logic 1, whilst for dynamic system operation logic activity is indicated by visible flashing.

3 The logic pulser

The logic pulser is a hand-held instrument, similar in external appearance to a logic probe, used for injecting controlled pulses into a nodal point of a

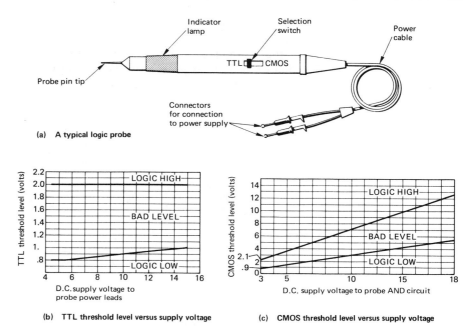

Fig. 4.24 Logic probe to indicate High, Low, and Bad logic levels

(a) A typical logic probe

(b) TTL threshold level versus supply voltage

(c) CMOS threshold level versus supply voltage

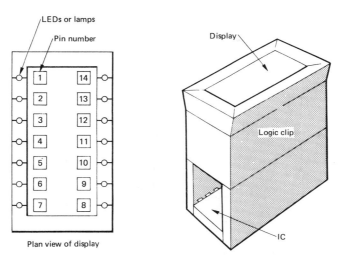

Fig. 4.25 Logic clip for indicating logic states of an IC (14-pin version shown where 1/0 state of each pin is indicated by LED being on/off)

Plan view of display

digital logic circuit. Its power supply leads should normally be connected to the power supply of the digital circuit under test and the pulser tip placed in contact with the node to be stimulated.

For the model shown in fig. 4.26a the frequency and number of pulses generated is controlled by a mode selection switch. This pulser can be used to generate either a single pulse; a continuous train of digital pulses, as shown for example in fig. 4.26b; a burst of 10 or a 100 pulses; or a pulse per second.

A simple example of the pulser's use in testing is illustrated in fig. 4.27. The pulser is used to generate a single pulse at the AND gate input; the output is monitored using a logic probe.

Fig. 4.26 The logic pulser

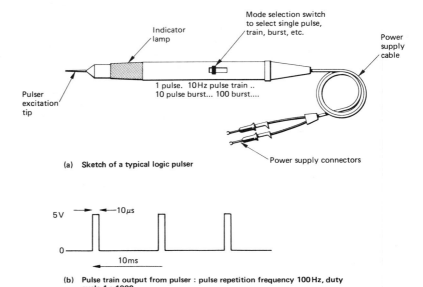

(a) Sketch of a typical logic pulser

(b) Pulse train output from pulser : pulse repetition frequency 100 Hz, duty cycle 1 : 1000.

Fig. 4.27 Simple test using logic pulser and logic probe. Probe in position (1) flashes, showing AND gate not faulty; probe in position (2) does not flash, so inverter faulty

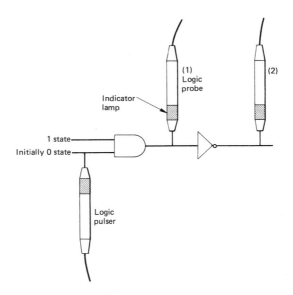

4 The current tracer

The current tracer is a hand-held instrument, similar in external apperance to the logic probe and pulser, used to locate low-impedance faults, e.g. to trace shorted inputs on ICs; solder bridging on printed circuit boards; shorted wires and conductors in cables; faulty tri-state gates.

The probe tip, which must always be held perpendicular to the conductor being traced, senses the a.c. magnetic field generated by a pulsating current and indicates the presence of current pulses by the lighting of the indicator lamp just above the current tracer tip. The sensitivity of the tracer can be adjusted over a typical 1 mA to 1 A range. Single pulses greater than 50 ns in width and pulse trains up to 10+ MHz can be detected.

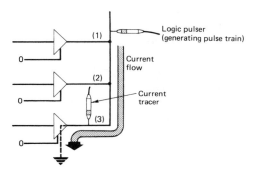

Fig. 4.28 Use of current tracer to locate faulty gate. The logic pulser is used to stimulate the gates; the current tracer does not light at positions (1) and (2) but does light at (3), indicating a low-impedance path through this gate and therefore that this gate is faulty.

The current tracer is normally used when logic probe trouble-shooting indicates a low-impedance fault. The user then adjusts, at some point distant from the suspected fault, the sensitivity control until the indicator lamp just lights. The current tracer is then moved along the conductor track or placed directly on the terminal point or an IC pin, while observing the indicator light. Fig. 4.28 shows an example of tracing a fault in a tri-state gate circuit.

5 Signature analyzers

Although logic probes, clips, pulsers and tracers find important application in testing and trouble-shooting, very much more powerful tools are usually required for testing the performance of complete microprocessor systems. Two important classes of test aids have been developed to aid us in these tasks: signature analyzers and logic analyzers.

Signature analysis is a technique used to identify faulty nodes in a microprocessor system by reducing or compressing the complex data bit streams into a simple "signature". The signature displayed on the signature analyzer test equipment indicates directly whether or not the node under examination is operating correctly.

In a typical signature analyzer a set of characters, e.g. 0–9, A, C, F, H, P, U, is used and for a given microprocessor system every node is identified by a 4-digit signature. For example, the correct operation of node 1 corresponds to (say) the signature A0C2; node 2 has the signature P666, and so on. The actual signatures are unique for the given system and are generated by running the test signature-analysis program developed for the system. This program exercises specific portions of the system in a controlled and repeatable manner. Two basic comments must be emphasized. First, the test program can only be used for the system for which it was developed—any system change will normally require a new test program and new signatures to cater for the change. Secondly, each node signature is unique; there is no question of being almost right, the signature is either right or wrong, e.g. if the signature given in the service manual for node 1 is A0C2, then if A0C1 is recorded, a fault occurs at node 1.

In general a typical procedure for fault finding using a signature analyzer would be as follows. Nodes in the suspected area of the fault are probed using the analyzer probe until a signature is found that does not agree with the one listed for that node. Signal paths are then traced back from this node until correct ones are found, thereby localising the fault. We can then resort to logic probe, current tracer, etc. techniques to find the faulty component(s).

6 Logic analyzers

Logic analyzers are powerful "data domain" test instruments used for examining logic signals in system development, production testing and trouble-shooting applications.

A logic analyzer can be thought of as the **data domain** equivalent to the oscilloscope. Whereas the oscilloscope is principally a time domain instrument used to display voltage waveforms as a function of time, a logic analyzer displays data (parts of programs) and timing diagrams for the system's digital control (timing signals).

A typical logic analyzer has between 16 and 32 inputs which can detect logic signals—the bits of digital information flowing along the buses of the microprocessor system. It can, for example, "trigger" on a particular address signal and capture a portion of the program being currently executed by the system undergoing test. It can then display typically 16 lines of the program content either immediately after or immediately before the trigger event. The latter capability is extremely useful in trouble-shooting, since by choosing a faulty system operation to be the trigger, the events that lead up to fault may be observed and analyzed. An analyzer can also be triggered by a control or data signal. For timing, most analyzers use the clock of the circuit under test. A new line of display is generated for each clock pulse input.

In general a logic analyzer allows an examination of specific portions of program sequences that occur in microprocessor systems and are especially useful for trouble-shooting new circuit designs. Many analyzers also incorporate a timing analysis feature. With the use of an internal time base, timing diagrams of the logic signals can be displayed on the analyzer screen in a manner similar to an oscilloscope. The difference is that the display is "rounded-off" to discrete time and voltage limits to give a clear graphic display without specific waveform information.

Logic analyzers can be regarded as very sophisticated "digital" oscilloscopes and are indeed just as important in microprocessor work as oscilloscopes are in analogue circuit testing and design. Although highly specialized, they, unlike signature analyzers, are not necessarily designed for a given system and they also provide much more detailed data and timing information.

Problems 4: Microprocessor architecture and system operation

1   Draw a block diagram showing the interconnection of the basic chips in a microcomputer system and explain briefly the function of *a*) the microprocessor, *b*) the ROM and RAM memory chips, *c*) the I/O unit, and *d*) the buses.

2   Describe the meaning of the following terms: memory location; address; kilobyte (Kbyte); memory map; chip-select, read and write signals.
Determine the size of the memory space in Kbytes for
a) an 8-bit microprocessor system with a 12-line address bus
b) a 16-bit microprocessor system with a 20-bit address word.

3   Describe with the aid of suitable diagrams how memory and I/O ports are accessed in a microcomputer system containing a number of ROM and RAM chips, an input and an output port.
An 8-bit microcomputer has the following memory map:
0000 to 07FF   ROM
0800 to 0BB0   RAM
2000 to 2003   input ports
3000 to 3002   output ports
Determine the amounts of ROM and RAM memory and the number of input and output ports.

Fig. 4.29

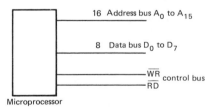

16   Address bus A_0 to A_{15}

8   Data bus D_0 to D_7

$\overline{WR}$ control bus
$\overline{RD}$

Microprocessor

4   Fig. 4.29 shows the block schematic of a microprocessor and its buses: 16 address lines A0 to A15, 8 data lines D0 to D7, control lines $\overline{WR}$ (write, active low), and $\overline{RD}$ (read, active low).
Determine the logic states on each line when:
a) memory location 00FF storing the single byte word 6D in a ROM chip is to be accessed and read;
b) the word 11 on the data bus is to be written into address 0100 in RAM;
c) to access an output port at address 2000 and to write the word BB on the data bus to this port.

Fig. 4.30

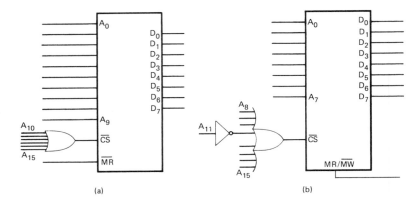

(a)   (b)

5   Determine for the memory chips shown in fig. 4.30a and b
     a) the type of chip and its memory capacity
     b) the range of addresses associated with each chip.

6   State briefly the function of the following internal logic circuits with a microprocessor chip:
     a) program counter, b) instruction register, c) instruction decoder, d) timing and control logic, e) accumulator, f) arithmetic logic unit, g) stack pointer, h) interrupt logic, i) status registers.

7   Part of the RAM in most microprocessor systems is allocated for the stack. Explain the function of the stack memory and how it is controlled by the microprocessor.
     List the differences in the 6502 and Z80 stacks and discuss the relative advantages of each stack system.

8   Explain the various operations which take place during the fetch-decode-execute cycle of a typical microprocessor.

9   Describe the difference between a memory mapped and an I/O mapped input/output port. Discuss the relative advantages of these two forms of input/output and explain why most microprocessors use a programmable input/output (PIO) for input/output.

10   a) State the possible consequences of enabling the WE and RE lines in the I/O port of fig. 4.19 simultaneously.
     b) State whether this situation is possible for the I/O port of fig. 4.20.

11   Design a logic circuit which would allow the RE and WE lines of the I/O port of fig. 4.19 to interface with
     a) a 6502 microprocessor   b) a Z80 microprocessor

12   Explain what additional features you would expect to find in a PIO other than I/O ports and what types of application these additional features would be used for.

13   Explain the difference between a *maskable* and *non-maskable* interrupt, illustrating your answer with examples from the 6502 and Z80 microprocessors.

14   If a microprocessor were not provided with interrupt facilities, explain what limitations this would place an I/O operations.

15 Describe briefly the use of the following logic fault finding devices: *a*) the logic probe, *b*) the logic clip, *c*) the current tracer.

16 Explain what is meant by "signature analysis" and describe briefly how you would check the operation of a given microprocessor-based system using a signature analyzer.

State the additional information it would be possible to obtain in testing the system if you had available a suitable logic analyzer.

5 Microprocessor Programming

5.1 Introduction

A microprocessor *instruction set* is, in effect, a rudimentary language which enables the programmer to "instruct" the microprocessor to carry out particular tasks and operations. The instruction set is designed by each of the individual manufacturers and, unfortunately, differs for each microprocessor; although presently there are attempts being made to introduce a degree of standardisation.

Any given microprocessor instruction may be presented in one of three forms. For example, the instruction to load the accumulator of the 6502 microprocessor with a particular number may be written as:

10101001	Machine code in *binary* form
A9	Machine code in *hex* form
LDA	Assembly code in *mnemonic* form

The **binary form** of the instruction is that used at *machine level* with the microprocessor, both fetching the instruction from memory and decoding it (i.e. deciding what it means) in the form of an eight-bit binary pattern.

The **hex code** is derived directly from the binary code by splitting the instruction byte into two four-bit words (or nibbles) and translating each nibble into hex, i.e.

$$1010_2 = A_{16} \qquad 1001_2 = 9_{16}$$

Hex code is designed to reduce the overall effort required by the programmer, since it is much easier to remember A9 than the byte 10101001. Furthermore, when entering the instruction into a microprocessor, via a keyboard, hex code requires only two key operations compared to the eight necessary for binary code. Note, however, that, since the microprocessor operates in binary, provision must be made to convert the hex code back into binary. This is easily accomplished by a small program (software decoding) or, less frequently, by a few integrated logic circuits placed between the keyboard and the microprocessor (hardware decoding).

Assembly code represents a half-way position between machine code and a high-level language (such as Pascal or Basic). The assembly code is usually a mnemonic derived from the instruction itself, i.e. LDA is derived from LoaD the Accumulator. Assembly code is thus very easy to remember and use when writing programs. When entering an assembly program into a

Table 5.1a Examples of 6502 instructions

Assembly code	Hex	Binary	Instruction
TAX	AA	10101010	Transfer Accumulator to X register.
DEY	88	10001000	DEcrement the Y register.
CLC	18	00011000	CLear the Carry flag.
JSR	20	00100000	Jump to SubRoutine.

Table 5.1b Examples of Z80 instructions

Assembly code	Hex	Binary	Instruction
LD A,B	78	01111000	LoaD the Accumulator from the B register.
DEC B	0D	00001101	DECrement the B register.
SUB E	93	10010111	SUBtract the E register from the accumulator.
JP ADDR	C3	11000011	JumP to the absolute address ADDR.

microprocessor, the assembly code must first be converted into machine code. For short programs, of a few lines, this is relatively easy and usually requires that the programmer has next to him or her a table which contains the assembly mnemonics and the equivalent machine code. This technique is known as *hand assembly* and is limited to programs of about one hundred lines or less. For longer programs a separate program—called an **assembler program**—is used to convert the assembly code into machine code which is placed directly into the microprocessor memory.

Tables 5.1*a* and *b* give some other examples of assembly, hex and binary code instructions for both the 6502 and Z80 microprocessors.

5.2 Introduction to the Instruction Set

All modern microprocessors have a relatively large number of instructions in their full **instruction set**. The 6502 has 151 separate instructions, whilst the Z80, with its many internal registers, has 722 instructions. (The 6502 and Z80 instruction sets are included in the appendix.)

The sheer number of available microprocessor instructions can, at first sight, be both daunting and bewildering to the newcomer, who may not fully appreciate the potential of operations such as ROL, NOP, BIT, etc. However, the instruction set is more easily understood once it is realised that the instructions may be grouped into subsets which perform similar operations. Whilst there is, as yet, no agreement between manufacturers as to what the subset groupings should be, the following find fairly widespread usage:

1 Data Transfer
2 Arithmetic operations
3 Logical operations
4 Shift and Rotate
5 Status testing
6 Jump and Branch
7 Special instructions

5.3 Data Transfer Instructions

This is the most numerous subset of instructions, both in number and frequency of usage. **Data transfer instructions** transfer data between microprocessor registers, between a microprocessor register and memory, or between a microprocessor register and an input/output device. Special transfer instructions may exist for microprocessor registers, or memory, which have a special role. For example, a PUSH or PULL [6502] operation is used for efficient stack implementation (for the Z80 the corresponding stack instructions are PUSH and POP).

Tables 5.2a and b list some of the more frequently used data transfer instructions for the 6502 and Z80 microprocessors.

Similarities between Tables 5.2a and 5.2b are immediately apparent. For example, both the 6502 and Z80 microprocessors use the same instruction mnemonic for Load the accumulator. However, it should be noted that, in the Z80 instruction, a "space" is inserted between the D and A of LD A. This difference, whilst slight, *is important*, particularly when assembler programs are used. The instructions TAX and TXA [6502] perform the same operation as LD A,C and LD C,A [Z80]; namely the transfer of data between the accumulator and an internal register of the microprocessor. Similarly, STA [6502] may be compared with LD (ADDR),A [Z80]. Such comparisons illustrate the need for standardisation of instruction sets as well as help understand the common complaint of programmers that "instruction sets are sufficiently similar as to be confusing."

Using the instructions given in Table 5.2a, the following simple program, which stores the number 24_{16} in the X register and at memory location $D1FE_{16}$ in a 6502 system, may be understood:

```
                   ┌─────────── Denotes a hex number
                   ↓
LDA   #$24
              ↑─────────── Denotes a literal (number)
TAX
STA   $D1FE
```

In the first line of the program, the number 24_{16} is loaded into the accumulator. In the second line, the contents of the accumulator are transferred into the X register. (A better description of the TAX instruction would be to say that the contents of the accumulator are *copied* into the X register since, during the operation, the contents of the accumulator remain unchanged.) In the third line of the program, the contents of the ac-

Table 5.2a Data transfer instructions [6502]

Assembly code	Instruction
LDA	Load accumulator.
STA	Store accumulator.
LDX	Load X register.
LDY	Load Y register.
TAX	Transfer accumulator to X register.
TXA	Transfer X register to accumulator.

Table 5.2b Data transfer instructions [Z80]

Assembly code	Instruction
LD A,n	Load the accumulator with the literal (number) n.
LD (ADDR),A	Load the absolute address ADDR from the accumulator.
LD C,n	Load the C register with the literal n.
LD A,C	Load the accumulator with the data in the C register.
LD C,A	Load the C register with the data in the accumulator.

cumulator are stored (or copied) into the memory location $D1FE_{16}$.

A brief explanation of the symbols # and $, which appear in the program, is necessary. The # (*hash*) symbol indicates that the accumulator is to be loaded with the literal (or number) which follows the instruction (as opposed to the accumulator being loaded with the contents of a specific memory location). The $ (*dollar*) symbol indicates that the number (or address as in line 3) is in hex. Symbols used to denote other radices are

$	Hex	base 16
@	Octal	base 8
%	Binary	base 2
No symbol	Decimal	base 10

Thus   % 0010 0111 ≡ @47 ≡ $27 ≡ 39

A similar program which stores the same number in the C register and at memory location $D1FE_{16}$ in a Z80 system is

LD   A,24H
LD   C,A └────Denotes a hex number
LD   D1FEH,A

A comparison of the two program examples illustrates further differences in the 6502 and Z80 assembly codes. The Z80 uses an H to indicate a hex address or number. As with the 6502, the Z80 assemblers assume a decimal base if no radix indicator is present. Octal and binary formats are not supported in Z80 assemblers. Note also that the addressing modes of the Z80 (see Section 5.10) are such that no special symbol is required to indicate that the 24 is a literal.

5.4 Arithmetic Operations

Arithmetic instructions may be broadly categorised into two classes. In the first class are those instructions which involve two separate bytes of data, one of which is usually resident in the accumulator. The result of the arithmetic operation is a single byte of data which is usually returned to the accumulator. Typical instructions of this type are ADD, ADD WITH CARRY, SUBTRACT, SUBTRACT WITH BORROW, etc. The essential difference between Add and Add with Carry is that, in the second instruction, any carry which is generated during an addition is automatically included in any subsequent arithmetic operation. Similarly the Subtract with Borrow instruction automatically implements a borrow. Contemporary eight-bit microprocessors, including the 6502 and Z80, do not implement the more complex arithmetic operations such as multiply and divide. These operations can, of course, be accomplished using sub-routines. (It should be noted, however, that some of the latest-generation 16-bit microprocessors do possess multiply and divide instructions in their instruction set, e.g. the Z8000 microprocessor.)

In the second class of arithmetic instructions are those which operate on a single byte of data. Typical instructions in this class are INCREMENT (increase by one) and DECREMENT (decrease by one) a microprocessor register or memory location.

Examples of arithmetic instructions are given in Tables 5.3a and b.

In Table 5.3b, (HL) is used to specify an absolute address whose high byte is contained in the H register and whose low byte is contained in the L register of the Z80. For example, if the H register contains $D1_{16}$ and the L register contains FE_{16}, the instruction ADC A,(HL) will result in the contents of address $D1FE_{16}$ being added to the accumulator.

Example 5.1 Using only the instructions already provided, write an assembly code program, for both the 6502 and Z80, which calculates the sum and the difference of the two numbers stored at $C000_{16}$ and $C001_{16}$ and stores the result at $B000_{16}$ (sum) and $B001_{16}$ (difference).

Solution 6502 program

Assembly (*or Source*) *code*	Comments
LDA $C000	; LOAD ACCUMULATOR WITH CONTENTS OF $C000_{16}$.
ADC $C001	; ADD CONTENTS OF $C001_{16}$ TO ACCUMULATOR.
STA $B000	; STORE THE RESULT AT $B000_{16}$.
LDA $C000	; LOAD ACCUMULATOR WITH CONTENTS OF $C000_{16}$.
SBC $C001	; SUBTRACT THE CONTENTS OF $C001_{16}$ FROM THE ACCUMULATOR.
STA $B001	; STORE THE RESULT AT $B001_{16}$.

└──────── indicates start of Comment field

Table 5.3a   Arithmetic instructions [6502]

Assembly code	Instruction
ADC	Add with carry.
SBC	Subtract with carry.
INX	Increment X register.
DEY	Decrement Y register.
INC	Increment memory.

Table 5.3b   Arithmetic instructions [Z80]

Assembly code	Instruction
ADD A,B	Add contents of B register to accumulator.
INC A	Increment the accumulator.
ADC A,(HL)	Add, with carry, contents of address specified by (HL) to accumulator
SBC A,(HL)	Subtract, with borrow, contents of address (HL) to accumulator.
DEC (HL)	Decrement contents of address specified by (HL).

Solution   Z80 program

Assembly (or Source) code	Comments
LD A,C000H	; LOAD ACCUMULATOR WITH CONTENTS OF C000$_{16}$.
ADC A,C001H	; ADD CONTENTS OF C001$_{16}$ TO ACCUMULATOR.
LD B000H,A	; STORE THE RESULT AT B000$_{16}$.
LD A,C000H	; LOAD ACCUMULATOR WITH CONTENTS OF C000$_{16}$.
SBC A,C001H	; SUBTRACT CONTENTS OF C001$_{16}$ FROM ACCUMULATOR.
LD B001H,A	; STORE THE RESULT AT B001$_{16}$.

—— indicates start of Comment field

The program listings given in the Solutions to Example 5.1 illustrate some of the features of a typical machine code program. The program is separated into two **fields**: the **assembly code** field (also called the **source code** or *operation code*) which contains the program instructions, and a **comment** field which allows the programmer to include, if necessary, useful explanatory comments. As will be seen later, a full machine code program contains a total of seven fields.

Examples of the use of the *increment* and *decrement* instructions will be left until the *branch*, *jump* and *status* instructions have been discussed since, in practice, these instruction subsets are often used together.

Table 5.4a Logical instructions [6502]

Assembly code	Instruction
AND	Logical AND between accumulator and data.
ORA	Logical OR between accumulator and data.
EOR	Logical Exclusive-OR between accumulator and data.

Table 5.4b Logical instructions [Z80]

Assembly code	Instruction
AND (HL)	Logical AND between accumulator and data in (HL).
OR (HL)	Logical OR between accumulator and data in (HL).
XOR (HL)	Logical Exclusive-OR between accumulator and data in (HL).

5.5 Logical Operations

Logical instructions involve the transformation of two separate bytes of data, one of which is usually resident in the accumulator. The result, a single byte, is usually returned to the accumulator.

Typical, and most frequently used, logical instructions are the AND, OR and Exclusive-OR instructions (Tables 5.4a and b).

Apart from usage as logical functions in their own right, the logical instructions are extremely powerful tools for bit, byte and character manipulation. The AND instruction may be used to force a 0 at any specified bit of a word (a process known as *masking*), whilst the OR instruction may be used to force a 1 at any specified bit. The Exclusive-OR instruction will produce the complement of a number and is thus used extensively to generate negative numbers via twos complement (see section 2.13.3).

The following examples, written for the 6502, illustrate uses of the logical instructions. The corresponding examples for the Z80 instruction set are given, in problem form, at the end of this chapter.

Example 5.2 Write a program which will change bits 0–3 in the data byte, stored at $C000_{16}$, to 0 *without altering* the bit pattern in bits 4–7.

Solution

Assembly (Source) code	Comments
LDA $C000	; LOAD ACCUMULATOR WITH THE DATA IN $C000_{16}$.
AND #$F0	; AND ACCUMULATOR WITH THE NUMBER $F0_{16}$.
	; (MASK OFF THE FOUR LSBS)
STA $C000	; STORE THE RESULT BACK IN $C000_{16}$.

To help understand the operation of the program, let us suppose that the data byte stored in $C000_{16}$ is $A6_{16}$. The program will thus result in

$$10100110 = A6_{16} = \text{Contents of } C000_{16}$$
$$\underline{11110000 = F0_{16}}$$
$$10100000 = (A6) \underset{\underset{\text{AND}}{\uparrow}}{.} (F0)$$

Thus the four MSBs of $C000_{16}$ remain unchanged, whilst the four LSBs are forced to zero or masked off. (The term *masking off* refers to the theoretical operation in which a screen, or mask, is placed over the number such that only certain parts of the number, in this example the four MSBs, are visible.)

Example 5.3 Write a program which will change bits 0–3 in the data byte, stored at $C000_{16}$, to a 1 without altering the bit pattern in bits 4–7.

Solution

Assembly (*Source*) code	Comments
LDA $C000	; LOAD ACCUMULATOR WITH THE DATA IN $C000_{16}$.
ORA #$0F	; OR ACCUMULATOR WITH THE NUMBER $0F_{16}$.
STA $C000	; STORE THE RESULT BACK IN $C000_{16}$.

Assuming that $C000_{16}$ contains $A6_{16}$ the above program would result in

$$10100110 = A6_{16} = \text{Contents of } C000_{16}$$
$$\underline{00001111 = 0F_{16}}$$
$$10101111 = (A6_{16}) \underset{\underset{\text{OR}}{\uparrow}}{+} (0F_{16})$$

Example 5.4 Write a program to negate the number stored at $C000_{16}$, twos complement assumed.

Solution

Assembly (*Source*) code	Comments
LDA $C000	; LOAD ACCUMULATOR WITH THE DATA IN $C000_{16}$.
EOR #$FF	; EXCLUSIVE-OR ACCUMULATOR WITH THE NUMBER FF_{16}.
	; (OBTAIN THE ONES COMPLEMENT)
ADC #$01	; ADD 1—OBTAIN THE TWOS COMPLEMENT
STA $C000	; STORE THE RESULT BACK IN $C000_{16}$.

Assuming, as before, that $C000_{16}$ contained A6, the program would result in

$$10100110 = A6_{16}$$
$$\underline{11111111 = FF_{16}}$$
$$\overline{01011001} = (A6_{16}) \oplus (FF_{16}) = \text{ones complement of } A6_{16}$$
$$+ \qquad \underline{\qquad 1}$$
$$\overline{01011010} = 5A_{16} = \text{twos complement of } A6_{16}$$

Note that $A6_{16} = -90_{10}$ and $5A_{16} = 90_{10}$ in twos complement.

5.6 Shift and Rotate Instructions

A **shift instruction** causes the bit pattern of a specific register or memory location to be displaced by one bit position (either to the right or to the left) (fig. 5.1). It is important to note that the bit which is shifted out of the byte is shifted into the carry flag register and that a 0 is placed in the end bit from which the shift is performed.

Fig. 5.1 Shift left and shift right operations

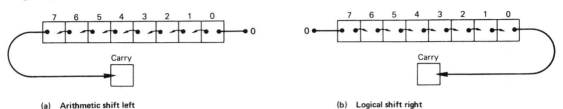

(a)   Arithmetic shift left

(b)   Logical shift right

The **rotate instruction** is similar to the shift (fig. 5.2). The fundamental difference is that, following a rotate instruction, the bit pattern is circularly permuted one bit, clockwise or anticlockwise, through the register, or memory, and carry flag register. Thus after nine *shift* operations, the register, or memory, and the carry flag will be set to 0, whilst after nine *rotate* operations the register, or memory, will contain the original bit pattern.

Fig. 5.2 Rotate left and rotate right operations

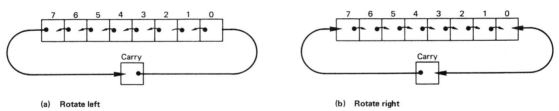

(a)   Rotate left

(b)   Rotate right

Typical shift and rotate instructions for the 6502 and Z80 are given in Tables 5.5*a* and *b*.

Shift and rotate instructions find extensive use in three types of operation. First, they allow the individual bits of a word to be examined separately. To achieve this, the word is either shifted or rotated (usually rotated) such that the bit to be examined is moved into the carry register. The carry flag is then tested (see sections 5.7 and 5.8) for a 1 or a 0.

Secondly, shift and rotate instructions are used for character manipulation, particularly during the transmission and reception of data between systems (e.g. microprocessor and printer, etc.). Prior to transmission, each byte of data is split into its high and low order nibbles which, after conversion to ASCII code, are transmitted as two separate pieces of information. Example 5.5 illustrates the use of the rotate instruction in separating a byte of data into its constituent high and low order nibbles. Rotate instructions are also used to reconstitute the data byte from the two transmitted nibbles at the receiver.

The third use of rotate and shift instructions occurs in multiplication and

Table 5.5a Shift and rotate instructions [6502]

Assembly code	Instruction
ASL	Arithmetic shift left.
LSR	Logical shift right.
ROL	Rotate left one bit.
ROR	Rotate right one bit.

Table 5.5b Shift and rotate instructions [Z80]

Assembly code	Instruction
SLA A	Arithmetic shift left—accumulator.
SRL (HL)	Logical shift right—address (HL).
RL A	Rotate left one bit—accumulator.
RR (HL)	Rotate right one bit—address (HL).

division. A shift, or rotate, left operation corresponds to a multiplication by two, whereas a shift, or rotate, right corresponds to a division by two. (Section 5.17.2 illustrates a typical multiplication program.)

Example 5.5 Write a program for the Z80 microprocessor which will place the low and high order nibbles of the data byte residing in $C000_{16}$ into $B000_{16}$ and $B001_{16}$ respectively.

Solution

Source code		Comments
LD	A,C000H	; LOAD ACCUMULATOR WITH DATA.
AND	A,0FH	; MASK OFF THE HIGH ORDER NIBBLE.
LD	B000H,A	; STORE RESULT (LOW ORDER NIBBLE) AT $B000_{16}$.
LD	A,C000H	; LOAD ACCUMULATOR WITH DATA.
SRL	A	; 1ST SHIFT RIGHT.
SRL	A	; 2ND SHIFT RIGHT.
SRL	A	; 3RD SHIFT RIGHT.
SRL	A	; 4TH SHIFT RIGHT.
LD	B001H,A	; STORE RESULT (HIGH ORDER NIBBLE) AT $B001_{16}$.

To help understand the operation of the program, assume that $C000_{16}$ contained $A6_{16}$. After masking $A6_{16}$ with 0F (line 2), the accumulator will contain 06_{16}—the low order nibble—which is stored at $B000_{16}$ (line 3). Lines 5–8 shift the high order nibble into the low order nibble of the accumulator (fig. 5.3), following which it is stored in $B001_{16}$ (line 9).

Fig. 5.3 Shifting the high nibble into the low nibble position

Accumulator

	1	0	1	0	0	1	1	0	LD A,(C000H) $(=A6_{16})$
$0 \rightarrow$	0	1	0	1	0	0	1	1	1st shift right $(=53_{16})$
$0 \rightarrow$	0	0	1	0	1	0	0	1	2nd shift right $(=29_{16})$
$0 \rightarrow$	0	0	0	1	0	1	0	0	3rd shift right $(=14_{16})$
$0 \rightarrow$	0	0	0	0	1	0	1	0	4th shift right $(=0A_{16})$

5.7 Status Flag Testing and Conditioning Instructions

As described in Chapter 4, all microprocessors are equipped with a **status register** or **flags register**, which records the *state* of the system or of the program under execution. Fig. 5.4 shows the bit pattern of the one-byte status registers of the 6502 and Z80 microprocessors.

In keeping with accepted terminology, a flag is said to be **set** if the corresponding bit is a binary 1 and **cleared**, or *reset*, if binary 0.

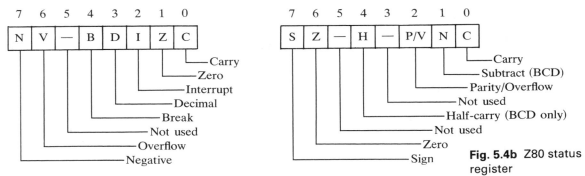

Fig. 5.4a 6502 status register

Fig. 5.4b Z80 status register

The operation of the full set of status flags is somewhat beyond the scope of these studies and, for present purposes, only the *carry*, *zero* and *negative* or *sign* flags will be considered. These three flags, which are the most frequently used—and consequently the most important of the status flags—function in both the 6502 and the Z80 as follows:

1 The **carry** (C) flag may be considered as the "ninth" bit of the accumulator, or register. It is set if a carry occurs from the eighth bit of the accumulator (or register) during an arithmetic addition. The carry flag, once set, is cleared by a borrow occurring during an arithmetic subtraction. Note that, whilst the 6502 carry flag can be cleared with the clear carry (CLC) instruction, the Z80 carry flag is cleared with the logical AND instruction. (The Z80 does not support a clear carry instruction as such.)

2 The **zero** (Z) flag is set if the contents of the accumulator, or register, are zero. Otherwise it is cleared.

3 The **negative** or **sign** (N or S) flag indicates that the number in the accumulator, or register, is negative in signed binary and twos complement representation. In practice N (or S) is identical to the seventh bit of the accumulator, or register.

Status instructions both test and condition the microprocessor status register. Examples of these types of instruction are given in Tables 5.6a and b.

Whilst the operation of the clear and set carry instructions are self-evident, the **compare instruction** requires further explanation. During a compare operation, the contents of the accumulator (or register) are compared with a specified byte of data, S, by computing the difference A−S. Neither A nor S are changed (i.e. the result of the subtraction is not stored)

Table 5.6a Status instructions [6502]

Assembly code	Instruction
CLC	Clear carry.
SEC	Set carry.
CMP	Compare.

Table 5.6b Status instructions [Z80]

Assembly code	Instruction
CCF	Complement carry flag.
AND A	Clear carry flag.
SCF	Set carry flag.
CP	Compare.

but the carry, zero and negative (or sign) flags are conditioned as follows:

$A-S$	Flags Conditioned
>0	Carry Set
$=0$	Zero Set
<0	Negative (or Sign) Set

The compare instruction invariably precedes, and is used in conjunction with, a conditional branch or jump instruction. Consequently further discussion will be left until the branch and jump instructions have been introduced.

It should be noted at this stage that, in some of the example programs given, e.g. Example 5.1, the implicit assumption was made that, prior to the arithmetic addition, the carry flag was cleared. In practice, of course, whether the carry flag is set or cleared depends upon the result of previous operations. Consequently, the first instruction in any arithmetic addition involving an add with carry instruction must be a *clear carry*, otherwise errors will occur. Similarly, prior to a subtract with borrow operation, the *set carry* (or borrow) instruction must be executed. This particular point is illustrated in Example 5.6.

Example 5.6 What will be the result, stored at $D000_{16}$, of the 6502 program listed below if prior to execution the carry flag is *a*) set, *b*) cleared?

PROGRAM
```
LDA   #$40
ADC   #$72
STA   $D000
```

Solution The program adds the numbers 40_{16} and 72_{16} together and stores the result at $D000_{16}$. Depending on whether the carry flag is initially set or cleared, the program will result in the following addition:

a) Carry set
$$40_{16}$$
$$+72_{16}$$
$$+ 1_{16} \longleftarrow \text{Carry} = 1$$
$$\overline{B3_{16}}$$

b) Carry cleared
$$40_{16}$$
$$+72_{16}$$
$$+ 0_{16} \longleftarrow \text{Carry} = 0$$
$$\overline{B2_{16}}$$

In *a*), the result stored at $D000_{16}$ is incorrect.

Table 5.7 Unconditional jump instructions [6502 and Z80]

Assembly code	Instruction
JMP ADDR	Jump to the absolute address ADDR [6502].
JP ADDR	Jump to the absolute address ADDR [Z80].

Table 5.8 Subroutine jump instructions [6502 and Z80]

Assembly code	Instruction
JSR ADDR	Jump to the subroutine starting at the absolute address ADDR [6502].
CALL ADDR	Call (≡Jump to) the subroutine starting at the absolute address ADDR [Z80].
RTS	Return from subroutine [6502].
RET	Return from subroutine [Z80].

5.8 Jump and Branch Instructions

This subset of instructions is extremely important and is often a deciding factor in the selection of a particular microprocessor. The terms *jump* and *branch* are used somewhat interchangeably by the various manufacturers, which can cause confusion. (In the following discussion it will be assumed that the terms jump and branch are completely interchangeable.)

A **jump instruction** (**branch instruction**) causes the program counter to be reloaded with a new address, which results in a modification to the normal sequential program flow. A jump instruction may be either unconditional or conditional.

An **unconditional jump** is an instruction which, when it is encountered during program execution, simply loads the program counter with an address which is specified in the instruction. The program thus "jumps" to the specified address. Both the 6502 and the Z80 have only one form of the unconditional jump (Table 5.7).

A special unconditional jump instruction, the **subroutine jump**, is also available in the 6502 and Z80 instruction set. The subroutine jump is similar to the unconditional jump with the exception that, prior to loading the program counter with the jump address, the contents of the program counter are first saved on the stack. Saving the program counter allows a return from the subroutine to be made using a Return from Subroutine instruction in which the saved program counter contents are pulled (or popped) off the stack and placed back in the program counter. Table 5.8 shows examples of subroutine jump instructions.

As the name suggests, a **conditional jump** is an instruction in which a jump to a particular address only occurs if a specified condition, as represented by the status flags register, prevails. For example, a Jump if Zero instruction will result in a jump to a specified address if, and only if, the zero flag is set.

Conditional jumps may be either absolute or relative. In an **absolute conditional jump** instruction, the instruction contains an absolute address which is loaded into the program counter if the jump conditions are met. An absolute conditional jump thus requires three bytes of memory, one for the instruction and two for the absolute address. In contrast, the **relative conditional jump** instruction only requires two bytes of memory, one byte for the instruction and one byte for an 8-bit offset which is added to the program counter, as a signed number, if the jump conditions are met. Thus the relative conditional jump permits jumps of up to ± 127 bytes of memory from the current program counter. Note, however, that since the program counter is incremented *before* the instruction is executed, the effective jump range is -126 to $+128$ bytes from the location of the jump instruction.

Example 5.7, which uses the Z80 jump if zero instruction, illustrates the difference between absolute and relative conditional jumps.

Example 5.7 *Absolute and relative conditional jumps*

a) JP Z,D000H   Jump if zero—*Absolute*
b) JP Z,25H   Jump (forwards) if zero ⎫
c) JP Z,A3H   Jump (backwards) if zero ⎭ *Relative*

Example 5.7*a* is an absolute conditional jump. If the zero flag is set, then this instruction will cause the program to jump to the absolute address $D000_{16}$. Examples 5.7*b* and 5.7*c* are both relative conditional jumps. These are easily distinguished from the absolute conditional jump since they have only one byte of data following the instruction. In Example 5.7*b* the program will jump to the address, which is at $+37_{10}$ bytes ($25_{16} = +37_{10}$ in signed binary) higher than the current program counter, if the zero flag is set. In Example 5.7*c* the program will jump back to the address which is 93 bytes lower than the current program counter ($A3_{16} = -93$ in signed binary) if the zero flag is set.

As already pointed out, the terms jump and branch are interchangeable. However, recently there has developed the tendency to refer to all conditional relative jumps as branch instructions, retaining the name jump for those instructions in which an absolute address is specified.

Tables 5.9*a* and *b* gives other examples of conditional jump (or branch) instructions for the 6502 and Z80 microprocessors respectively. (It should be noted that the 6502 does not support absolute conditional jumps.)

Example 5.8 Write a program, in Z80 machine code, that will execute the subroutine, beginning at $E000_{16}$, eight times.

Solution

Line No.	Label	Source code	Operand	Comments
1		LD	H08H	; Load H register with 8_{10}.
2	LOOP	CALL	E000H	; Jump to subroutine at $E000_{16}$.
3		DEC	H	; Decrement H register.
4		JP	NZLOOP	; Jump if not zero to loop.

The program listed above will execute the subroutine, beginning at $E000_{16}$, eight times. However, before discussing the operation of the program it must first be noted that the program listing has five fields as opposed to the two fields given in the earlier examples (e.g. Example 5.5). A brief explanation of these additional fields follows.

The program **line number**—the first field—is a programmers' aid which allows the program writer to refer, either in the comment column or in text, to a specific line of the program.

The **label** field allows the use of **symbolic addresses**, a very powerful tool when writing machine code programs. In the previous examples it was assumed that a particular piece of data was stored at a specified address (e.g. $D000_{16}$ in many of the examples quoted). Whilst this may be satisfactory for simple demonstration programs, having to specify a particular address for data storage for more complex programs would be a distinct disadvantage. First, when commencing writing a program it may not be obvious where a piece of data should be stored in memory. Secondly, it is both inefficient, and frustrating, to have to remember that a piece of data—which may correspond to a physical quantity such as volts—is located at, say, $D000_{16}$. By introducing a symbolic address, which may be given a name such as VOLTS, these particular problems are resolved. (Note however, that during program assembly the symbolic address must be replaced by the appropriate absolute or relative address.)

The third and fourth fields of the program listing contain the source (or OP) code and the operand respectively. (In the previous examples these fields were combined for convenience.)

Returning to the program, it may be seen (line 1) that the H register, which is used as a counter, is loaded with the number 8—the number of times the subroutine is to be executed. Line 2 of the program jumps to the subroutine at $E000_{16}$. Line 3 decrements the H register whilst line 4 tests to see if, after decrementing H, the result is zero. If the result is not zero, the program jumps to the symbolic address called LOOP which calls the subroutine again. If the result is zero—which occurs after the subroutine has been executed 8 times—the program continues to the next instruction (which would be at line 5).

A similar program, for the 6502, which uses the X index register as a counter is given below Table 5.9b.

Table 5.9a Conditional jump instructions [6502]

Assembly code	Instruction	Address mode
BMI	Branch if minus (negative)	Relative
BEQ	Branch if equal to zero	Relative
BCS	Branch if carry set	Relative
BNE	Branch if not equal to zero	Relative

Table 5.9b Conditional jump instructions [Z80]

Assembly code	Instruction	Address mode
JP Z,ADDR	Jump if zero	Absolute
JP C,ADDR	Jump if carry set	Absolute
JR Z,d*	Jump if zero	Relative
JR NZ,d	Jump if not zero	Relative

*d = displacement in signed binary

Line No.	Label	Source code	Operand	Comments
1		LDX	#$08	; LOAD X REGISTER WITH 8_{10}.
2	LOOP	JSR	$E000	; JUMP TO SUBROUTINE AT $E000_{16}$.
3		DEX		; DECREMENT X.
4		BNE	LOOP	; BRANCH IF $\neq 0$ TO LOOP.

5.9 Special Instructions

Microprocessor instruction sets usually contain a few instructions which fall outside of the categories already discussed. These **special instructions** usually reflect the philosophy of the particular microprocessor design, and their relative importance depends upon the use for which the microprocessor is intended. The only special instruction, common to both the 6502 and Z80 microprocessors, which will be discussed here is the *no-operation* instruction which has the mnemonic **NOP** for both microprocessors.

The NOP instruction has two basic uses. First, it can be used to create a delay by using time during which the microprocessor does nothing. Second, it may be used to temporarily fill lines where, at a later stage in the program development, additional instructions may be easily inserted. (This particular use is usually reserved for hand-assembled programs.) Similarly, NOP instructions may be used to fill lines where instructions have been removed.

5.10 Introduction to Addressing Modes

Almost all of the instructions discussed so far result in the microprocessor either moving or operating on data stored in memory. In all of these cases the instruction must contain information relating to where the data to be operated on, or moved, resides (the *data source*) and where the data, once operated on, is to be moved to (the *data destination*).

In some of the instructions discussed, the data source and destination is contained in the instruction itself (e.g. TAX and LD A,B in Table 5.1), whilst in other instructions there is, apparently, no information concerning the data source or destination (e.g. AND in Table 5.4a).

Instructing the microprocessor as to the data source and destination is called **addressing** and, for versatility, each microprocessor is equipped with a variety of **addressing modes**. (The 6502 has thirteen addressing modes whilst the Z80 has seven basic modes.) To be able to write machine code programs, an understanding of the various addressing modes is essential.

It is beyond the scope of the present work to include all addressing modes for the 6502 and the Z80 microprocessors. Consequently only the five most important, and most frequently used, addressing modes will be discussed.

5.11 Implicit (Register) Addressing

In **implicit addressing**, the instruction itself specifies the data source and destination. Typical examples of implicit addressing are given in Table 5.10. Since implicit instructions can, by their very nature, only refer to registers within the microprocessor, this form of addressing is often called **register addressing**.

5.12 Immediate Addressing

With **immediate addressing** the data to be operated on follows *immediately* after the instruction in the form of a one-byte word. The data is essentially a numerical constant, usually called a *literal*. In the 6502 assembly code a special symbol, a # (or hash), is used to differentiate immediate addressing from page zero addressing (see 5.14) since both forms of addressing have one data byte following the instruction. The Z80 does not support page zero addressing and, consequently, requires no such symbol. Table 5.11 illustrates typical examples of immediate addressing.

5.13 Absolute Addressing

In **absolute addressing** the data to be operated on resides at the absolute memory location given by the two bytes of data immediately following the instruction (Table 5.12).

Table 5.10 Examples of instructions using implicit addressing

Assembly code	Instruction
TAX	Transfer accumulator to X register [6502].
TYA	Transfer Y register to accumulator [6502].
LD A,C	Load accumulator with contents of C register [Z80].
ADD A,B	Add contents of B register to accumulator [Z80].

Table 5.11 Examples of immediate addressing

Assembly code	Instruction
LDA #$40	Load the accumulator with the number 40_{16} [6502].
LD A,40H	Load the accumulator with the number 40_{16} [Z80].

Table 5.12 Examples of absolute addressing

Assembly code	Instruction
LDA $D000	Load accumulator with the data stored at $D000_{16}$ [6502].
STA $E000	Store accumulator contents at $E000_{16}$ [6502].
LD A,D000H	Load accumulator with the data stored at $D000_{16}$ [Z80].
LD E000H,A	Store accumulator contents at $E000_{16}$ [Z80].

Table 5.13 Examples of page zero addressing [6502]

Assembly code	Instruction
LDA $40	Load accumulator with the contents of address 0040_{16}.
ROL $40	Rotate left contents of address 0040_{16}.
CMP $40	Compare accumulator with the contents of address 0040_{16}.
ADC $40	Add, with carry, contents of address 0040_{16} to accumulator.

5.14 Page Zero Addressing

In **page zero addressing** the data to be operated on resides in page zero, at an address given by the one byte following the instruction. (Page zero is memory locations 0–225, i.e. the first 256 locations in memory.) Page zero addressing is similar to absolute addressing, the main difference being that it uses one less byte in the overall instruction (and thus less memory).

It must be pointed out that the Z80 does not support this very useful form of addressing. (The Z80 does, however, support a modified page zero addressing used to initiate jumps to subroutines. Modified page zero addressing will not be discussed here.)

Typical examples of page zero addressing, for the 6502, are given in Table 5.13.

5.15 Indexed Addressing

The main objective of **indexed addressing** is to allow manipulation of tables of data in memory. Indexed instructions specify both an address and an index, or displacement. During program execution, the displacement is added to the address to provide a final address.

Both the 6502 and the Z80 have several modes of indexed addressing. However, for present purposes only one of the indexed addressing modes will be discussed. Furthermore, the philosophy of indexing is different for the 6502 and Z80 and, consequently, these two microprocessors will be discussed separately.

5.15.1 Absolute Indexed Addressing [6502]

In **absolute indexed addressing**, the contents of either the X or Y *index registers* are added, as a one-byte unsigned number, to the absolute address specified in the instruction to compute the final address. As an example, consider the instruction

    LDA $D000,X

If the X register contained the number 40_{16}, then execution of this instruction would result in the accumulator being loaded with the data stored at $D040_{16}$ ($=D000_{16}+40_{16}$). Similarly the instruction

    STA   BASE,Y

would store the contents of the accumulator at the symbolic address BASE+the contents of the Y register.

Other examples of absolute indexed addressing are given in Table 5.14.

There are two points to be noted concerning absolute indexed addressing. First, since the X and Y index registers are both one-byte registers, only tables of not more than 256 words can be addressed using indexed addressing alone. Second, since the index is added as an unsigned number, only memory locations higher than the absolute base address may be addressed. In practice these two restrictions rarely present any real problem.

5.15.2 Indexed Addressing [Z80]

As with the 6502, the Z80 also has two index registers, IX and IY. However, these are both sixteen-bit registers which contain an absolute base address to which is added a displacement. An example of indexed addressing in the Z80 is the instruction

    LD   A,(IX+d)

which loads the accumulator with the contents of the absolute address given by IX+d, where d is a one-byte *signed* displacement. For example, if IX contained $D000_{16}$ and $d=40_{16}$, the instruction would load the accumulator with the contents of address $D040_{16}$. As with the 6502, the one-byte displacement only allows tables of up to 256 words to be addressed but note

Table 5.14 Examples of absolute indexed addressing [6502]

Assembly code	Instruction
CMP BASE,X	Compare contents of address BASE+X with accumulator.
LSR BASE,Y	Logical shift right of contents of address BASE+Y.
SBC BASE,X	Subtract contents of address BASE+X from accumulator.
EOR BASE,Y	Exclusive-OR contents of address BASE+X with accumulator.

Table 5.15 Examples of indexed addressing [Z80]

Assembly code	Instruction
LD A,(IY+d)	Load accumulator with the contents of address (IY+d).
RL (IX+d)	Rotate left contents of address (IX+d).
ADD A,(IY+d)	Add contents of address (IY+d) to accumulator.
DEC (IX+d)	Decrement contents of address (IX+d).

that a signed displacement allows access to memory location −127 to +127 above the base address given by IX. It should be noted that, since IX (and IY) can be incremented and decremented, all of the Z80 64 Kbytes of memory can be easily addressed with indexed addressing.

Other examples of Z80 indexed addressing are given in Table 5.15.

5.16 Writing Machine Code Programs

In the preceding paragraphs almost all of the elements of a written machine code program have been introduced. In addition to the five program fields already discussed (e.g. Example 5.8) two further pieces of information are required before a machine code program can be entered and run on a given microprocessor system.

First, it is necessary to know where, in memory, the program is to be stored. Second, the object (or machine) code for the program instructions must also be known. These two pieces of information are usually placed between the line number and label fields and thus comprise the second and third fields (Example 5.9).

Example 5.9 Write the full 6502 machine code program for the problem given in Example 5.8. The program is to be stored in memory commencing at page 3.

Solution The full 6502 machine code program is given in fig. 5.5. The operation of the program has already been discussed in Example 5.8 and

Fig. 5.5 Program
listing

Line No.	Memory location (hex)	Object code	Label	Source code	Operand	Comments
1	0300	A2 08		LDX	#$08	; LOAD X REGISTER WITH 8_{16}.
2	0302	20 00 E0	LOOP	JSR	$E000	; JUMP TO SUBROUTINE AT $E000_{16}$.
3	0305	CA		DEX		; DECREMENT X REGISTER.
4	0306	D0 FA		BNE	LOOP	; BRANCH IF $\neq 0$ TO LOOP.

will not be repeated here. There are, however, several points to be noted concerning the program listing.

The object code has been hand-assembled, from the source code, using the 6502 instruction set given in the Appendix. In the first line of the program, A2 is the hex code for the instruction LDX (immediate addressing). Following A2 is the operand, or data, 08_{16}. The memory location field, line 1, shows that the instruction A2 is to reside at 0300_{16} in memory with the data, 08_{16}, at 0301_{16}. (Note that, in all lines of the program, only the memory location of the instruction is given. It is assumed that the operand—if present—follows consecutively the instruction in memory.)

In the second line, 20 is the hex code for the instruction JSR (absolute addressing) which is stored at location 0302_{16}. The two-byte absolute-address operand $E000_{16}$ is stored at locations 0303_{16} and 0304_{16}. Note that the absolute address $E000_{16}$ is stored in the order "low byte first, high byte second". (All absolute addresses are stored as low byte first, high byte second in 6502 object code.)

In the third line, CA is the hex code for the instruction DEX (implied addressing) which is stored at 0305_{16}.

In line 4, D0, the hex code for the instruction BNE (relative addressing), is stored at 0306_{16}. The operand FA (FA = −6 in signed binary) will result in the program counter being loaded with 0302_{16}—the absolute address of the symbolic label LOOP—if the test fails. ($0302_{16} = 0308_{16} - 06_{16}$ where 0308_{16} is the content of the program counter when the microprocessor *commences* execution of the instruction BNE—see section 5.8.)

5.17 Example Machine Code Programs

The following two programs, the first to find the maximum and minimum values in a table of data, the second to multiply two one-byte numbers, are both routines which find a wide application as well as being typical machine code programs. It must, however, be stressed that, since the programs are based upon only the instructions introduced in this chapter, they are neither as efficient nor as elegent as programs which could be written using the *full* instruction set of the 6502 and Z80 microprocessors.

5.17.1 Maximum and Minimum Values of a Data Table

The flowchart for the program to determine the **maximum and minimum values** of a data table is shown in fig. 5.6. The program uses an index counter to determine when all of the elements of the data table have been examined. Two registers, or memory locations, with the symbolic names MINV and MAXV, are used to store the minimum and maximum values respectively.

Fig. 5.6 Flowchart of program to find minimum and maximum values in a table of data

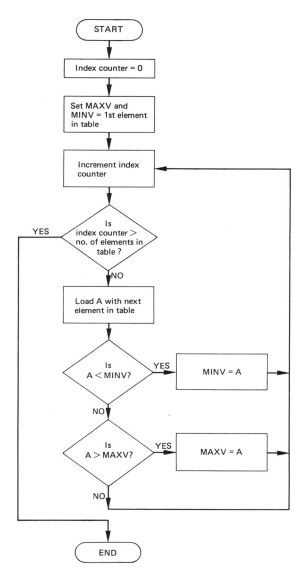

The program first sets the index counter to zero and sets MINV and MAXV equal to the first element in the table. (All subsequent elements in the table are then tested to see if they are less than MINV or greater than MAXV.) The index counter is incremented and tested to see if it is greater than the number of elements in the table. If all elements in the data table have been examined, the test succeeds and the routine ends. If the test fails, the accumulator is loaded with the next element in the table and a second test performed to see if the accumulator is less than MINV. If this second test succeeds, the new minimum value in the accumulator is stored in MINV. Should the test for a new MINV fail, a third test is made to see if the accumulator holds a new maximum value.

Fig. 5.7 6502 program listing for program to determine minimum and maximum values in a data table

Line No.	Label	Source code	Operand	Comments
1	START	LDX	#$00	; SET X INDEX REGISTER = 0.
2		LDA	TABLE	; LOAD A WITH FIRST ELEMENT OF TABLE.
3		STA	MINV	; LOAD MINV AND MAXV WITH
4		STA	MAXV	FIRST ELEMENT OF TABLE.
5	LOOP	INX		; INCREMENT INDEX REGISTER.
6		CPX	LENGTH	; IS X > LENGTH?
7		BCS	END	; IF YES THEN END ROUTINE.
8		LDA	TABLE,X	; LOAD A WITH NEXT DATA ELEMENT.
9		CMP	MINV	; IS A < MINV?
10		BCS	MAXV	; IF NO TEST FOR A > MAXV.
11		STA	MINV	; STORE NEW MINIMUM AT MINV.
12		JMP	LOOP	; EXAMINE NEXT ELEMENT.
13	MAX	CMP	MAXV	; IS A > MAXV?
14		BCC	LOOP	; IF NO EXAMINE NEXT ELEMENT.
15		STA	MAXV	; STORE NEW MAXIMUM AT MAXV.
16		JMP	LOOP	; EXAMINE NEXT ELEMENT.
17	END	RTS		; RETURN FROM ROUTINE.

Fig. 5.7 gives the program listing for the 6502 microprocessor in which the symbolic address TABLE is the first element in the data table and LENGTH is the address containing the total number of elements in the table. Note that the table cannot have more than 256 entries. In practice this is not, usually, a limitation.

The program listing is self-explanatory and the only point to note is that the X index register serves both as a counter, which is used to determine when all of the elements in the table have been examined, and as the address index as well (line 8).

The same program, written in Z80 assembly code, is given in the solution to problem 5.4.

5.17.2 One-byte by One-byte Multiplication

Before discussing the program to perform **one-byte by one-byte multiplication** it is useful to recall the basic rules of multiplication using fig. 5.8 which illustrates the multiplication of two numbers.

Fig. 5.8 Multiplication of two (decimal) numbers

137	Multiplicand
×108	Multiplier
1096	Partial product
000	Partial product
137	Partial product
14796	Result

Fig. 5.9 Multiplication of two one-byte numbers

10001001	Multiplicand ($=137_{10}$)
×01101100	Multiplier ($=108_{10}$)
00000000	Partial product
00000000	Partial product
10001001	Partial product
10001001	Partial product
00000000	Partial product
10001001	Partial product
10001001	Partial product
00000000	Partial product
011100111001100	Result ($=14796_{10}$)

The multiplication is performed by first multiplying the multiplicand (137) by the right-hand digit (8) of the multiplier to produce the partial product 1096. The next digit to the left of the multiplier (0) is then used to multiply the multiplicand and the result is *shifted to the left* by one position before it is added to the partial product. The process is repeated for all digits of the multiplier.

Fig. 5.9 shows the same calculation performed in binary as a one-byte by one-byte multiplication. Due to the simple rules of binary multiplication ($1 \times 0 = 0$ and $1 \times 1 = 1$), the multiplicand need only be shifted left before being included as a partial product if the corresponding multiplier bit is a 1. Note that the one-byte by one-byte multiplication leads to a two-byte (16 bit) result and that, if a program were to be based on the multiplication shown in fig. 5.9, eight registers or memory locations would be required to hold the partial products.

Fig. 5.10 gives the flowchart of a program to perform a one-byte by one-byte multiplication. The flowchart algorithm follows the example shown in fig. 5.9 with the exception that, instead of storing the partial products in eight separate registers, the multiplicand is added to the result, if the corresponding multiplier bit is a 1 and the result *shifted right*. Note that the carry flag is used to determine whether a particular bit of the multiplier is a 0 or a 1.

Fig. 5.10 Flowchart for one-byte by one-byte multiplication

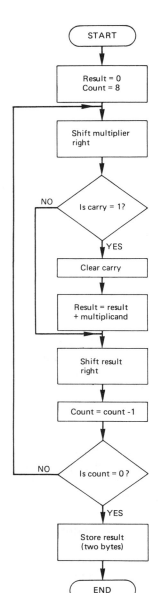

Line No.	Label	Source code	Operand	Comments
1	START	LD	H,08H	; MULTIPLIER BIT COUNT (H) SET = 8.
2		LD	B,00H	; CLEAR THE B REGISTER.
3		LD	A,(MPLY)	] ; LOAD D REGISTER WITH
4		LD	D,A	MULTIPLIER.
5		LD	A,(MPLD)	] ; LOAD E REGISTER WITH
6		LD	E,A	MULTIPLICAND.
7		LD	A,B	; CLEAR ACCUMULATOR (B = 0).
8	NXTBIT	SRL	D	; SHIFT NEXT MULTIPLIER INTO CARRY.
9		JP	NC,(SHIFT)	; IS MULTIPLIER BIT = 1?
10		CCF		] ; IF YES CLEAR (COMPLEMENT) CARRY AND
11		ADC	A,E	ADD MULTIPLICAND TO ACCUMULATOR.
12	SHIFT	SRL	A	] ; TRANSFER LSB OF ACCUMULATOR
13		RR	B	TO RLOB (VIA CARRY FLAG).
14		DEC	H	] ; DECREMENT BIT COUNTER. IF ZERO
15		JP	NZ,(NXTBIT)	EXIT FROM ROUTINE.
16		LD	(RHOB),A	] ; STORE HIGH BYTE OF RESULT.
17		LD	A,B	] ; STORE LOW BYTE OF RESULT.
18		LD	(RLOB),A	
19	END	RET		; EXIT FROM ROUTINE.

Fig. 5.11 One-byte by one-byte multiplication: Z80 assembly code

Fig. 5.11 shows the corresponding assembly code program for the Z80 microprocessor. The program uses the symbolic addresses MPLY (multiplier), MPLD (multiplicand), RHOB (result: high-order byte) and RLOB (result: low-order byte). The H register is used as the multiplier bit counter and the D and E registers are used as temporary storage for the multiplier and multiplicand respectively. Similarly the B register is used as temporary storage for the low byte of the result. Throughout the program the accumulator is used as a temporary register for the eight most significant bits of the result. Note that in the program listing symbolic addresses are enclosed in parenthesis, a feature of Z80 assembly code.

It is well worth spending time to understand how the program operates and, in particular, how in lines 12 and 13 the least significant bit of the temporary result is transferred to RLOB.

The same program, written in 6502 assembly code, is given in the solution to problem 5.5.

Problems 5: Microprocessor programming

1   Write a program in Z80 assembly code to mask off (i.e. set to 0) bits 0–3 of the data byte stored at $C000_{16}$ without altering bits 4–7.

2   Write a 6502 assembly program which will place the high and low order nibbles of the data byte residing at $C000_{16}$ into $B000_{16}$ and $B001_{16}$ respectively.

3   Write a Z80 assembly program to set bits 0–3 of the data, stored in address $E000_{16}$, to 1 without altering bits 4–7.

4   Develop a Z80 assembly code program to determine the minimum and maximum values in a data table, using the flowchart given in fig. 5.6.

5   Explain the difference between an *add* and an *add-with-carry* instruction. Explain also why it is sometimes necessary to clear the carry flag before using an add-with-carry instruction.

6   Write a 6502 assembly code program to perform a one-byte by one-byte multiplication using the flowchart given in fig. 5.10.

7   Explain the meaning of the term "addressing" in the context of a microprocessor instruction set, and why manufacturers produce microprocessors with many addressing modes.

8   The time taken to execute each 6502 and Z80 instruction is given in the instruction sets listed in the appendices. These times are expressed in terms of the number of clock cycles. Using the times given, write an assembly code subroutine, called DELAY, for a 6502 system which will introduce a 1 msec delay when executed. The clock frequency of the 6502 system is 1 MHz. [Hint: use the X, or Y, index registers as counters for a loop which performs no-operation (NOP) instructions.]

9   Write a Z80 subroutine, called PAUSE, which will introduce a delay of 2·25 msec when executed. The clock frequency of the Z80 system is 2 MHz.

10   Explain the meaning of the following terms used in assembly programming:
   a) Symbolic labels   *b*) Source code   *c*) Op code.

11   Using the program listing shown in fig. 5.5 as an example, write a full 6502 program for problem 5.8. The program is to be stored in memory commencing at 0400_{16}.

12   Compare, and contrast, the indexed addressing modes of the 6502 and Z80 microprocessors. State which of these two microprocessors has the more versatile indexed addressing.

6 Computer Storage Devices

6.1 Introduction

All computing systems require some form of *memory* to store both programs and program data. Most systems require both **volatile memory** (memory which "forgets" or loses its contents when the supply power is removed) and **non-volatile memory** (memory which retains its contents even when the power is removed). In general, volatile memory is used as *workspace* for storing temporary data and the results of calculations during program execution; whilst non-volatile memory is used to store programs, permanent records, etc.

It is useful, at this stage, to define the more frequently used terms associated with computer memory and storage. These terms include:

a) **Access time** The delay which occurs between the initiation of a *read-from-memory* operation and the time when the required information is available.

b) **Access cycle time** (usually referred to as the *cycle time*) The minimum time between successive read-from-memory operations.

c) **Read cycle time** The same as access cycle time.

d) **Write cycle time** The minimun time between successive *write-to-memory* operations.

e) **Memory size** The amount of data (often expressed in bytes) which can be held in memory.

f) **Random access memory** or **RAM** A volatile (usually solid state) memory for which the access time is independent of the location of the information. (In practical terms, any word in a RAM may be accessed without having to go through all the preceding locations.)

g) **Read only memory** or **ROM** A non-volatile memory in which the access time is (usually) independent of the location of the information. Information is entered into memory during the manufacturing process and *cannot be altered* (without destroying the memory) by the user. Consequently only read operations are permitted.

h) **Programmable read only memory** or **PROM** A ROM in which information may be stored—or programmed—by the user. Once programmed the contents of the PROM cannot be altered.

i) **Erasable programmable read only memory** or **EPROM** A PROM the contents of which may be erased and re-programmed with new data.

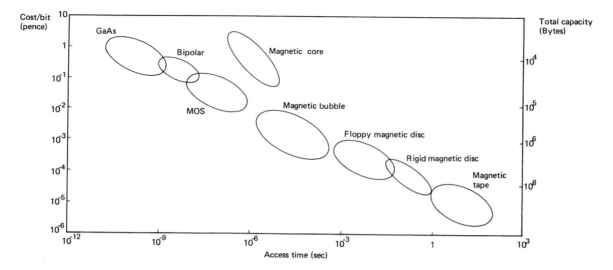

Fig. 6.1 A comparison of cost, access time and total capacity for various memory technologies (projected costs for 1984–85)

Memory erasure usually requires a "special" process such as exposing the EPROM to intense ultra-violet radiation.

The type of memory employed in any computer system depends, to a very large extent, upon the particular application, and is usually determined by three factors:

1   The storage space (memory size) required
2   The access time
3   Cost.

As might be expected, economics is often a decisive factor in memory selection, with a general rule applying that the larger the memory and the smaller the access time, the greater the cost (fig. 6.1). As a consequence of this, together with limitations imposed by physical size, power dissipation and address bus structures, most computing systems use two or more types of storage medium. Fig. 6.2 illustrates a typical computer memory configuration comprising three storage areas. These are

1   Microprocessor registers   All microprocessors are constructed with several (typically 2–12) registers in which data may be temporarily stored. This internal memory, which can also function as index and address registers (see sections 5.11 and 5.15), is characterised by a very small access time, typically 20–40 nsec. Although the storage area is small, its use can result in considerable time-saving in such operations as multiplication, bit manipulation, etc., when compared with the case in which the data operated on is stored in external memory.

2   Main store   As the name suggests, the main store is used to store the program currently executed, together with temporary data and results. Originally a magnetic core store was used for this purpose and, although

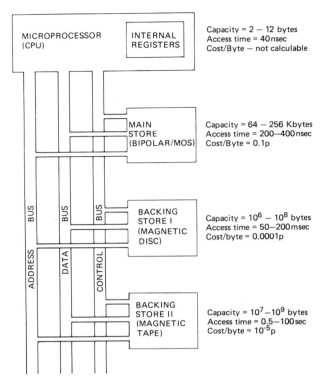

Fig. 6.2 Typical computer memory configuration

MICROPROCESSOR (CPU)

INTERNAL REGISTERS

Capacity = 2 − 12 bytes
Access time = 40 nsec
Cost/Byte — not calculable

MAIN STORE (BIPOLAR/MOS)

Capacity = 64 − 256 Kbytes
Access time = 200−400 nsec
Cost/Byte = 0.1p

BACKING STORE I (MAGNETIC DISC)

Capacity = 10^6 − 10^8 bytes
Access time = 50−200 msec
Cost/byte = 0.0001p

BACKING STORE II (MAGNETIC TAPE)

Capacity = 10^7−10^9 bytes
Access time = 0.5−100 sec
Cost/byte = 10^{-5}p

ADDRESS BUS   DATA BUS   CONTROL BUS

almost completely superseded by modern solid state memories, the terms "main core" and "core store" are still occasionally used to describe the main store irrespective of the storage medium. The chief requirement of the main store is that the read and write cycle times are comparable with the read and write cycle times of the microprocessor, thus making the memory *transparent* to the microprocessor. If this is not the case then the microprocessor will be "kept waiting" for data transfers to and from memory. Not only does this waste time but introducing a WAIT state into the microprocessor cycle usually requires additional circuitry.

The size of the main store varies considerably, depending upon the microprocessor or CPU. "Established" 8-bit microprocessors (e.g. 6800, 6502, Z80) are limited to 64 Kbytes of main store by the 16-bit address lines. The latest generation of 16-bit microprocessors (e.g. Z8000, 8086) possesses the facility to address multiple blocks of 64 Kbytes, with the APX 234 capable of addressing in excess of 1 Gbyte.

3 Backing store The backing store is a non-volatile mass-storage area characterised by relatively long access times. Modern backing stores are usually either magnetic tape or magnetic disc. Both of these devices are of similar cost, the essential difference being that magnetic tape has a higher storage capacity and longer access times compared to magnetic disc.

As the above discussion implies, a variety of physical effects and techniques have been developed for computer storage. However, only two technologies find a widespread application with microprocessor-based systems. These involve either magnetic effects or solid state devices and will be discussed separately.

6.2 Introduction to Magnetic Storage Systems

Five basic types of memory have been developed which utilise the magnetic properties of materials to store information. These are

1 Magnetic core
2 Magnetic card
3 Magnetic bubble
4 Magnetic disc
5 Magnetic tape.

Of these only 4 and 5 have any real practical significance for microprocessor-based computing systems.

It is, however, worth mentioning the present status of the first three. Magnetic core memories have almost all been replaced by solid state memories which offer larger capacity with a faster access time at a reduced cost (fig. 6.1). Magnetic card memories, which operate on the same principle as magnetic tape or disc (i.e. magnetic surface recording, see 6.3), are now considered to be obsolete, although "mini" magnetic cards are used as storage by some pocket calculators. Magnetic bubble memories, the latest development in magnetic memories, are now finding an ever-increasing usage. Currently, their cost and performance figures limit their use to more specialised applications (e.g. telephone exchanges) where their main advantage of having no moving parts, which results in excellent reliability and almost zero maintenance, is of paramount importance. However, there is little doubt that within the next few years they will find applications in microprocessor and microcomputer systems.

Both magnetic disc and magnetic tape use the same physical effect, that of *magnetic surface recording*, to store information. The only essential difference in the two systems lies in the mechanical arrangement of the read/write circuitry and the recording medium.

6.3 Magnetic Surface Recording

Fig. 6.3 illustrates the principle of **magnetic surface recording** (MSR). The WRITE HEAD consists of a coil wound on a core material which has a high magnetic permeability. The air gap in the core allows magnetic flux, produced by the write current, to pass into the magnetic surface of the recording medium, resulting in a small area of the surface becoming magnetised. Reversing the write current results in a reversal of the magnetisation, thus allowing a binary pattern to be recorded.

The READ HEAD is constructed in a similar fashion to the write head. As the magnetised surface passes the read head, some of the magnetic flux

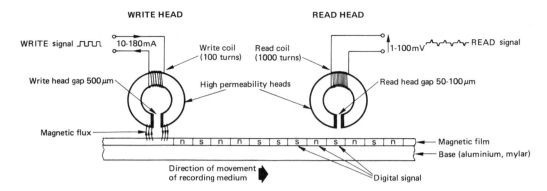

Fig. 6.3 Magnetic surface recording

passes into the head via the read head gap. The changing flux induces a voltage ($E = -d\phi/dt$) in the read head windings which reflects the state of magnetisation—and hence the data recorded—of the recording surface.

The only essential difference between the read and write heads lies in the number of turns on the head coil and the size of the air gap. For the write operation, a large air gap is required to minimise the write current. Additionally, a small number of turns on the write coil results in a coil with a low inductance which permits high switching speeds. The read head, on the other hand, requires a small air gap to provide good read-pulse resolution, necessary to maximise the total number of bits recorded per unit track length. A large number of turns on the read coil is necessary to produce an adequate signal level. In some systems the read and write heads are combined, which requires a degree of compromise in the conflicting design requirements. Usually the compromise is made in favour of the read operation.

The recording surface is traditionally a 25 μm film of gamma ferric oxide (Fe_3O_4), although more recently 0·2–2·0 μm films of either nickel-cobalt (Ni–Co) and chromium dioxide (CrO_2) have been introduced. Both CrO_2 and Ni–Co possess superior recording properties when compared with Fe_3O_4, albeit at a higher cost.

6.3.1 Recording Codes

Some thirteen different **recording codes** have been employed for magnetic surface recording. Of these only three are used to any extent and are illustrated in fig. 6.4 (*d*, *e*, and *f*) which shows the serial recording of one data byte. Each bit of data occupies one **cell bit** (fig. 6.4*a*). Clock signals (fig. 6.4*b*) are also shown and, in practice, would be used by recording codes (*c*) and (*d*) for purposes of synchronisation. The recording codes operate as follows:

(*c*) RETURN TO ZERO (RZ) In this code a 1 is represented by one state of magnetization (i.e. either "north" or "south" pole) for the central region of the cell bit. During the remainder of the cell bit, the magnetization is

Fig. 6.4 Magnetic
surface recording
codes

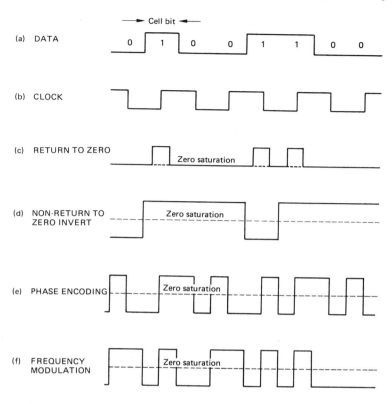

returned to zero (i.e. not magnetized). A 0 is represented by no
magnetization of the cell bit. In practice RZ code is no longer used and
is only included for purposes of reference.

(*d*) NON-RETURN TO ZERO INVERT (NRZI) In this code a 1 is represented
by a change in magnetization at the beginning of the cell bit and a 0 by
no change.

(*e*) PHASE ENCODING (PE) Here a 1 is represented by a change of magnetisation, in a specified direction (i.e. "north" to "south"), at the centre of
the cell. A 0 is represented by a change of magnetisation in the opposite
direction. An advantage of PE is that it is *self-clocking* in that it
produces regular read signals at the centre of the cell which can be used
for synchronisation. An external clock is not required.

(*f*) FREQUENCY MODULATION (FM) In FM, a 1 is represented by a change
of magnetization at the centre of the cell and a 0 by no change. In
addition a change of magnetization occurs at the beginning of each cell.
As with PE, FM is self-clocking with the clock signals occurring at the
start of each cell.

6.3.2 Error Detection

One of the disadvantages of magnetic surface recording is that it is susceptible to the generation of errors, particularly during the read operation.

Consequently there is a need to include in the read/write process some form of **error detection**. As might be expected, a variety of error detection methods have been developed of which the following three are the more frequently encountered:

1   Parity checks   In this—the simplest of the methods—a **parity bit** is added to each word during the write operation such that the total number of bits in each word is either even (*even parity*) or odd (*odd parity*). During the read operation a check is made to ensure that the mode of parity is maintained. Parity checks can only be regarded as a "first filter" error check since multiple errors (e.g. two missing bits in a word) will escape detection.

2   Check sums   With check sums the numerical value of each byte, in a given block of data, is summed with any carries which are generated being ignored (fig. 6.5). The result of the summation—the *check sum*—is recorded

Fig. 6.5 Generation of a check sum for the data block
$$X = Y + Z + P$$

	Character	ASCII Code	Binary Code
	X	88	01011000
	=	61	00111101
	Y	89	01011001
Data	+	43	00011011
Block	Z	90	01011010
	+	43	00011011
	P	80	01010000
	Total Sum	494	111101110

Carry (ignored)

∴ Check sum = 11101110 = 238_{10}

at the end of the data block. During reading, the check sum is again calculated and compared with the recorded check sum. Any difference indicates the presence of an error. Whilst more reliable than the simple parity check, check sums can, on occasions, fail to detect multiple errors.

3   Cyclic redundancy check (CRC)   In this, a block of data is simply regarded as being one very long binary number. The cyclic redundancy check is obtained by dividing this long number by a second, known and agreed number called the *generator*. The remainder of the division is recorded at the end of the data block as the CRC character. During reading, the CRC is again calculated and compared with the recorded CRC.

Whilst it is beyond the scope of the present work to discuss the underlying theory, CRCs have a much higher probability of error detection than other techniques.

6.4 Magnetic Disc Recording

As the name suggests, in a **magnetic disc recorder** the recording surface comprises a disc which revolves about a central—and usually vertical—axis. The READ/WRITE HEAD is situated close to the disc surface such that concentric tracks on the disc can be recorded or read back (fig. 6.7).

One feature which is immediately obvious is that data can only be written to, or read from, a particular region of the disc when that region is below the read/write head. Thus the disc access times, also called *rotational latency*, are dependent, amongst other things, upon the speed of revolution of the disc.

Fig. 6.6 Comparative sizes of commonly encountered foreign bodies in disc environment

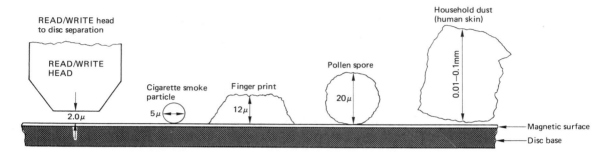

To avoid intolerable wear, due to friction, the read/write head does not make physical contact with the recording surface, being separated by an air gap of $1 \cdot 0$–$10 \cdot 0\ \mu$m. Maintaining this small separation is essential for reliable operation, something which requires precision engineering and is partially responsible for the relative high cost of disc systems. One technique—the *flying head disc*—uses an aerodynamically designed recording head and mounting, such that the disc, revolving at high speed, draws air between the disc and recording head, resulting in the recording head resting on a cushion of air. With this method, air gaps as small as $0 \cdot 5\ \mu$m can be established. Small disc/record head separations require that the disc be operated in an environment which is free from dust and other foreign bodies. To help appreciate the nature of this problem fig. 6.6 illustrates the typical sizes of the more commonly encountered air-borne foreign bodies.

There are two basic types of magnetic disc currently in use:
- *a) Rigid or hard disc*   fixed head
                             moving/multiple moving head
- *b) Floppy or soft disc*   moving head only

6.4.1 Rigid Discs

Rigid or **hard discs** are usually associated with mainframe or the larger mini computers. The disc is usually constructed from aluminium with a recording surface of either ferric or chromium oxide. Disc diameters range from 25–38 cm. Only the outer 10–15 cm of the disc are used for recording purposes, with the diameter of the inner track being determined by the maximum packing density (bits per unit length) of track.

Fig. 6.7 Magnetic surface recording: disc

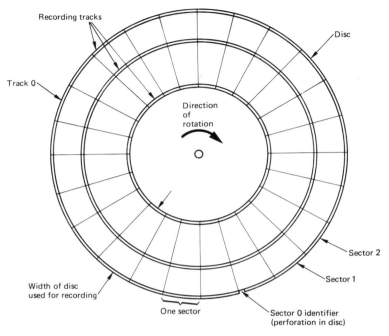

(a) Disc format

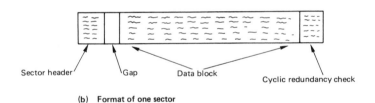

(b) Format of one sector

The disc recording surface can accommodate up to 256 separate tracks with each track subdivided into some 32 sectors (fig. 6.7). Each sector can hold up to 256 bytes of data giving a total disc capacity of approximately 2M bytes. One sector is the smallest block of data which can be written to or read from the disc. The position of the sectors may be determined by *sector headers* written onto the disc by a computer program (*soft sectoring*, see fig. 6.7*b*) or, more rarely, by perforations around the edge of the disc which are detected by photoelectric sensors (*hard sectoring*). The position of the first sector is specially marked, usually by a physical perforation on the disc. The most usual method of recording is phase encoding with at least one level of error detection, usually CRC.

Fixed recording head As the name suggests, in this system the position of the recording head remains fixed (fig. 6.8*a*). Thus each track requires its own read/write head, making a total of 256 recording heads for a full-size

Fig. 6.8 Rigid (hard) disc systems

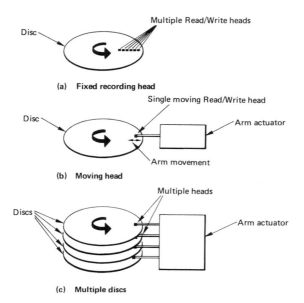

(a) **Fixed recording head**

(b) **Moving head**

(c) **Multiple discs**

system. Such large numbers of recording heads clearly represent a disadvantage in terms of multiple read/write circuitry, signal cross-talk, etc. However, the fixed disc does offer the advantage of permitting high rotational speeds—up to 70 revolutions/second—and correspondingly small access times, typically a few msec. Most fixed head systems are constructed such that the disc cannot easily be removed or exchanged. Consequently the capacity of a fixed head system is 2 Mbytes.

Moving and multiple moving recording heads Moving head discs contain only one read/write head which moves across the disc, on the end of an arm, until it is positioned above a particular track (fig. 6.8b). Since the width of each track is very small (typically 0·1–0·15 mm), precision engineering is required to ensure that the recording head both reaches and remains over a particular track.

The moving head disc has a longer access time when compared with the fixed head system. This is due to the time taken to move the head to a new track position, as well as the slower rotational speeds used by the moving head systems. However, this disadvantage is partially, if not totally, offset in the multiple disc unit which may have up to twelve stacked discs, each with its own read/write head attached to a common arm (fig. 6.8c). One advantage of the multiple disc unit is that data may be read, and written, in parallel, allowing byte storage and effective access times of eight times faster than the single disc.

The mechanical arrangement of the moving head disc usually results in a smaller number of tracks than the fixed head, typically 200 tracks. The total capacity is thus approximately 1·5 Mbytes/disc giving a total capacity of 30–40 Mbytes on a multiple double-sided-recording disc system.

Single moving head disc systems are usually constructed to allow exchangeable discs to be employed in which the discs are kept in a special plastic cassette-type cover. Multiple disc cassettes are also available (called *disc packs*) but as would be expected are only used on very large systems.

6.4.2 Floppy Discs

The **floppy disc** is a more recent, and from the point of view of the microprocessor-based mini-computer, significant development in disc storage. The disc itself comprises a flexible (hence *floppy*) disc with a ferric oxide recording surface on one (*single-sided disc*) or both (*double-sided disc*) sides. The standard disc has a diameter of 20 cm (8 inches) and is contained in, and protected by, a plastic sleeve (fig. 6.9).

Fig. 6.9 A floppy disc

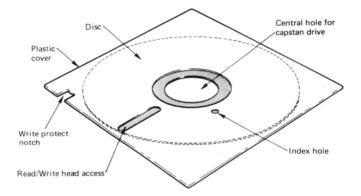

An oblong slot, cut in the plastic sleeve along a radius, allows access for the read/write head, whilst a circular hole in the centre permits the disc to be rotated, inside the plastic cover, on a capstan drive. A single index hole enables the position of the first sector to be determined by an external photoelectric sensor. In addition, a *write protect notch* is cut in the side of the plastic sleeve which engages with a micro-switch inside the disc drive. To prevent accidental write operations to the disc, which could alter or destroy data already written on the disc, the write protect notch is covered by an adhesive foil. The presence of the foil is detected by the micro-switch and any attempt to write to the disc will result in either the generation of an error message or the abortion of the program (or both) (fig. 6.10).

In use, the disc is inserted into a disc drive unit. Closing the drive unit door automatically engages the capstan drive which, in some systems, runs continuously. The disc may rotate in either the vertical or horizontal plane. The single or double (for double-sided discs) read/write head is moved from track to track by a stepper, or incremental, motor. Frequency modulation (FM) recording code is used together with a cyclic redundancy check.

Two types of floppy disc are currently in use. In addition to the floppy disc described above there is a mini version known as the *mini-floppy*, or *flippy*, disc. The characteristics of both discs are listed in Table 6.1.

Fig. 6.10 Floppy disc drive

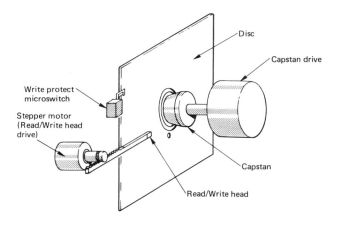

Table 6.1 Floppy disc characteristics

	Floppy disc	Mini-floppy disc
Disc diameter	8 inch	5·25 inch
Rotational speed	360 rpm	300 rpm
Maximum number of tracks	77*	38
Sectors per track	26*	18
Bytes per sector	128 *	128
Total capacity	256 Kbytes	64 Kbytes
Access time (average)	100 msec	≃300 msec

* IBM 3740 format

Early floppy disc systems were constructed with read/write heads which were in direct and constant contact with the floppy disc. The subsequent frictional wear limited the life of the floppy disc to about 500 hours continuous use. All modern floppy disc units use non-contact read/write heads, with one design incorporating a flying head. However, many mini-floppy drive units still use direct-contact read/write heads which does represent a limitation for these devices.

6.5 Magnetic Tape Recording

Magnetic recording tape consists of a polyester, or mylar, base coated with either a layer of ferric oxide or chromium dioxide, with the latter being used only in very specialised applications. The thickness of the tape base is typically 25 μm and the magnetic surface approximately 10 μm. The tape width can vary between 0·25 cm and 2·54 cm and its overall length between 100 m and 500 m. Typical tape spool diameters range from 7 cm to 20 cm with the spools sometimes forming part of an integral tape cassette.

Fig. 6.11 Magnetic tape transport

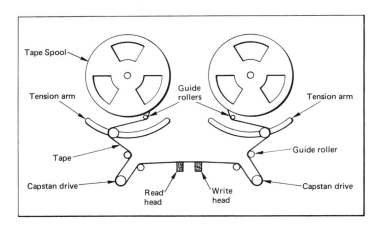

Fig. 6.11 illustrates a typical tape transport system, such as might be used in a mini-computing system. The two tape spools, each driven by separate motors, rotate in opposite directions, whilst spring-loaded tension arms absorb any temporary slack in the tape which may arise when the tape drive starts, stops or changes direction. Twin capstan drives, rotating at a uniform rate, move the tape at a uniform velocity (typically 1 m/sec) over the multi-track read and write heads, with the tape maintaining direct contact with the read and write heads. Whilst this arrangement results in tape wear, due to friction, its effect in practice may be ignored since the overall time which a given region of the tape spends in contact with the recording heads (and hence tape wear) is extremely small. In practice, tape life is limited by mechanical fatigue induced by the continual acceleration and deceleration of the tape during record searches. For a similar reason, the tape drive is less susceptible than disc drives to the presence of foreign bodies (see 6.4). Even so, most tape drives are operated in a closed environment into which filtered air is pumped at a pressure slightly higher than the ambient pressure.

Unlike disc systems, magnetic tape recorders usually employ separate read and write heads. Not only does this avoid design compromises (see 6.3) but it also allows the immediate reading of data, during a write operation, providing early error detection.

Data is usually recorded on nine tracks across the width of the tape (fig. 6.12) using a non-return to zero invert (NRZI) code. Seven-track recording, whilst still used extensively, is nevertheless regarded as obsolete. As with disc recording, data is recorded in blocks which comprise a block header, the data block and a cyclic redundancy check (CRC). In addition a *longitudinal redundancy check* (LRC)—essentially a check sum of each data track—is usually included. Gaps in the tape, between data blocks and block headers, allow the tape to be positioned before a read or write operation.

Data packing densities vary, with 2000–4000 bytes/cm more commonly used. On a 500 m length tape, with a read/write velocity of 1 m/sec, this corresponds to a maximum storage capacity of approximately 10^8 bytes with a data transfer rate of approximately 200 Kbytes/sec. Access times are

Fig. 6.12 Record
format: magnetic tape

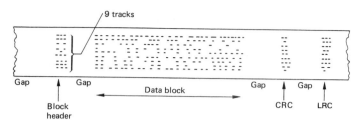

strongly dependent upon the read/write velocity, data packing densities and
record format, and range from a few seconds to one or two minutes.

6.6 Disc and Tape Controllers

Disc drivers and tape recorders, whilst capable of storing large quantities of
data, are nevertheless inefficient in the sense that most of their operational
time is spent searching for a particular record. This is particularly true of
tape systems. Connecting such devices directly to a microprocessor or CPU
would result in an intolerable waste of computing time whilst the microprocessor performed record searches.

To overcome this particular problem, disc and tape systems are interfaced
to the main computing system via a **controller circuit**. When a particular
record is required, the computer informs the controller of the whereabouts
of the data record (i.e. track and sector number or tape section header). The
controller first searches for the record and loads it directly into memory with
a *direct memory access* (DMA) routine. The controller then generates a *data
ready* interrupt to inform the microprocessor that the record is available.
During a write to disc or tape operation, the microprocessor places the data
block to be recorded into a known area of memory called the *disc* or *tape
buffer* store. The microprocessor then informs the controller of the data
destination (track and sector number or tape section) and then leaves the
controller to perform the write operation whilst it continues with more
"useful" computations.

6.7 Semiconductor Memories

One of the major problems facing the technical author is that in the interval
between the writing and the publication of technical material, substantial
developments may have taken place which tend to render the contents
obsolete.

This is particularly true of **semiconductor memories** where, in recent
years, a major development has been announced almost every three months.
For example, when the present text was commissioned, 32K semiconductor
memories, capable of storing $32 \times 1024 = 32\ 768$ bits, represented the limits
to the "state of the art". At the time of completion of this text (10 months
later), 64K memories are in volume production with 256K memories just

commencing production. In addition the 512K memory has successfully completed research and development and one company has announced its intention of developing a 4M bit memory.

As a consequence the reader is advised to consider the present work as representing semiconductor memories of a previous generation and should consult the professional and trade magazines for state-of-the-art information.

There are, however, two good reasons for presenting semiconductor memories here. The first is that the rapid advances in semiconductor memories are due, primarily, to advances in an existing technology rather than the development of new technologies. Consequently the basic technology remains unchanged as does its relative advantages and disadvantages. Second, there is an indication that a saturation point has almost been reached, regarding the number of devices which may be fabricated per unit area on an integrated circuit (the so called *quantum limit*). As a result, certain manufacturers have expressed a cautious belief that in the next few years semiconductor memory development will be less rapid once the 1 Mbyte (=8M bit) memory has been achieved.

The basic unit of the semiconductor memory is the **memory cell** which is capable of storing just one binary digit. The memory cell may be constructed from either bipolar or field effect transistors, the complete memory being formed by fabricating many such cells on a single chip. Bipolar memories are characterised by relatively small memory capacity (typically 16K bits) and a fast access time (15–40 nsec), whilst field effect memories are characterised by a high memory capacity (64K–256K bits) and a long access time (100–300 nsec).

6.8 Bipolar Memories

6.8.1 Bipolar Random Access Memories (RAM)

Fig. 6.13 illustrates the basic **bipolar random access memory** cell. It comprises two dual-emitter bipolar transistors cross-coupled to form a bistable circuit (or *flip-flop*). In operation, one transistor is conducting (ON) whilst the other transistor is non-conducting (OFF). Either of the emitters, on each transistor, is capable of conducting base/emitter current and may thus be used, independently, to turn the transistor ON.

When the memory cell is in the *standby mode* (i.e. not part of a read or write cycle), the cell select line is held at a lower potential (0·3 V) than either the DATA or DATA lines (1·0–2·0 V). Under these conditions, the cell current through the ON transistor is conducted through the cell select line, leaving the DATA and DATA lines in a high impedance state (i.e. effectively disconnected from the cell).

To READ data from the cell, the select line is raised high (3·0 V), resulting in the cell current flowing through either the DATA (T1 ON) or DATA (T2 ON) lines. A differential amplifier (not shown in fig. 6.13) connected to the DATA and DATA senses the *state* of the cell. If T1 is ON, the output of the

Fig. 6.13 Bipolar random access memory cell

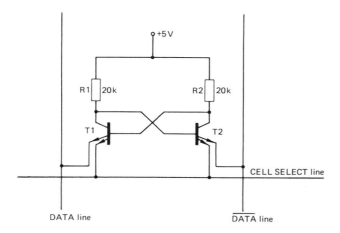

differential amplifier will be high, indicating that a 1 is stored in the cell. If T2 is ON, the amplifier output will be low, indicating that a 0 is stored in the cell. Note that since the DATA and DATA lines are in a high impedance state when the cell is on standby, many such cells may share the same differential amplifier provided that only one cell is selected for a READ operation at any given time.

To WRITE to the cell, the cell select line is raised high (3·0 V) and either the DATA (write a 1 into the cell) or DATA (write a 0 into the cell) line is lowered to 0 volts.

Fig. 6.14 illustrates how 64 such memory cells may be connected to form a memory which is organised as 16 words with 4 bits per word. (For a full explanation of the organisation and control of a memory, such as that shown in fig. 6.14, see section 6.10.)

The memory cell shown in fig. 6.13 dissipates approximately $800\,\mu W$, when on standby, and has an access time of about 40 nsec. The standby power limits the size of memory, constructed from such cells, to approximately 512 bits. A 512-bit memory would dissipate a total of $0·7$ watts ($512 \times 800\,\mu W +$ drive and decode circuits dissipation) which is about the upper limit to the power dissipation of a single chip.

In order to reduce the power dissipation per cell, and hence increase memory size, the collector current in T1 and T2 must be reduced. This, in turn, requires that R1 and R2 be increased. However, a 20 k resistance is about the maximum value which can be created in bipolar structures using present-day technology. A solution to this problem is shown in fig. 6.15 in which two additional transistors, T3 and T4, are used as high impedance collector loads. Using this memory cell, 4096-bit memories may be constructed which have a total power dissipation of approximately 600 mW.

Table 6.2 lists state-of-the-art performance figures for bipolar RAMs together with comparable data for other types of semiconductor memory.

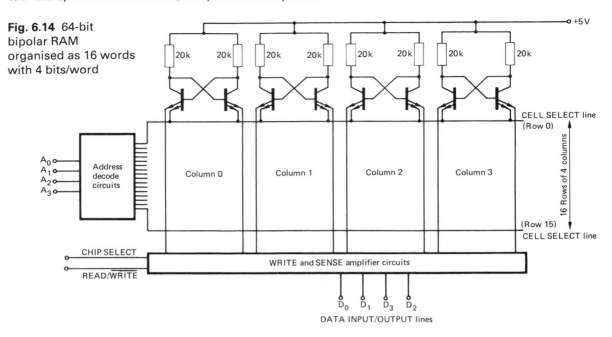

Fig. 6.14 64-bit bipolar RAM organised as 16 words with 4 bits/word

Table 6.2 Semiconductor memories: summary

Memory	Capacity (K bits)	Access Time (nsec Read & Write)	Power Consumption (μW/bit) ACTIVE	STANDBY
Bipolar				
RAM	4	25 R/W	140	
ROM	32	40 R	20	
PROM	32	40 R	16	
MOS/SOS				
RAM	32 (NMOS)	70 R/W	10·0	0·001
	16 (PMOS)	70 R/W	7·0	0·001
	16 (CMOS)	90 R/W	0·12	0·0001
Dynamic RAM	256	100 R/W	3·0	0·03
ROM	64 (NMOS)	150 R	0·2	0·004
	256 (CMOS)	200 R	0·35	0·005
EPROM	128	200 R 50 msec W	3·0	0·001
EEPROM	16	250 R 10 msec W	30·0	30·0

R/W READ and WRITE
R   READ only
W   WRITE only

Fig. 6.15 Low-power bipolar memory cell

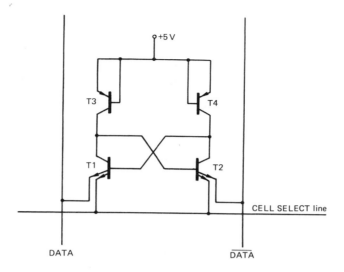

6.8.2 Bipolar Read Only Memories (ROM and PROM)

There are two types of read-only memory: *masked* and *programmable*. Masked programmed memory is usually referred to as ROM, whilst PROM is reserved for programmable memory.

1 Fig. 6.16 illustrates a 4×4 **masked ROM** organised as 4 words with 4 bits per word. It comprises a 4×4 diode matrix with, or without, conducting links between the diodes and the data output columns. During operation a particular row is selected (i.e. raised to $+5$ V) using the address and chip select inputs. The data output lines will be logical 1 if a diode-conducting link exists between the row and data column and 0 if the conducting link is missing. For example, if Row 3 is selected (by raising A_0, A_1 and the chip select lines high), the data output will be $1101 \equiv 13_{10}$.

Programming of the masked ROM, which effectively consists of inserting

Fig. 6.16 Masked ROM

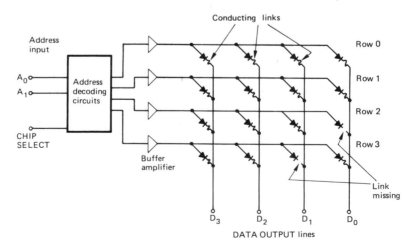

the conducting links at the appropriate positions in the matrix, is performed by the manufacturer when the memory chip is made. A photographic mask (hence *masked*) is constructed, to the customer's specifications, which during production masks out the positions where conducting links are *not* required. Masked ROMs, which have a typical capacity of 32 768 bits and an access time of 40 nsec, offer a very cheap ROM where large-volume production is required.

2 Fig. 6.17 illustrates a **PROM memory**. Each PROM memory cell consists of a transistor whose collector is tied to the +5 V rail. A fusible link, or "fuse", in the emitter circuit determines whether the output from the cell is a 1 (fuse intact) or a 0 (fuse blown) when the cell select line (transistor base) is raised high.

Following manufacture, with the fuses intact, the output of each memory cell is a binary 1. To program a 0 into the cell, the fuse is blown by passing a sufficiently high current (typically 50 mA) through the fuse element. The process of fuse-blowing requires close-tolerance conditions. If the fuse current is too large, damage to the cell select and sense circuits can occur. If the fuse current is too small, the conductor will only separate for a short while, after which the fuse will *grow back* destroying the programmed information.

PROM fusible links are constructed from nichrome barrier metals such as titanium-tungsten or polysilicon materials. Present state-of-the-art bipolar PROMs offer a 32K bit storage capacity with an access time of approximately 40 nsec.

6.9 Field Effect Memories

Semiconductor memories based on field effect devices are constructed using either MOS (metal-on-silicon) or SOS (silicon-on-sapphire) technologies.

6.9.1 Field Effect RAMs

1 Fig. 6.18 illustrates an **NMOS random access memory** cell. Its mode of operation is similar to the low-power bipolar memory cell shown in fig. 6.15. Referring to fig. 6.18, T1 and T2 (NMOS transistors) comprise a bistable element which stores the cell data. T3 and T4 serve as very high impedance drain loads for T1 and T2, respectively, which minimises the cell current.

To read data from the cell, the cell select line is raised high, switching on T5 and T6, thus connecting the cell to the DATA and DATA lines. To write data to the cell, the cell select line is again raised high and the DATA or DATA line set low to force the bistable into the required state.

The NMOS memory cell can be designed with a power consumption as low as 5 μW (standby), although 10–20 μW is more typical of currently available devices. Due to both the low-power consumption and the relatively small physical geometry of the NMOS transistor, many memory cells may be fabricated in a single integrated circuit.

Fig. 6.17 PROM

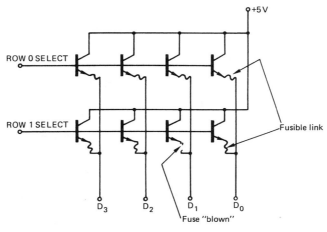

Fig. 6.18 NMOS RAM cell

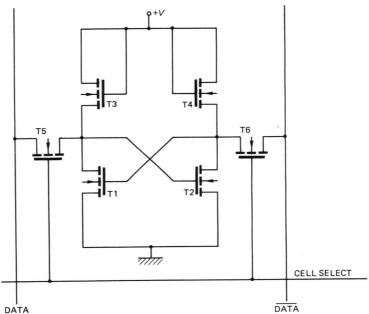

State-of-the-art NMOS memories offer a 32K bit storage capacity with access times of 100–300 nsec. The relatively long access times reflect long circuit time constants created by the high gate resistance of field effect transistors and circuit stray capacitance.

2   PMOS memory cells may be constructed in a similar fashion to the NMOS memory cells. Unfortunately the PMOS memories suffer from long access times, typically 500–800 nsec, as a consequence of the low carrier mobility (the ratio of electron mobility to hole mobility $\simeq 3:1$). PMOS memories have, in the past, offered advantages of lower power consumption and lower cost than their NMOS counterparts although this situation no longer exists.

Fig. 6.19 CMOS
memory cell

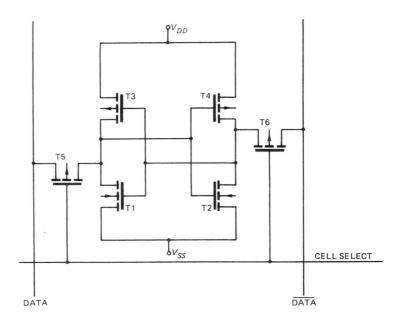

3 The **CMOS** (complementary metal-on-silicon) **memory** cell, which is constructed from NMOS and PMOS inverters connected in series, is shown in fig. 6.19. T1–T4 form the bistable data storage element with T5 and T6 acting as switches during read/write operations.

CMOS memories exhibit all the characteristics of NMOS and PMOS memories with some very important extras. These extras include very low power dissipation, typically $0·2$ μW/cell, and high noise immunity. The very low power requirements allow the memory to be operated from small batteries for considerable periods. In this context, CMOS memories may be used as RAM in computer systems with a battery-powered back-up for information retention should the main system power supply fail. Fig. 6.20 illustrates a typical back-up supply circuit which automatically operates should the main power supply fail. Under normal operating conditions, the memory receives power from the main supply via D1. D2 is reverse biased, leaving the back-up battery (a mercury cell) isolated. Should the main power supply fail (i.e. $V_p = 0$ volts), the power is supplied from the mercury cell via D2, with D1 becoming reverse biased to prevent the mercury cell supplying power to the rest of the circuit. In a typical application the mercury cell will supply power for a few hundred hours.

The CMOS memory cell suffers from two basic disadvantages. The first is that the CMOS memory circuit (memory cell + drivers) requires a larger number of active devices than comparable NMOS and PMOS memories. This results in CMOS memories having a smaller total storage capacity than the NMOS and PMOS devices. The second is that CMOS memories suffer from the effects of parasitic capacitance between the gate and substrate of the active devices. An obvious solution to this problem is to reduce the

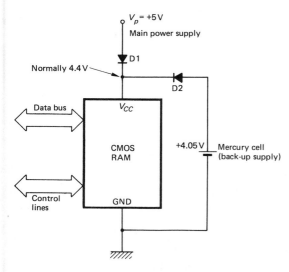

Fig. 6.20 CMOS RAM
with back-up supply

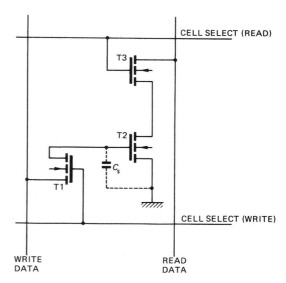

Fig. 6.21 NMOS
dynamic RAM cell

parasitic capacitance by minimising the gate area. However, there are limits to what may be achieved by this approach. Another solution is to use a different substrate material which has led to the development of CSOS (complementary silicon-on-sapphire) memories.

CMOS memories offer storage capacities of 16K bits with access times of about 90 nsec.

6.9.2 MOS Dynamic RAM

Fig. 6.21 shows an NMOS dynamic RAM cell which uses the gate-to-source stray capacitance C_s of an NMOS transistor T2 as a data storage element. The presence of charge on C_s may be used to represent one logic state and its absence the other logic state.

To write data into the cell, the data is first placed on the write data line and the cell select (write) line raised high. This switches on T1 and allows the write data to either charge or discharge C_s. To read data from the cell, the cell select (read) line is raised high, switching on T2 and T3. The output on the read data line then represents the state of C_s.

Fig. 6.22 shows a dynamic RAM cell which uses just one NMOS transistor. The cell is selected by raising the cell select (gate) high which turns T1 on. In the read mode, the change on C_s is transferred to the data line and sensed by charge-sensitive amplifiers (not shown in fig. 6.22). In the write mode, the data line is used to either charge or discharge C_s, thus writing a 1 or a 0 into the cell.

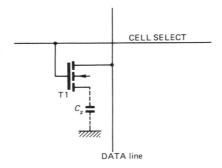

Fig. 6.22 Single-transistor NMOS dynamic RAM cell

The dynamic RAM cell is the simplest of the MOS memories, requiring a minimum number of active devices and consuming very little power in the standby mode. Using such cells very large memories may be fabricated on a single integrated circuit. State-of-the-art dynamic RAMs provide 256K bit storage capacity with 100 nsec access times. At the time of writing, the 512K bit dynamic memory has successfully completed the research and development stage.

The dynamic RAM cell suffers from one major disadvantage in that the capacitance C_s will discharge through the input resistance R_{in} of T2 (fig. 6.21) or the leakage resistance R_c of T1 (fig. 6.22). Typical values of $C_s = 0.2$ pF, $R_{in} = R_c = 10^{10}\,\Omega$ give a discharge time constant of approximately 2 msec. Consequently the dynamic memory cell must be *refreshed* (i.e. have the data re-written into it) at least every 2 msec, otherwise the stored data will be lost. It is from this need to constantly refresh the memory that the name *dynamic* is derived.

To assist with the refresh operation, dynamic RAMs are constructed with additional circuits such that, following a read cycle, the addressed memory cell(s) is automatically refreshed. [*Note*: this is essential for the single transistor memory cell (fig. 6.22) where the stored data is destroyed during the read operation.] The user of such a dynamic RAM only has to ensure that each cell is read at least every 2 msec (even if the read data is not used) to preserve the stored information.

As a further development, many dynamic RAMs are equipped with a *refresh counter* driven from the system clock. The counter steps through each memory address in turn, executing a read/refresh cycle with the memory output disabled, usually during the period when the main processor is decoding an instruction The refresh cycle is thus transparent to the main processor and no processor time is lost for refresh purposes.

Certain microprocessors (e.g. the Z80) are equipped with an internal refresh register (in the Z80 this is the R register) to allow easy interfacing with dynamic RAMs. The contents of the refresh register are placed on the address bus and a refresh line (the $\overline{\text{RFSH}}$ in the Z80) activated during the period when the microprocessor is decoding an instruction. The refresh register is automatically incremented during each *fetch-decode-execute* cycle, providing an automatic refresh sequence which is transparent to the microprocessor.

Fig. 6.23 NMOS ROM
cell

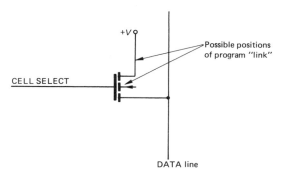

A second, minor disadvantage of dynamic RAMs is that existing devices require multi-voltage supplies, typically +5 V, −5 V and +12 V. This can represent a nuisance, as well as additional cost, in systems which would otherwise only require a +5 V supply. However, this additional cost is usually offset by the advantages of cheap, high capacity storage which dynamic RAMs provide.

6.9.3 MOS ROMs

The operating principle of the **NMOS maskable ROM** cell (fig. 6.23) is identical to that of the bipolar ROM (see 6.8.2) but with one fundamental difference. Due to the manufacturing process, the programming "link" consists either of a conducting link in the drain circuit or of an enhancement/depletion implantation in the gate region.

In the case where a drain link is employed, including the drain to +V connection, or link, a 1 is programmed into the cell. Absence of the drain to +V link programs a 0 into the cell. The enhancement/depletion implantation causes the NMOS transistor either to turn ON (a 1 programmed in the cell) or to stay permanently OFF (a 0 programmed into the cell) when the cell select (gate) line is raised high.

Currently available NMOS ROMs offer 64K bit storage with 150 nsec access time.

Very large maskable ROMs may be constructed using CMOS cells with enhancement/depletion implantation as the programming process. 256K bit ROMs with 200 nsec access time and extremely low power consumption represent the current state of the art. Such ROMs—the so-called Big ROMs—are finding an ever-increasing application in word processors, speech synthesisers and graphics generators particularly where a large number of graphics characters are required (e.g. Japanese and Chinese script).

6.9.4 EPROM (FAMOS and UVPROM) memories

The need for a flexible PROM which can be used for software development and single-unit applications has led to the development of an ultra-violet light **erasable programmable read only memory**, known simply as an **EPROM** (erasable-PROM) or, alternatively, as UVPROM (*ultra-violet PROM*).

Fig. 6.24 Structure of a FAMOS (UVPROM)

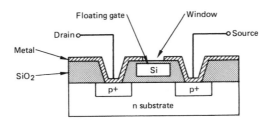

The heart of the EPROM is a FAMOS (floating-gate avalanche-injection MOS) cell illustrated in fig. 6.24. The FAMOS cell is similar to a PMOS transistor except that the silicon gate is floating, i.e. electrically isolated from the drain, source and substrate by a layer of silicon dioxide (SiO_2).

Following manufacture, the gate electrode is uncharged. The source-to-drain resistance is high and the cell is said to be in the logic 1 state. To program a logic 0, a high-voltage pulse is applied between the source and drain (typically 25 V for a period of 50 msec). The high voltage causes an injection of avalanche electrons into the gate region, causing the gate to become negatively charged. Due to the high insulating properties of SiO_2, the gate-substrate discharge time constant is sufficiently long (fig. 6.25) such that, for all practical purposes, the programming is permanent. With the gate negatively charged, the PMOS channel is enhanced and the drain-to-source resistance is low.

Fig. 6.26 illustrates a complete EPROM FAMOS memory cell in which T1 is used to switch the FAMOS cell to the data line when the memory cell is selected.

To erase the programmed information, the FAMOS cell is exposed to intense ultra-violet radiation via a window in the surface of the cell (fig. 6.24). The resultant flow of photoelectrons from the gate to substrate discharges the gate, leaving the cell in a logic 1 state.

Current EPROMs offer a storage capacity of 128K bits with an access time of 200 nsec. Typical erasure times (which are very dependent upon the u-v source) are 15–30 minutes. The EPROM lifetime is, typically, 500–1000 program/erase cycles.

The main disadvantage of EPROMs, especially for development work, lies in the relatively long time it takes to erase and re-program data—a process which usually requires the EPROM to be removed from the development board so that it may be placed in a u-v cabinet.

In single-unit applications, care must be taken to ensure that the EPROM is not constantly exposed to bright sunlight which, over a period of several months, would erase the stored data. To avoid this problem an opaque material (black tape) is usually stuck over the EPROM window once programming is complete.

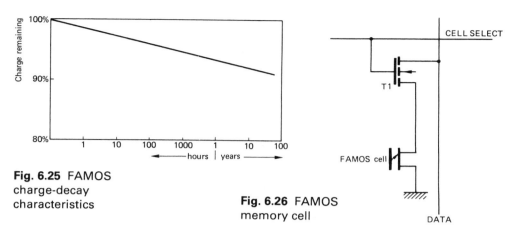

Fig. 6.25 FAMOS
charge-decay
characteristics

Fig. 6.26 FAMOS
memory cell

6.9.5 EEPROMs (EAPROMs)

Electrically erasable programmable read only memories (EEPROM), also
known as *electrically alterable programmable read only memories* (EAP-
ROM), are the more recent addition to the semiconductor memory family.
They are similar, in principle, to EPROMs but with two fundamental
differences. The first is that, during programming, electrons are injected into
the floating gate by the tunnel effect rather than by avalanche injection. The
second is that both programming (writing a 0 to a cell) and erasure (writing a
1 to a cell) are performed by applying a high-voltage pulse (typically 24 V for
10 msec) across the cell, after the appropriate control lines have been
conditioned.

The EEPROM possesses some distinct user advantages when compared
with the EPROM. First, it can be programmed and erased in situ with
considerably shorter erasure times. Second, it is not affected by sunlight.
Third—and most important for software development—individual cells may
be erased and then reprogrammed, whereas with the EPROM exposure to
u-v erases the whole memory.

Current EEPROMs offer 16K bit storage capacity with 250 nsec (read)
access and 10 msec write/erase time. Memory lifetime is approximately
1000 erase/write cycles.

The main disadvantages of EEPROMs are at present the relatively high
cost.

6.10 Semiconductor Memory Organisation and Control

Table 6.2 summarises the more important characteristics of currently available semiconductor memories. As already stressed, due to the rapid developments in semiconductor memories, Table 6.2 must be regarded only as

useful, comparative performance data. For similar reasons no attempt will be made to draw any applications-oriented conclusions from the data.

In addition to those listed, a characteristic which is of considerable practical importance is the way in which a semiconductor memory is **organised**. For example, a memory with a 32K bit capacity may be organised as $32K \times 1$ bit, $16K \times 2$ bits, $8K \times 4$ bits, $4K \times 8$ bits, etc. In the $32K \times 1$ bit configuration, only one of the 32K memory cells may be selected or addressed (i.e. written to or read from) at any one time. In the $4K \times 8$ bit configuration eight out of the 32K memory cells may be addressed simultaneously. The $32K \times 1$ bit memory requires 15 address lines and one data line whilst the $4K \times 8$ bit memory requires 12 address lines and 8 data lines (fig. 6.27).

Fig. 6.27 Organisation of a 32K-bit memory

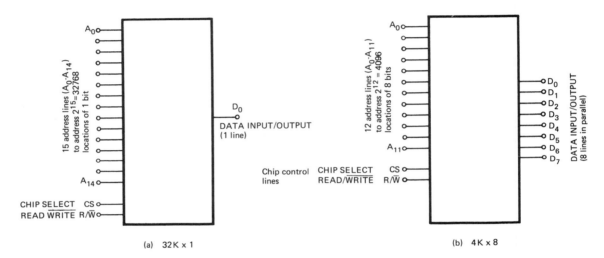

(a)   32K x 1

(b)   4K x 8

The $4K \times 8$ bit memory allows the storage of byte-wide (8 bits at a time) data and is clearly a more useful arrangement for an 8-bit microprocessor than the $32K \times 1$ bit memory. Similarly, for a 16-bit microprocessor, a 32K memory would need to be organised as $2K \times 16$ for optimum usage. At present 16-bit-wide memory chips do not exist. However, a 16-bit-wide memory may be constructed by, for example, connecting two-byte-wide memories in parallel (fig. 6.28).

In addition to the address and data lines, semiconductor memories are equipped with at least two **control lines**. These are the READ/WRITE ($R/\overline{W}$) and the chip select (CS) lines (fig. 6.27). The $R/\overline{W}$ line is used to inform the memory as to whether the central processor is performing a read or write to memory operation. If the $R/\overline{W}$ line is at logic 1, the microprocessor is reading from memory, whereas if the line is at logic 0 ($\overline{WRITE}$) the microprocessor is writing to memory.

The chip select line is used to enable the microprocessor to select just one chip in memory. For example, a 48K byte memory may be constructed from twelve 4K byte memories of which only one may be addressed at any one

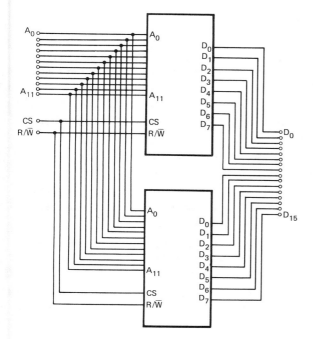

Fig. 6.28 Two 4K × 8 memories connected to form a 4K × 16 memory

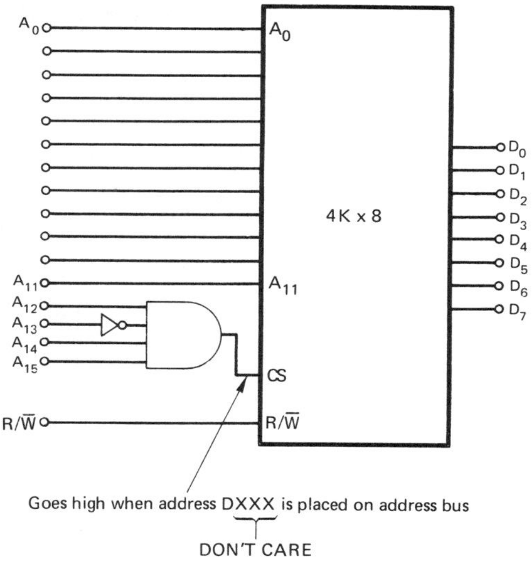

Fig. 6.29 Chip select circuitry for a 4K × 8 memory occupying memory locations D000 − DFFF

time. Until the CS line is activated, the memory is *disabled,* i.e. effectively disconnected from both the address and data buses. The chip select line is usually controlled by the most significant system address lines usually via hard-wired logic gates. Fig. 6.29 illustrates a chip selection circuit for a $4K \times 8$ memory chip which occupies the memory location $D000_{16}$ to $DFFF_{16}$. The chip select line is only activated (raised to logic 1) when the address lines A_{12}–A_{15} are set to D_{16}. The address lines A_0–A_{11} then select one of the 4K bytes in memory from 0 to FFF_{16}.

Problems 6: Computer storage devices

1 Explain why most minicomputers use more than one type of storage medium. Draw a block diagram of a typical computer memory system and describe the rôle and characteristics of each storage system.

2 Describe the features of the various magnetic recording systems currently in use and explain why magnetic disc recorders demand more stringent environmental conditions than magnetic tape recorders.

3 A fixed-head hard disc is formatted with 26 sectors per track. If the disc revolves at 40 revolutions/sec estimate the average sector access time.

4 Explain why it is necessary to have some form of error checking procedure in magnetic disc and tape recording systems. Name, and briefly describe, error checking methods currently used in magnetic tape recording.

5 Describe the more commonly encountered recording codes used in magnetic surface recording and, for each code described, give one application. Explain the advantages of using self-clocking codes.

6 Calculate the time for which a mercury cell, rated at 10 mA hours, will provide back-up support for a 32 Kbyte CMOS memory which draws a total of 32 μA when on standby.

7 Distinguish between a ROM, PROM and EPROM and give typical applications for these devices.

8 Draw and explain the operation of a dynamic RAM memory cell. Explain why it is necessary to make a dynamic RAM *transparent* to a microprocessor and describe the methods by which this may be achieved.

9 Using the values quoted in the text calculate the minimum programming time of
a) a 32K bit EPROM organised as $4K \times 8$
b) an 8K bit EEPROM organised as $1K \times 8$.

10 Compare, and contrast, the characteristics of bipolar and MOS RAM and ROM. Select the type of memory (i.e. bipolar or MOS) you would use in a mini-computing system which requires a 32K RAM with an access time of 250 nsec.

11 Describe a disc controller and explain how it can be used to lead to more efficient use of a microprocessor.

12 Using just standard logic gates design a circuit which will select (i.e. enable the chip select line) of two 4 Kbyte RAMs occupying memory locations 0000_{16} to $1FFF_{16}$.

7 Peripheral Equipment

7.1 Introduction

In any microprocessor system, approximately 70–80% of the cost and development effort is associated with peripheral equipment, whose sole purpose is to allow communication between the microprocessor and the "outside" world (usually the user). The type of peripheral used in a particular system depends purely upon the system application and may range from a few push-button switches for input, and relays for output, such as may be found in a microprocessor-controlled washing machine; to several visual display units (VDUs), printers, graph plotters, etc. as may be found in a fully interactive mini-computing system.

In this chapter, the characteristics and principles of operation of the more commonly encountered computer peripherals will be discussed, together with the ways in which they are connected, or *interfaced*, with the microprocessor systems.

Fig. 7.1 The QWERTY alpha-numeric keyboard layout

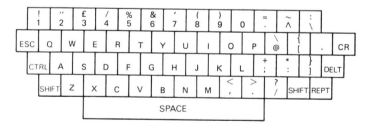

7.2 Input Devices—Keyboards

Fig. 7.2 The hexadecimal keyboard

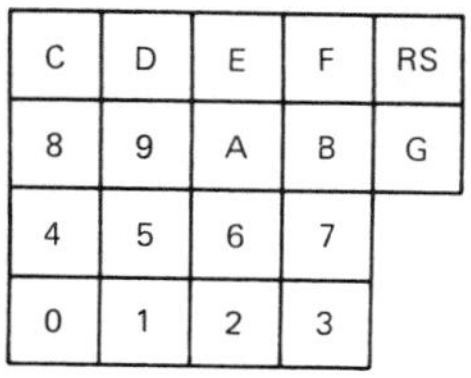

C	D	E	F	RS
8	9	A	B	G
4	5	6	7	
0	1	2	3	

The **keyboard** is the most widely used peripheral for entering information into the computer. The most common form is the **QWERTY** keyboard (fig. 7.1) which allows the full alpha-numeric set (0 to 9 and A–Z) to be entered, together with control characters such as ESC (escape). On small microprocessor development systems, the HEX keyboard (fig. 7.2) which inputs the numerals 0 to 9 and the letters A–F with control characters such as G (go) and RS (reset) is sometimes used.

The desirable qualities of any keyboard are reliability, quiet operation, light operating pressure and positive action (i.e. the user can tell by the feel

Fig. 7.3 Contact switch

that a key is operating properly) which in turn depends upon the type of key-switch used.

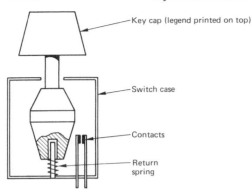

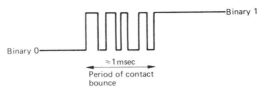

Fig. 7.5 Pulse train due to contact bounce

7.2.1 Keyboard Switches

1 Whilst considerable effort has been made to obtain better methods, the **contact switch** (fig. 7.3) is still the most popular form of keyboard switch. Pressing the switch key causes the contacts to touch (or in certain types open) which, with associated circuitry, will produce a binary 1 or 0 (fig. 7.4).

The contact switch is simple to produce and is, consequently, cost effective with a life of about 10^7 operations (Au-Ag-Pt contacts). However, it suffers from mechanical contact "bounce" which results in a series of ones and zeros being produced during the short period (1 msec) when the contacts close or open (fig. 7.5). Problems with contact bounce may be easily overcome by software, which requires that the output from a given key remains unchanged for a set period (typically 5 msec) before recognising the key as having been pressed.

Fig. 7.4 Typical contact switch circuit configurations

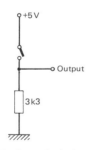

(a) Output 0→1 when switch is pressed

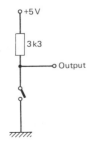

(b) Output 1→0 when switch is pressed

2 The **magnetic reed key-switch** (fig. 7.6) comprises a pair of contacts enclosed in a glass envelope. The contacts, which are made from ferrous and precious metals, are opened and closed by a permanent magnet set in the key plunger. When the key is pressed, the increased magnetic field closes the switch contacts. Since the key contacts are enclosed, the switch has a longer lifetime (10^8 operations) and reduced contact bounce time (≈ 0.8 msec) than the simple contact switch. It is, however, expensive (three times the cost of the simple contact switch).

3 The **Hall-effect key-switch**, which also utilises a magnetic field, is a non-contact switch that has become popular in recent years. It depends for its operation on the Hall-effect (fig. 7.7) in which a voltage is developed across a slab of semiconductor, through which a current flows, when a magnetic field is applied perpendicular to the current flow. The generated voltage, the Hall voltage, is both perpendicular and proportional to the current flow and the applied magnetic field.

The construction of the Hall-effect key is similar to the magnetic reed switch, with the semiconductor slab replacing the reed contacts. Since the

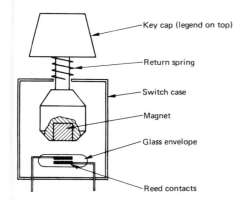

Fig. 7.6 Magnetic reed switch

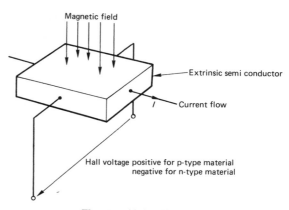

Fig. 7.7 Hall effect

switch does not rely on moving contacts it has excellent reliability ($\approx 5 \times 10^8$ operations) and does not suffer from contact bounce. However, it does have the disadvantages of being costly (four to five times the cost of the simple contact switch) and of requiring an external current source (typically 6–10 mA). In addition, the generated Hall voltage (typically 20–50 mV) requires amplification before it can be compatible with TTL or CMOS circuit elements. In practice this is not really a problem since most Hall devices, including key-switches, are constructed with an integral amplifier providing standard logic levels at the output.

4 The **capacitive key-switch** (fig. 7.8) is also a non-contact switch and consists, typically, of two conducting plates mounted on the base of the switch. One of the plates is connected to an a.c. source (typically 10^5 Hz) and, when the key is depressed, a conducting disc capacitively couples the a.c. signal to the second conducting plate. The coupled a.c. signal is then used to sense the key as being pressed. Like the Hall-effect switch, the capacitive switch has a long lifetime ($\approx 4 \times 10^8$ operations) and does not suffer from contact bounce. Its main disadvantage lies in its cost (three to four times the simple contact switch) and the need for additional circuits to source and detect the a.c. signal.

Fig. 7.8 Capacitive key-switch

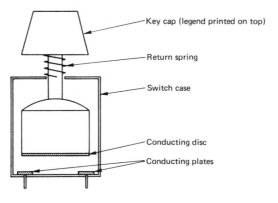

7.2.2 Keyboard Encoders

In systems where only a few key-switches are required to enter information (e.g. a microprocessor-controlled dishwasher), the key-switches are usually connected directly, albeit via a suitable buffer circuit, to the microprocessor buses. The microprocessor then **polls** (looks at in turn) each key to see if a particular key has been pressed.

With Hex and QWERTY keyboards this direct approach would be extremely inefficient since the microprocessor would spend an appreciable amount of its time just polling the many key-switches instead of performing more useful tasks. Where many keys are involved, a dedicated keyboard circuit is used which continually scans the key-switches, detects when one is pressed, and then places the appropriate code (usually ASCII) on the data bus. In addition an interrupt may be generated to inform the microprocessor that input information is present.

Fig. 7.9 illustrates a typical keyboard and keyboard encoder arrangement. The keyboard switches are mounted in a matrix structure such that, when a switch is pressed, contact is made between one column and one row of the matrix. Various matrix configurations are used although in recent years, for QWERTY keyboards, a matrix of nine rows and ten columns has become a semi-standard. The keyboard encoder is usually a single-chip integrated circuit which selects, in turn, a column in the matrix and places a known signal level (usually a 0) on it. The nine rows are then scanned and, if a key is depressed, this will be detected as the column voltage is transferred to the row. The whole process is repeated for each column-row combination and the complete cycle repeated continuously with a typical scanning time of approximately 900 μsec (10 μsec clock period $\times$ 90 possible characters).

The row and column select signals also address the ROM which holds the output code for each key. Once a key-pressed state has been detected, the key code is placed on the tri-state output bus and an interrupt generated to alert the microprocessor to new input informations.

The keyboard encoder is also designed to cope with the problems of contact bounce, and the situation where more than one key is pressed at a given time. Contact bounce is overcome by stopping the scanning cycle for a period of 5 msec once a pressed key is detected. The key input is subsequently ignored until the end of the 5 msec period by which time contact bounce will have ceased. Two methods are used to deal with the case where keys are pressed simultaneously:

a) *Key lockout* in which the first key detected as being pressed is accepted, and all other keys ignored until the first key is released.
b) *Key rollover* in which, once a key has been detected as pressed, it is ignored in all subsequent scanning cycles until it has been released and pressed again. Thus, if several keys are pressed they will be detected in successive scanning cycles.

With an average key-pressed detect time of 6 msec (900 μsec keyboard scan + 5 msec anti-contact-bounce delay), the maximum possible rate of

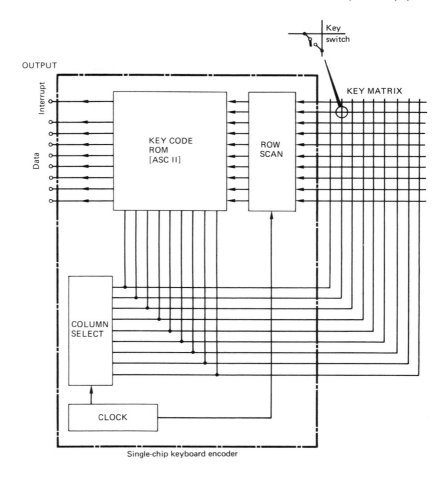

Fig. 7.9 Matrix keyboard and keyboard encoder

input from the keyboard and encoder is 170 characters per second. This limitation is of little practical significance since even a typist holding the First Class Certificate (120 words/minute) will only input information at the rate of 10 characters/second.

7.3 Output Devices—Printers

The **printer**, which produces a permanent record of characters on paper, known as **hardcopy**, is an essential peripheral in most modern microprocessor computing systems. Obvious examples range from the printing of salary slips, in an accounting office of a commercial institution, to the "final" results and tables of a scientific application. Of equal importance in all cases is the need to be able to produce program listings and run-time information.

Printers may be classified as either *impact* or *non-impact* devices. In **impact printing** a *print head* strikes an inked ribbon, placed immediately in front of a sheet of paper, leaving an imprint of the print head on the paper.

Fig. 7.10 Basic impact printer configurations: serial printers

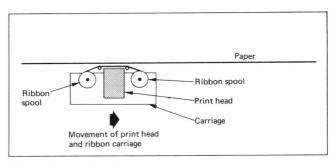

(a) **Integral print head and ribbon carriage**

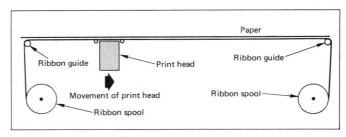

(b) **Moving print head only (permits larger ribbon spools)**

The two basic print head–ribbon–paper configurations in current use are shown in fig. 7.10. In both cases the print head is mounted on a carriage which traverses across the paper from left to right (*serial printing*) with the inked ribbon moved in incremented steps between character printing.

In **non-impact printing**, the character is formed on the paper by what is, essentially, a non-mechanical process. One example of this method is *electrophotography* in which a laser beam, deflected by an acoustic–optical system, produces images on paper by a process similar to that used in photocopiers. For present purposes, only impact printers will be discussed since not only are they the most popular type of printer in use but they are the only printer which the non-specialist is likely to encounter. (At the time of writing the cost of a laser–electrophotography printer is about £200 000 and is, consequently, only employed in large specialised applications, e.g. military systems.)

Impact printers may be classified, depending upon the type of print head used, as:

a) Cylinder head
b) Ball head
c) Daisy wheel or Diablo
d) Needle head or dot matrix.

Fig. 7.11 Cylinder printer

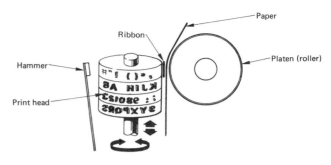

Clockwise rotation								Anticlockwise rotation							
'	8	%	\$	#	"	!		(	)	*	,	–	.	/	+
G	F	E	D	C	B	A		H	I	J	K	L	M	N	O
7	6	5	4	3	2	1		0	8	9	:	;	<	=	>	?
W	V	U	T	S	R	Q		P	X	Y	Z	]	/	[	↑	–

(a)   **Typical character set**

(b)   **Print mechanism**

Fig. 7.12 Teletype terminal

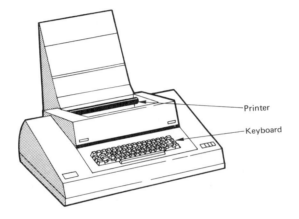

7.3.1 Cylinder Head Printers

The **cylinder printer** head (fig. 7.11) has the print symbols embossed on a metal cylinder. Up to 64 characters are available (4 rows of 16 characters), the usual character set being the upper case alpha-numeric set together with other standard symbols (fig. 7.11*a*). The ribbon and paper are placed in front of the cylinder which has a hammer positioned at the rear. During operation, the head is rotated clockwise, or anticlockwise, and moved vertically until the symbol to be printed is positioned next to the ribbon and the paper. The hammer then strikes the back of the cylinder head, forcing the head forward, which prints the character on the paper.

The cylinder print head is now only to be found in the older *teletype* terminals (fig. 7.12) which combine a cylinder head printer with a (mechanical) keyboard for input. Whilst the teletype is no longer in production it is included in the present discussion since there are still large numbers in existence, acting as general "work horses" for small computing systems.

The teletype has a maximum print rate of 12 characters/sec with a standard 80 characters per line. The ribbon configuration is that shown in fig. 7.10*b*.

Fig. 7.13 Ball-head printer

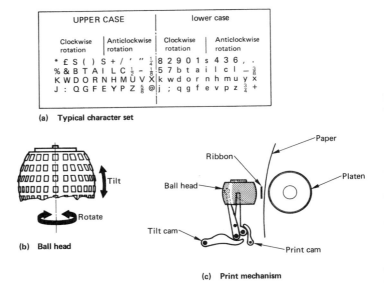

UPPER CASE		lower case	
Clockwise rotation	Anticlockwise rotation	Clockwise rotation	Anticlockwise rotation
* £ S ( )	S + / ' " $\frac{1}{4}$	8 2 9 0 1	s 4 3 6 , .
% & B T A I L	C $\frac{1}{2}$ – $\frac{1}{8}$	5 7 b t a i l	c l – $\frac{3}{8}$
K W D O R N H M U	V X	k w d o r n h m u	y x
J : Q G F E Y P Z	$\frac{5}{8}$ @	j ; q g f e v p z	$\frac{3}{4}$ +

(a) **Typical character set**

(b) **Ball head**

(c) **Print mechanism**

7.3.2 Ball Head Printers

The **ball head** or **golfball printer** (fig. 7.13) was primarily developed by IBM as a print mechanism for electric typewriters. It was later developed further as a computer printer. The print characters are embossed on the surface of a metal sphere which, having a larger surface area than a cylinder of comparable size, allows a greater character set than the cylinder print head. Typically the full alpha-numeric set, with upper and lower case, together with other symbols are available (fig. 7.13).

A character is selected by first rotating, and then *tilting*, the ball head until the desired character is positioned next to the ribbon and paper. During the print operation the ball is moved forward by the print cam to strike the ribbon and paper.

Print rates of 12 characters/sec are possible with a maximum of 150 characters per line. A special feature of golfballs printers is that the ball heads are interchangeable, thus allowing different character sets to be used. The ribbon configuration is that shown in fig. 7.10*a* and usually employs a "cartridge" ribbon.

7.3.3 Daisy Wheel (Diablo) Printers

The **daisy wheel** or **Diablo print** head (fig. 7.14) consists of up to 96 spokes on a spindle assembly. Attached to the end of each spoke is an embossed print symbol such that the complete assembly resembles the petal arrangement of a daisy (from which the name is derived) (fig. 7.14*b*).

The daisy wheel is positioned such that a symbol on the uppermost spoke lies directly in front of the printer ribbon and paper (fig. 7.14*c*). During the

Fig. 7.14 Daisy wheel
(Diablo) printer

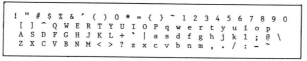

```
!  "  #  $  %  &  '  (  )  0  *  =  {  }  ~  1  2  3  4  5  6  7  8  9  0
[  ]  ^  Q  W  E  R  T  Y  U  I  O  P  q  w  e  r  t  y  u  i  o  p
A  S  D  F  G  H  J  K  L  +  `  |  a  s  d  f  g  h  j  k  l  ;  @  \
Z  X  C  V  B  N  M  <  >  ?  z  x  c  v  b  n  m  ,  .  /  :  -  ~
```

(a)   Typical character set

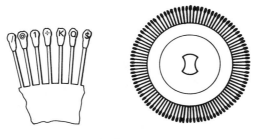

(b)   Daisy wheel print head

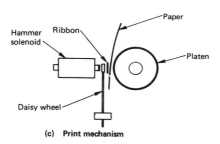

(c)   Print mechanism

print cycle the daisy wheel is first rotated, until the desired character lies in the uppermost position, following which a solenoid-operated hammer, positioned behind the daisy wheel, prints the character on to the paper.

Like the ball head the daisy wheel, with its possible 96 characters set, allows both upper and lower case alpha-numerics as well as other symbols (fig. 7.14a). The daisy wheel can also be easily changed for one with a different character set. Print rates of up to 30 characters/sec are possible, with a maximum of 150 characters per line. The ribbon configuration is that shown in fig. 7.10a and a ribbon cartridge is invariably used.

The daisy wheel printer provides excellent copy, and is both versatile and reliable. As such it has become the most-favoured form of serial printer in the "middle" market range, particularly with word processor and similar systems. An additional advantage is that most daisy wheel printers are controlled by a dedicated, internal microprocessor, making them an "intelligent" printer (see 7.3.5).

Fig. 7.15 Dot matrix printer

1234567890!£%&'()*=–
ABCDEFGHIJKLMNOPQRSTU
VWXYZabcdefghijklmnop
qrstuvwxyz

1234567890!£%&'()*=–
ABCDEFGHIJKLMNOPQRSTU
VWXYZabcdefghijklmnop
qrstuvwxyz

Double-size characters — effective matrix size 9 × 14

Basic 9 × 7 dot matrix characters

(a) **Typical character set**

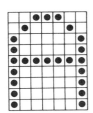

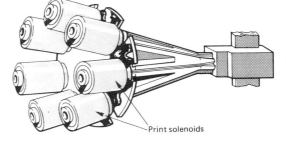

Print head
(front elevation)

Print solenoids

(b) **9 × 7 dot matrix formation of the letter A**

(c) **Needle print head (radial arrangement)**

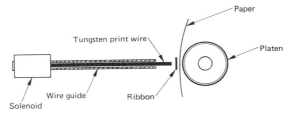

Paper

Tungsten print wire

Platen

Solenoid

Wire guide

Ribbon

(d) **Print mechanism**

7.3.4 Needle Head or Dot-matrix Printers

With the **needle head printer** each character is formed from a matrix of dots, from which this printer derives its alternative name (fig. 7.15). The basic print mechanism is a thin tungsten wire which is driven, by a solenoid, onto the inked ribbon and paper, thus printing one "dot" (fig. 7.15d). In most dot matrix printers, seven such print elements are arranged such that up to seven dots may be printed in a vertical line to form one column of the dot matrix. Successive columns are then printed such that a character is formed in a matrix which is, usually, 9×7 dots. Various types of print head are available although the radial arrangement of the print solenoids (fig. 7.15c) is the more usual. The physical size of the solenoid, in relation to the print wire, prevents an in-line print head arrangement.

The dot-matrix printer has become almost a standard as a reliable medium-speed cheap printer. The print quality, whilst not as good as either the daisy wheel or golfball printers, is, nevertheless, quite acceptable. Both types of ribbon arrangement (fig. 7.10) are used, some with cartridge ribbons.

A unique feature of the dot-matrix printer is that the size and shape of the print character is entirely under software control. For example, printing a character in a matrix of 18×14 dots (which would require printing two rows) produces a character twice the size of a 9×7 dot character. Since the character size may be varied, characterising a dot-matrix printer in terms of the number of characters per line is meaningless. Print speeds of 15 lines per minute with 720 dot columns per line are typical, although it must be pointed out that dot-matrix printers cannot operate continuously for all types of printing due to overheating of the print solenoids. This is particularly true of scientific applications where the dot-matrix printer, with its high resolution capabilities, is used to display graphical data, histograms, etc. which may require shaded (dense) print.

Since the dot-matrix printer can only be controlled by software, most printers are constructed with integral dedicated microprocessors and several standard EPROM character sets. Such a printer is a very intelligent device (see below).

7.3.5 Intelligent Printers

As already mentioned (7.3.3 and 7.3.4) some printers are constructed with an integral microprocessor and data buffer, to both control the print operation and provide for a variation in the print type and formatting. Such devices are known as **intelligent printers**. The additional features which microprocessor control allows includes the following.

Variable print   The dot matrix printer (7.3.4) has already been cited as an example where print size can be varied under software control. With the daisy wheel and ball head printer, the print size is determined by the particular print head. However, with both of these printers the print density can be varied by altering, also under software control, the current passing through the solenoid print hammer. In addition, the character print is formatted to allow for the different character size. For example, the letter i occupies less horizontal space than the letters m or w. Conventional printers allow equal horizontal spaces for all characters. Formatted characters produce a more uniform print which is pleasant to the eye.

Vertical and horizontal formatting of text   A wide variety of vertical and horizontal formatting is possible under microprocessor control. Standard operations such as margins, tabulation and line feed are available, together with such specialised features as "skip to a specific line/position on a line" (useful in printing over semi-prepared documents such as cheques, "personalised" letters, etc.), subscript, superscript and high resolution graph plotting.

Optimised printing can produce a considerable increase in printing speed. With optimised printing the print head will print either from left to right, as in conventional serial printers, or right to left, depending upon which direction will result in least movement of the print head. The necessity for a high-speed carriage return is thus obviated, which results in not only a faster print speed, but a less noisy printer which has an increased reliability.

A **data buffer** at the input allows the printer to receive and store a complete piece of text. Typically the buffer will be capable of storing 64 to several thousand characters. Since a computer can output data at a much higher rate than present-day printers can print, the inclusion of a data buffer allows the computer to output text to the printer at high speed and then continue with other computational tasks whilst the text is being printed.

7.4 Output Devices—LEDs, LCDs and Seven-segment Displays

1 The **light-emitting diode**, or **LED**, is the most simple of output devices. As its name suggests it is a junction diode which emits light when forward biased. In all forward biased junction diodes, energy is released by the recombination of the unbound "free" electrons and holes in the junction region. This energy is emitted as either infra-red (heat) or visible radiation. For silicon and germanium diodes the greater percentage of energy is emitted in the infra-red. However, for certain other materials, e.g. gallium phosphide (GaP), the majority of the energy is emitted in the visible region. By varying the junction material, the frequency, and hence colour, of the emitted light may be altered. At present, red, green, yellow and blue LEDs are available.

Fig. 7.16 LED circuit

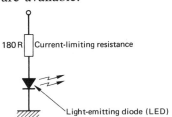

180 R | Current-limiting resistance

Light-emitting diode (LED)

Fig. 7.16 illustrates the simple circuit of an LED output. If the input is at binary 1 (2·8–3·5 V) the LED is illuminated. The 180 Ω resistance is used to limit the current through the LED to approximately 12 mA. If the input is at binary 0 (0–0·8 V), the LED is off. Eight such LED circuits may be connected to a byte-wide data bus, via buffer amplifiers, to indicate the current status of the data bus. Similarly, the status of the address and control buses may be displayed.

Fig. 7.17 Seven-segment LED display

2 The **seven-segment display** (fig. 7.17) is an extension of the simple LED. Using seven LEDs, each constructed in the physical shape of a short bar, most alpha-numeric and all of the Hex characters may be displayed by illuminating the appropriate segments (fig. 7.18).

Seven-segment displays may be connected directly to four binary data lines, via a suitable decoder/driver circuit (fig. 7.19), such that the status of the data lines is automatically displayed as a hex digit. The decoder/driver is

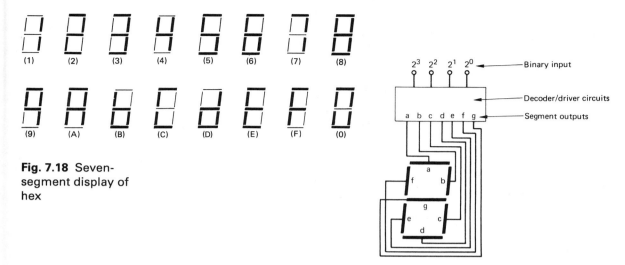

Fig. 7.18 Seven-segment display of hex

Fig. 7.19 Use of decoder circuit to drive a seven-segment display

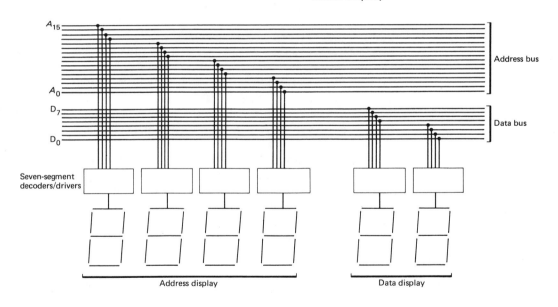

Fig. 7.20 Address and data bus status display using seven-segment LEDs

a self-contained integrated circuit consisting of combinational logic circuitry which decodes the four-bit binary input pattern into the appropriate seven-bit code to drive the seven segments of the display.

Fig. 7.20 illustrates the use of six seven-segment displays to display the state of the address and data buses, on an eight-bit microprocessor system, as four-digit and two-digit hex numbers respectively.

Fig. 7.21 Reflective
LCD

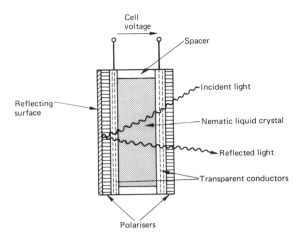

3   Seven-segment displays may also be constructed from **liquid-crystal displays**, **LCDs**. Liquid crystals are organic molecules which flow like a liquid and yet possess certain properties normally associated with crystals. Fig. 7.21 illustrates a reflective LCD. With zero voltage across the cell, any light entering the cell passes through the polarisers, the transparent conducting electrodes and the liquid crystal, and is then reflected back out of the cell by the reflecting back surface. If a voltage of 2–8 V is applied across the cell, the plane of polarisation of the incident light is rotated as it passes through the liquid crystal such that, following reflection, it is not transmitted by the polarisers. The cell thus appears dark to an observer. Seven-segment LCD displays may be constructed from seven such cells fabricated in the shape of a short bar (fig. 7.17).

The main advantage of LCD displays is that their power consumption is very small, typically microwatts, when compared with LED displays which require, typically, 0·5 W. However, LCD displays do require ambient lighting to operate, whilst LED displays are self-illuminating. Furthermore, multi-coloured LED displays may be used to display different sets of data for easy identification.

7.5   Input and Output Devices—the Visual Display Unit (VDU)

The **visual display unit**, or **VDU**, is a self-contained terminal peripheral consisting of a keyboard for input, and a television-type display for output (fig. 7.22). At present the VDU is the most common interactive computer input/output peripheral; and is likely to remain so for the foreseeable future. Its popularity arises from its versatility, ease of use, quietness in operation, cheapness, and excellent reliability which stems, in turn, from its use of a well-established technology.

Fig. 7.22 Visual display unit (VDU)

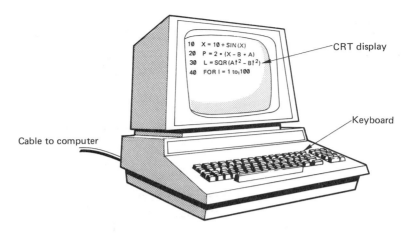

CRT display

Keyboard

Cable to computer

```
10  X = 10 + SIN (X)
20  P = 2 * (X - B * A)
30  L = SQR (A↑2 - B↑2)
40  FOR I = 1 to 100
```

Fig. 7.23 VDU cathode ray tube (schematic)

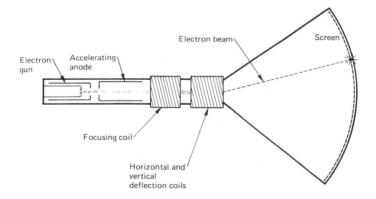

Electron beam

Screen

Electron gun

Accelerating anode

Focusing coil

Horizontal and vertical deflection coils

The principal component of the VDU display is the cathode ray tube (CRT) which utilises an electron beam to produce a spot of light on a phosphor-coated screen (fig. 7.23). The CRT screen size is, typically, 12–15 inches (diagonal measurement, rectangular screen) and the phosphor coating is either of type P4 (white image) or P31 (green image). The electron beam is deflected, vertically and horizontally, by two mutually-perpendicular magnetic fields produced by current flow in external coils (electrostatic deflection is rarely used in VDU displays). [A full description of the CRT will be found in most physics, electronics or television textbooks].

Fig. 7.24 CRT raster scan

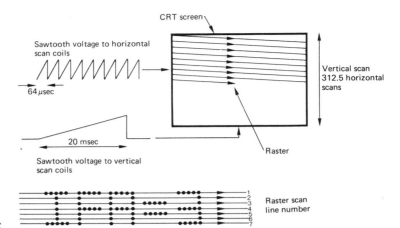

Fig. 7.25 Text display of IFA = 3 using the raster-scan dot-matrix technique

7.5.1 The Use of the CRT as an Alpha-numeric Text Display

For almost all alpha-numeric text displays the **raster-scan** technique, as employed in domestic television receivers, is used. Saw-tooth waveforms are applied to the horizontal and vertical deflection coils, such that the electron beam scans the whole of the CRT screen in a series of horizontal traces or scans (fig. 7.24).

Following standard television receiver principles, the time for the beam to make one horizontal (or *line*) scan is 64 μsec. The vertical (*field*) scan time of 20 msec (flyback included) results in a total of $312\frac{1}{2}$ lines in a full picture (or *frame*), with a repetition rate of 25 frames/sec. Frames may be interlaced when high resolution graphics are required. In most cases, where only alpha-numeric text is to be displayed, interlaced scanning is not employed.

To display text, the raster-scan is combined with the dot-matrix character representation (fig. 7.25). A dot matrix of 5×7 is almost universally employed, which requires a minimum of seven raster lines to display each line of text. As the raster beam moves along the first raster line, the top row of the 5×7 dot matrix for each character is displayed. As the beam moves along the second raster line, the second row of the dot matrix is displayed. This is repeated for the next five rows until the first line of text is fully displayed. The raster then (usually) scans two blank lines before displaying the second row of text.

Fig. 7.26 illustrates the principal components of a raster-scan dot-matrix display. The characters are stored in memory—the *video RAM*—in the serial sequence in which they will appear in the displayed text. A clock, consisting of an oscillator and a chain of bistable counters, generates the raster scan signals and selects, via the video RAM address lines, the appropriate character in memory. A ROM *character generator* then combines the character and row scan information and generates, using an internal *look-up table*, the appropriate dot pattern. This is then converted into serial form in a shift register (parallel-in/serial-out) before being applied to the brightness circuits of the CRT.

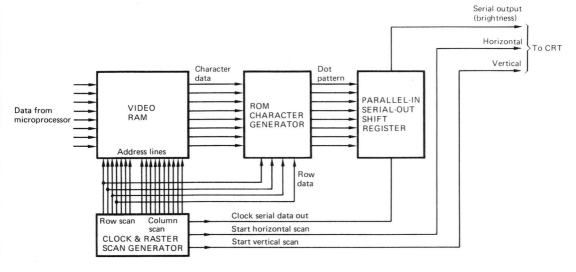

Fig. 7.26 Principal components of a raster-scan dot-matrix display .

Up to 32 lines (although 24 lines is the normal format) of text, with 80 characters per line, may be displayed on the CRT. As with the dot-matrix printer (7.3.4), the character set and size may be varied although this usually requires that the ROM character generator be physically changed. However, in the modern "intelligent" (microprocessor-controlled) VDU, several character sets may be held in ROM, with a user programmable set in RAM, and changed under software control.

As mentioned, the VDU consists of both a CRT-type display, described above, and a keyboard, described in 7.2, combined in an integal unit. Fig. 7.27 illustrates the architecture of a typical non-intelligent VDU with cursor control. Text typed in at the keyboard is sent to the computer, via the

Fig. 7.27 Architecture of a typical VDU system

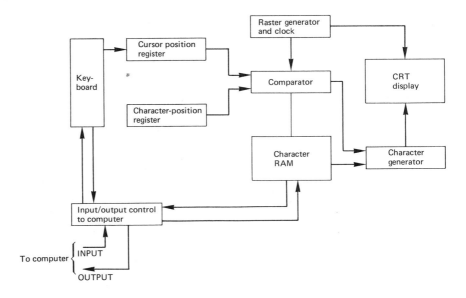

204 Microprocessors: Essentials, Components and Systems

output lines, and is also displayed on the VDU screen. In most systems an input character is transmitted from the keyboard to the computer, which then *echoes* that character back to the video RAM to be displayed on the screen. Thus when a character, input from the keyboard, appears on the VDU screen, it indicates that not only has a key been pressed, but that the *correct* key information has been entered into the computer system. The computer can also send information direct to the VDU screen.

7.6 Graph Plotters

The **graph plotter** is used primarily to produce graphical diagrams and drawings on paper. Although often considered to be a specialised device, it nevertheless finds wide application, which includes the graphical display of scientific data, multi-section architectural plans, pseudo three-dimensional (e.g. isometric and similar) engineering drawings, printed circuit layouts and map drawing.

Additionally, if the ink pen is replaced by, for example, a scribe or a cutting edge, the graph plotter may be used to etch and cut patterns in metals, plastics and other materials.

Figure 7.28 illustrates the two basic types of graph plotter currently in use.

1   The **flat-bed plotter** is the less expensive of the two and, consequently, is more commonly found on the smaller computing systems. The paper is held horizontally on a flat bed, usually by an electrostatic field. The pen is moved across its surface in two orthogonal (the X and Y) directions. In addition the pen may be raised and lowered onto the paper, as necessary, during the drawing sequence. The pen holder can be equipped with up to four different pens to allow multi-colour plots and drawings. In the modern intelligent flat-bed plotters, several pens are kept in a *nest* and exchanged under software control.

The flat-bed plotter drive mechanism usually involves servo control (fig. 7.29). The reversible-drive motor drives both the pen carriage and a multi-turn potentiometer. The input (analogue) signal is compared with the output from the multi-turn potentiometer by a differential amplifier. Any difference in signal level is amplified, and used to turn the drive motor until the potentiometer output is equal to the signal. The more modern intelligent flat-bed plotters use a *stepper*, or *incremental* drive motor, which rotates under digital control in fixed steps, typically 3°. To move the pen, the drive motor is stepped, under software control, a known number of steps or increments. The mechanical gearing is such that each rotational step produces a 0·005 cm movement of the pen. This exceedingly small increment permits the drawing of curves from a sequence of pen steps, which cannot be detected as being such by the naked eye.

The main advantage of the flat-bed plotter is its relatively low cost. Its main disadvantage is that it can only produce drawings up to maximum size of about 30 cm × 20 cm.

Fig. 7.28 Graph
plotters

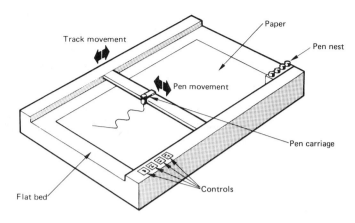

(a)   **Flat bed plotter**

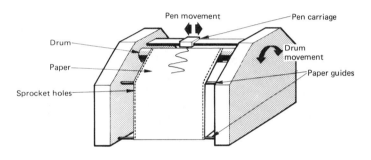

(b)   **Drum or incremental plotter**

Fig. 7.29 Graph
plotter servo-drive

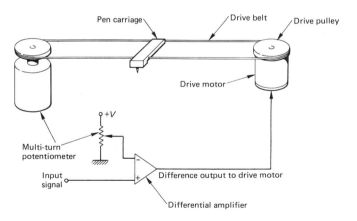

2   The **drum** or **incremental plotter** is usually only found on mainframe computing systems or in systems where the need for high-precision large drawings justifies the high cost of this device (e.g. a dedicated architectural-plan development system). The pen is mounted on a carriage which moves across the width of the paper only. The paper is mounted around a horizontal drum and held in position by sprocket holes and pins at the paper edge. In very high quality systems a vacuum may be used for this purpose. During the plotting sequence, the drum drives the paper, backwards and forwards, as the pen moves across the width of the paper. The pen may be raised and lowered onto the paper as required and, like the flat-bed plotter, a multiple-pen head is usually installed.

As the name suggests, both the drum and pen carriage use incremental, or stepper, drive motors, which can produce a step resolution as high as 0·002 cm. The plot sizes may be very large with paper widths of up to 1 metre and almost indefinite paper lengths (paper rolls of length 100 m can, theoretically, be used).

7.7 Digitiser Table

The **digitiser table** is used to input drawings and graphical information. It consists of a flat horizontal table (fig. 7.30) whose size may be up to 3 m × 3 m. A stylus, or sensing, head is placed on the table surface and its positional information, in terms of the table X and Y coordinates, determined and entered into the computer. The digitising table may thus input graphical information and, as such, is used in such applications as map drawing (input information from aerial photographs), transferring and modifying engineering and architectural plans, printed circuit design and particle tracking (nuclear physics).

Fig. 7.30 Digitiser table

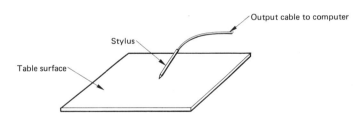

A variety of methods may be used to determine the stylus position, of which the following are the more common.

1 Wire mesh table An X-Y matrix of wires is embedded in the surface of the table. Unique coded pulse trains are applied to the matrix wires and detected via capacitative coupling to the stylus. From the received pulse train the stylus position may easily be determined.

2 Acoustical table Ultrasonic transmitters are positioned at either the corners or edges of the table. The stylus comprises an ultrasonic receiver. Either the time delay or phase difference between the transmitted and received signals is measured, from which the stylus position may be determined.

3 Voltage gradient table The table surface consists of a sheet of resistive material across which two a.c. signals, of differing frequencies, are applied in the X and Y directions respectively. The stylus effectively measures the a.c. voltage on the table surface and, since the voltage gradient across the table surface is known, its position may be determined. This particular type of digitiser table suffers from the disadvantage that direct physical contact must occur between the stylus and table surface. The stylus usually consists of a sharp point which must pierce any drawing on the table in order to make contact with the table surface.

Each of the three types of digitiser table described above can give a resolution of approximately 0·05 cm over a surface area of 3 m × 3 m.

7.8 Light Pen

A **light pen** is used to either "draw" on, or point to part of, a VDU display. It consists of a light-sensing element (usually a photo-diode or photo-transistor) set in the end of a pen or stylus-like holder (fig. 7.31). In use the pen tip is held close to the VDU screen. As the raster scan passes and

Fig. 7.31 Principal components of a light pen

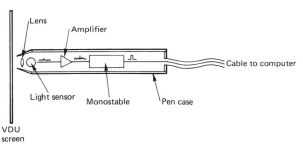

illuminates the pen tip, the light sensor produces a signal which is then amplified and used to trigger a monostable circuit. The short output pulse from the monostable is input to the computer, via an interrupt line or a standard input/output port. The position of the light pen is easily determined by reading the raster scan generator registers, which gives the current position of the raster (fig. 7.26) when the monostable pulse occurs.

7.9 Interfacing Techniques

Before a peripheral can be of any practical use, it must first be connected to a microprocessor or computing system in such a way that data and instructions may be transferred between the computer and peripheral. This connecting or **interfacing** a computer with peripherals can be the source of formidable problems, which are due to the range of peripherals available as well as the large number of manufacturers whose individual design is almost always different (and hence "superior") to similar devices on the market.

Communication between a computer and a peripheral may be

a) **Simplex** where information can be transmitted in one direction only, e.g. computer to (non-intelligent) printer, keyboard to computer.

b) **Half duplex** where information may be transmitted in both directions but in only one direction at a time, e.g. IEEE 488 bus (see 7.9.1).

c) **Full duplex** where information may be transmitted in both directions simultaneously, e.g. VDU.

It is now a universal standard to transmit computer data in bytes comprising a seven-bit ASCII code with the eighth bit as a parity test. The data byte may be transmitted **in parallel**, when all eight bits are transmitted on eight separate transmission lines, or **serially** when the data bits are transmitted separately, in a serial sequence, down a single transmission line (fig. 7.32). In both cases the data may be transmitted with synchronous clock pulses (**synchronous transmission**). Additional lines for *handshaking* (see 7.9.1) may also be present.

Fig. 7.32 Parallel and serial transmission of the data byte A6 = 10100110

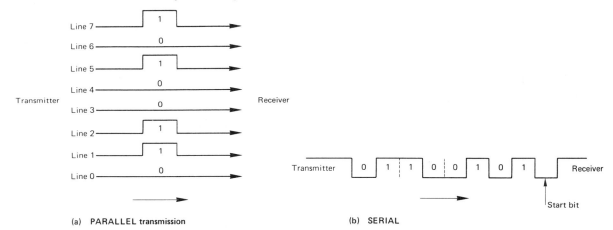

(a) PARALLEL transmission

(b) SERIAL

Parallel transmission has the advantage of speed (about eight times faster than serial transmission). However, it requires eight times as many transmitting and receiving circuits, at increased cost, which are also prone to *cross-talk* and have poor noise immunity. Parallel transmission is usually limited to cases where the transmitter and receiver are situated close to each other, resulting in connecting cable lengths of 20 m or less.

Serial transmission is used for long-range (20 m to many kilometres) communications where the cost of multiple data transmission lines would be high, and where facilities for multiple lines may not even exist (e.g. telephone lines). The use of a single transmission line can allow circuits with good noise immunity properties to be used at an overall economic cost.

To allow different peripherals to be interfaced to different computing systems, with minimal hardware and software effort, standard interfacing systems have been developed. Of these the IEEE 488 (GPIB) bus (parallel transmission) and the RS 232C (serial transmission) are now universally recognised standards.

7.9.1 IEEE 488 (GPIB) Bus

The standards for this bus were set by the Institute of Electrical and Electronics Engineers (USA) in October 1975 (IEEE document number ANSI MC 1.1, 1975) and accepted as an international standard in 1980. This interface is also known as the HP-IB (Hewlett Packard Interface Bus) and, more recently, as the GPIB (General Purpose Interface Bus).

Fig. 7.33 IEEE 488 bus structure

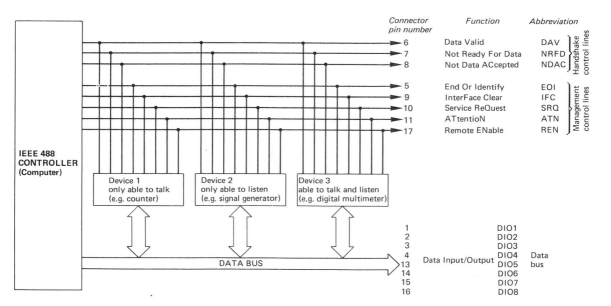

The **IEEE 488 bus** is primarily designed for connecting instrumentation to a central controller (usually a computer) for purposes of creating fully automated/data-logging measurement systems. At present some 220 different manufacturers produce equipment which is either partially or wholly IEEE 488 bus compatible.

The basic bus structure is shown in fig. 7.33. Devices connected to the bus may be

a) A controller
b) A talker only
c) A listener only
d) A talker and a listener.

The **controller** is responsible for the overall operation of the system by issuing the appropriate commands to other devices on the bus. As might be expected any system may only have one controller, which is usually a minicomputer with data-recording facilities. A **talker only** is a peripheral which can only transmit information (e.g. a frequency counter), whilst a **listener only** can only receive information (e.g. a signal generator). A **talker and listener** can both transmit and receive information (e.g. a digital multimeter). During operation, the controller will dictate whether a given device is a talker, listener or is idle (disconnected from the bus). Several listeners can be active simultaneously but only one talker can be active at a given time. For purposes of identification, each IEEE 488 bus device is allocated a unique 5-bit address—or *device number*—from five address switches situated on the (rear of the) instrument (fig. 7.34*b*). The controller may thus specify which devices it wishes to communicate with by placing the device address on the data bus.

The bus consists of 24 lines, of which 16 carry TTL-compatible signals, the other 8 being ground returns (fig. 7.34*a*). The 16 signal lines may be divided into three groups:

a) Data input/output bus
b) Handshake control lines
c) Management control lines.

The **data bus** comprises 8 bi-directional lines along which data, address information, and instructions from the controller, are sent as seven-bit ASCII characters. When not in use, the data lines are set "high". The management lines inform the devices as to whether the data bus contains data, address information, or instructions. All information is transmitted along the data bus under sequential control. No new step in the sequence can be initiated until the previous step is complete. Information transfer can proceed as fast as the devices can respond, but no faster than that allowed by the slowest listening device.

It is the task of the **handshake control lines** to control the passage of information from talker to listener(s). There are three such lines:

a) NRFD (not ready for data) which is held "low" by a listener until it is ready to accept a data byte. When "high", new data can be placed on the data bus by either a talker or the controller.
b) NDAC (not data accepted) which is held "low" by a listener until it has accepted the data byte. When "high", old data can be removed from the data bus by a talker or controller.
c) DAV (data valid) which is set "low" by the talker to indicate that valid data is present on the data bus.

The five **management control lines** issue instructions and, in conjunction with the handshake control, manage an orderly flow of information along the data bus. The individual lines function as follows:

a) ATN (attention) is set only by the controller. When "low", it indicates that the data bus is carrying either an address or an instruction.
b) IFC (interface clear), when set "low" by the controller, places the system in a known quiescent state (usually idle).
c) REN (remote enable) is used by the controller to set devices to either local (i.e. front panel) or bus control. For bus control REN is held "low".
d) SRQ (service request) which may be set "low" by any device on the bus to indicate that the device requires attention by the controller.
e) EOI (end or identify) which is set "low" by a talker to indicate that the data on the bus is the last byte of a multi-byte transfer sequence.

Fig. 7.34 IEEE 488 bus connector

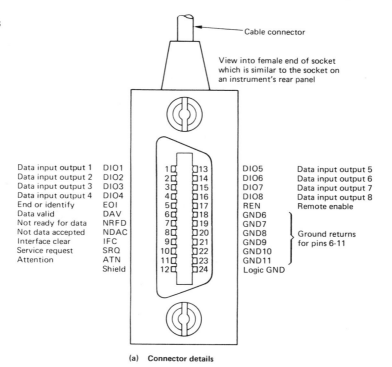

Cable connector

View into female end of socket which is similar to the socket on an instrument's rear panel

Data input output 1	DIO1	1	13	DIO5	Data input output 5
Data input output 2	DIO2	2	14	DIO6	Data input output 6
Data input output 3	DIO3	3	15	DIO7	Data input output 7
Data input output 4	DIO4	4	16	DIO8	Data input output 8
End or identify	EOI	5	17	REN	Remote enable
Data valid	DAV	6	18	GND6	
Not ready for data	NRFD	7	19	GND7	
Not data accepted	NDAC	8	20	GND8	Ground returns
Interface clear	IFC	9	21	GND9	for pins 6-11
Service request	SRQ	10	22	GND10	
Attention	ATN	11	23	GND11	
	Shield	12	24	Logic GND	

(a) **Connector details**

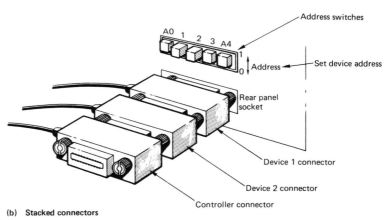

Address switches

A0 1 2 3 A4

Set device address

Address

Rear panel socket

Device 1 connector

Device 2 connector

Controller connector

(b) **Stacked connectors**

Physically the IEEE 488 bus consists of a 24-way (usually ribbon) cable connected to a standard, stackable 24-pin plug (fig. 7.34). Connections between devices may be either "star" or "chain" format provided that

(i) the total cable length is not greater than 20 m
(ii) the length of any single cable is not greater than 4 m
(iii) the total number of devices present on the bus, including the controller, does not exceed 15.

Under worst-case conditions (15 devices with a total cable length of 20 m) the maximum data transfer rate is 125 000 bytes/sec.

7.9.2 EIA RS 232C Serial Interface

The Electronics Industry Association (EIA) RS 232C interface standard allows for two full duplex data channels transmitting serial data, either synchronously or asynchronously, with or without handshake. The RS 232C (versions A and B are now obsolete) signal levels are shown in fig. 7.35 from which it should be noted that the binary 0 (also called a Space or ON condition) is more positive than the binary 1 (also called the Mark or OFF condition). This can present problems when interfacing RS 232C to TTL (a common requirement) since not only is there a considerable difference between the two signal voltage levels but the signal logic is inverted as well.

Connection between RS 232C devices is via a standard 25-pin connector (Cinch or Cannon chassis-mount, female-type DB-25S) illustrated in fig. 7.36, which also lists the pin connections. Unlike the IEEE 488 bus, the RS 232C interface is designed for connection between two devices only—usually a computer and a peripheral. Consequently if a computer wishes to communicate with more than one peripheral, a separate RS 232C interface must be provided for each peripheral. In addition, all RS 232C lines, unlike the IEEE 488 bus, are unidirectional, transfering data in one direction only, a factor which greatly simplifies both the hardware and software control of the interface.

Rarely is the full RS 232C standard implemented, with the majority of systems requiring only a subset of the electrical circuits. This has led to a re-defining of the RS 232C interface in terms of subsets called Level I, Level II and Level III which are defined as:

LEVEL I	Pin 2 Transmitted Data } Pin 3 Received Data } Channel 1	
	Pin 7 Logical Ground	
	Pin 1 Protective Ground	
LEVEL II	Level I+	
	Pin 6 Data Set Ready	
	Pin 8 Data Carrier Detect	
	Pin 20 Data Terminal Ready	
LEVEL III	Level II+	
	Pin 4 Request to Send } Pin 5 Clear to Send } Channel 1	
	Pin 22 Ring Indicator	

Level I is normally used with equipment tied directly to each other, such as a terminal or a printer connected directly to a computer. Level II is normally used where a certain amount of handshaking is required, and is most often encountered in acoustic couplers (for transmission over a normal GPO telephone line, etc). Level III is used where a more precise and detailed control over data flow is required, such as in auto-answer modems. As such, Level III implementation may be considered as reserved for specialist equipment.

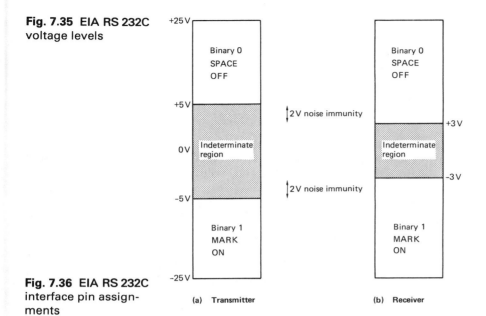

Fig. 7.35 EIA RS 232C voltage levels

(a) Transmitter

(b) Receiver

Fig. 7.36 EIA RS 232C interface pin assignments

Pin number	Circuit Mnemonic	Description	
1	AA	Protective Ground	⎫
2	BA	Transmitted Data	
3	BB	Received Data	
4	CA	Request to Send	⎬ CHANNEL 1
5	CB	Clear to Send	
6	CC	Data Set Ready	
7	AB	Logical Ground	⎭
8	CF	Data Carrier Detect	
9	—	⎫ Reserved for testing	
10	—	⎭	
11	—	Unassigned	⎫
12	SCF	Received Line Signal Detector	
13	SCB	Clear to Send	⎬ CHANNEL 2
14	SBA	Transmitted Data	⎭
15	DB	Transmitter Signal Element Timing	
16	SBB	Received Data CHANNEL 2	
17	DD	Receiver Signal Element Timing	
18	—	Unassigned	⎫
19	SCA	Request to Send	⎬ CHANNEL 2
20	CD	Data Terminal Ready	⎭
21	CG	Signal Quality Detector	
22	CE	Ring Indicator	
23	CH/CI	Data Signal Rate Select	
24	DA	Transmit Signal Element Timing	
25	—	Unassigned	

DB-25S connector

Fig. 7.37 Connection between two RS 232C devices (level 1)

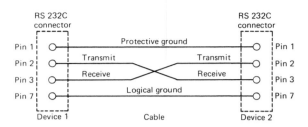

Levels I and II are frequently encountered and consequently a few further notes on the associated electrical circuits will be useful:

Pin 1   Protective ground   This pin is tied to the equipment frame and other external grounds as required.

Pins 2 and 3   Transmitted and received data, respectively   Data is transmitted in the serial format shown in fig. 7.32b.

Pin 7   Logical ground   Ground return for all RS 232C signals.

Pin 6   Data set ready   An outgoing signal indicating that the local device is ready for operation.

Pin 8   Data carrier detect   An incoming signal indicating that the remote device is ready for operation.

Pin 20   Data terminal ready   An incoming signal used to "prepare" a device for connection to an RS 232C channel.

Connecting two RS 232C devices together requires a little care since one cannot simply join like-numbered pins on two connectors. If this were to happen it would lead to the potentially disastrous situation where, for example, the transmitters from two devices were connected together. Consequently RS 232C connecting cables must be constructed such that appropriate lines "cross over" (fig. 7.37).

The maximum RS 232C signal path length is determined by the requirement that the line capacitance does not exceed 2500 pF, permitting a maximum data transmission rate of 2×10^4 baud [1 **baud** = 1 bit/sec]. For a typical transmission cable, possessing a line capacitance of 80 pF/m, this corresponds to a maximum cable length of approximately 30 m (100 feet).

7.10   Analogue-to-Digital and Digital-to-Analogue Conversion

In many practical situations the microprocessor is required to interface with an analogue system, in which the data may be input or output as an analogue (voltage) signal. Common examples are to be found in the control of graph plotters, servomechanisms, etc. which require digital signals to be converted to analogue form; or in the measurement of voltage, temperature (via a thermocouple, resistance thermometer, etc.), mechanical displacement, velocity or acceleration, all of which require an analogue signal to be converted to a digital form.

7.10.1 Digital-to-Analogue Conversion (DAC)

Almost all **digital-to-analogue convertors** use the principle of a summed current flow through a resistive *ladder network*, of which the most frequently encountered circuit is the R-2R ladder (fig. 7.38).

Simple circuit analysis shows that the output voltage of the operational amplifier is given by

$$V_{out} = -V_{ref}\left(\frac{R_f}{2R_L}\right)\left[\frac{A_0}{1} + \frac{A_1}{2} + \frac{A_2}{4} + \frac{A_3}{8}\right] \qquad (7.1)$$

where $A_0 = 1$ if the switch S_0 is connected to V_{ref} and $A_0 = 0$ if the switch S_0 is connected to ground. Similarly A_1–A_3 are 1 or 0 depending upon the position of S_1–S_3 respectively. Thus since A_0–A_3 represent a binary number, the circuit can convert a 4-bit input digital signal ($S_0 \equiv$ MSB, $S_3 \equiv$ LSB) into an output analogue signal.

Fig. 7.38 A four-bit R-2R ladder DAC

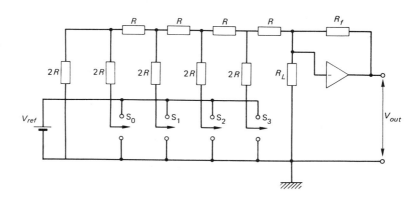

Whilst the circuit illustrated in fig. 7.38 could easily be constructed from discrete components, using transistors as switches for S_0–S_3, there is, for most practical purposes, little point in doing so. There are available, at present, integrated circuit DACs offering 4, 8, 10, 12, 14 and 16 bit conversion, all costing less than their discrete component counterparts. An example is the Ferranti ZN 425E DAC which is a high-performance monolithic integrated 8-bit digital-to-analogue convertor currently costing about £3·00 (one-off price).

This device (fig. 7.39) contains its own internal reference voltage (which is available for external use, pin 16) although an external reference voltage may be used if desired, pin 15. (To use the internal reference voltage, pin 15 is connected to pin 16.) The ZN 425E will accept either an 8-bit parallel input (pins 5–7, 9–13) or a "serial" input in the form of clock pulses (pin 4), which are used to set up an 8-bit number of a binary counter. A *logic select* (pin 2) determines whether the analogue output represents the parallel or serial inputs. Table 7.1 gives typical performance data for the ZN 425E.

Fig. 7.39 ZN 425E
digital-to-analogue
convertor

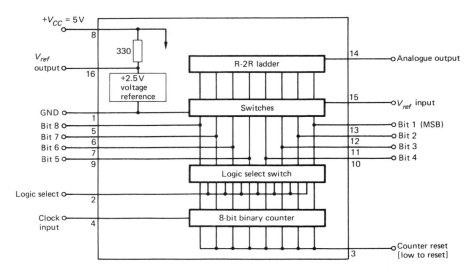

Table 7.1 ZN 425E—Performance data

Accuracy	±0·19%
Settling time	1·0 μsec
Offset voltage	3·0 mV
Linearity	±0·5 of least significant bit
Linearity temperature coefficient	7·5 ppm/°C

7.10.2 Analogue-to-Digital Conversion [ADC]

A variety of methods are available for performing **analogue-to-digital conversion** (ADC). However, for most practical purposes only two basic techniques are used which either

a) Compares the voltage to be measured with a known voltage produced by a DAC, i.e. utilises a DAC, or

b) Uses the method of *dual slope integration*.

As with the DACs, a wide variety of integrated ADCs are currently available, although the merits of an integrated ADC versus a (semi) discrete component ADC depends purely upon the requirements and economics of a particular application. For example, an 8-bit stand-alone integrated ADC with a conversion time of 20 msec currently costs about £10·00. However, if a conversion time of 20 μsec is required, the cost rises to £80·00. On the other hand an ADC constructed from (semi) discrete components (see, for example the circuit shown in fig. 7.40) would cost about £8·00 and, with the appropriate software, would have a conversion time of 25 μsec.

Fig. 7.40 ADC utilising
the ZN 425E DAC

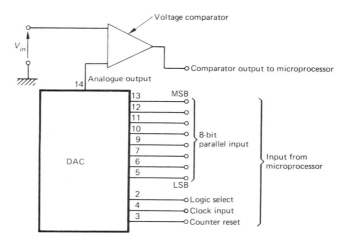

7.10.3 ADCs utilising DACs

Fig. 7.40 illustrates a typical circuit of this type of ADC, based on the
Ferranti ZN 425E DAC, discussed in 7.10.1.

Operation is as follows. The output of the DAC is first set to zero
(initialisation) and then incremented, via the 8 parallel input lines or internal
serial counter, until the output from the voltage comparator is observed to
change state. At this point the output from the DAC just exceeds V_{in} which
is thus represented by the binary input to the DAC.

Two modes of operation are possible, depending on whether the DAC is
controlled by the counter (*incremental ADC*) or the 8-bit parallel input lines
(*successive approximation ADC*).

1   Incremental ADC   In this, the simplest of the two modes, the DAC
counter is incremented, in steps of 1 LSB, from zero. The conversion time is
of the order of 2^n clock cycles where n is the number of binary digits in the
conversion. Thus for an 8-bit ADC with a typical effective clock rate of
$2 \, \mu$sec the conversion time is $512 \, \mu$sec.

2   Successive approximation ADC   In this mode, the input to the DAC is
first set to half its maximum value (2^{n-1}) via the 8-bit parallel input. A test is
then made to determine whether the output from the comparator has
changed state, which will show whether 2^{n-1} represents a voltage greater or
smaller than V_{in}. If greater, the binary input is decreased by 2^{n-2}; or if
smaller, increased by 2^{n-2}; and the comparator once again tested for a
change of state. This process is repeated until the binary input is changed by
1 LSB. Graphically the conversion is as shown in fig. 7.41.

The conversion time is n clock cycles which, for an 8-bit ADC with an
effective clock rate of $2 \, \mu$sec, is $16 \, \mu$sec.

Whilst faster than the incremental mode, the successive approximation
mode does require a more sophisticated (and time-consuming) software

control, which increases the conversion time to 25–30 μsec for the example quoted.

Fig. 7.41 ADC using method of successive approximation

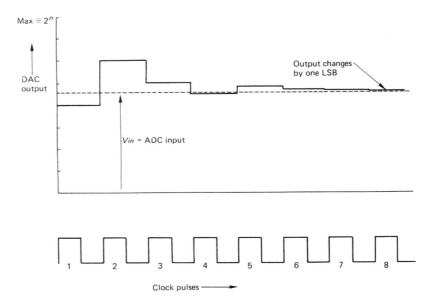

Both the incremental and successive approximation ADCs suffer from one major limitation, in that they are susceptible to noise, particularly "spikes", in the system. For accurate trouble-free operation, noise levels must be less than 0·5 LSB, which can be difficult to obtain in the somewhat noisy environment of a microprocessor system.

7.10.4 Dual Slope Integration ADCs

The principle of the **dual slope integration ADC** is illustrated in fig. 7.42. Operation is as follows. A "start convert" pulse clears the binary counter and removes any charge from the integrator capacitor C by closing the electronic switch S_2 briefly. The switch S_1 is then connected to the analogue input voltage V_{in}, allowing C to charge. As soon as C commences charging, the output of the comparator, which switches to a low level, is used to gate clock pulses to the binary counter until the binary counter overflows. At this point, the voltage on C is V_A where $V_A < V_{in}$. The switch S_1 is now connected to the negative reference voltage $-V_{ref}$, causing C to discharge. C continues to discharge with clock pulses feeding into the binary counter (note that at overflow the binary counter is effectively reset to zero). When C is fully discharged, the output from the comparator once again changes state and clock pulses cease to be gated into the binary counter.

It may easily be shown that, at this point,

$$V_{in} = \left[\frac{V_{ref}}{2^n}\right] \times \text{BC} \tag{7.2}$$

Fig. 7.42 Dual-slope integration ADC

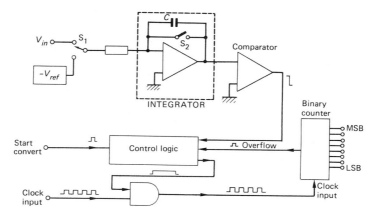

where n = number of bits in the binary counter
BC = binary counter reading when the comparator changes state for the second time.

Almost all commercial integrated circuit ADCs use the dual slope method. These integrated devices usually perform a continuous conversion, updating the binary counter output into latches (not shown in fig. 7.42) at the end of each conversion cycle. Alternatively the conversion cycle may be initiated by a start pulse from a microprocessor, etc.

The dual slope ADC has excellent noise immunity (hence its widespread use) since the system will "integrate out" any noise in the system. Its main disadvantage is that the conversion time is 2^{n+1} clock cycles which for an 8-bit convertor with a clock rate of 2 μsec is 1·24 msec.

Problems 7: Peripheral equipment

1 Discuss, giving one example of each, the difference between an "intelligent" and a "non-intelligent" (or dumb) computer peripheral.

2 Using a suitable block diagram describe the operation of a VDU such as might be found in a minicomputing system.

3 Compare the operational characteristics and applications of dot-matrix and daisy wheel printers. Describe the facilities you would expect an "intelligent" dot-matrix printer to possess.

4 Two major problems associated with keyboards are (i) contact bounce and (ii) situations in which more than one key is pressed simultaneously. Discuss the various hardware and software methods used to overcome these particular problems.

5 Fig. 7.43 illustrates a seven-segment display connected to seven output lines of an I/O port. A segment is illuminated when the corresponding output line is set to 1. Construct a look-up table giving the numbers which must be written to the output port to display the hexadecimal character set 0–F.

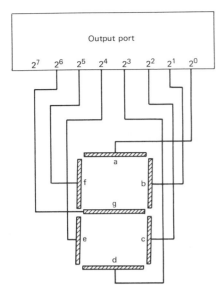

Fig. 7.43 Seven-segment display

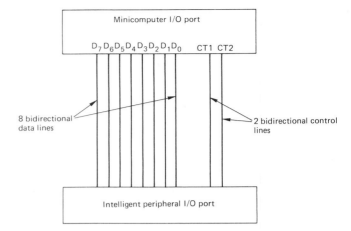

Fig. 7.44 Minicomputer parallel interface

6 Describe, and list the characteristics, of two of the following:
a) Flat-bed graph plotter
b) Digitiser table
c) Light pen.

7 Discuss the operating principle of the dual slope integration ADC. State the advantages that dual slope integration ADC possesses compared with an incremental ADC.

Using the values given in the text calculate the approximate conversion time for 16-bit ADCs employing:
a) Incremental ADC
b) Successive approximation ADC
c) Dual slope integration ADC.
The clock frequency in each case is 1 MHz.

8 Give the advantages and disadvantages of transmitting data in parallel format over *a*) short distances, *b*) long distances.

Assuming a clock frequency of 1 MHz calculate the minimum time required to transmit 2 Kbytes of data in (i) parallel format, (ii) serial format.

9 Fig. 7.44 illustrates a simple interface between a minicomputer and an intelligent peripheral. The I/O port provides ten bidirectional lines of which eight are required for data. Suggest a possible handshaking sequence for the two control lines which would allow:
a) The minicomputer to inform the peripheral it has data to transmit.
b) The peripheral to inform the minicomputer it is ready to receive data.
c) The peripheral to inform the minicomputer that it has received the transmitted data.

8 Microprocessor Applications

8.1 Introduction

In this chapter three typical applications of microprocessors are discussed. The three examples chosen not only demonstrate how a microprocessor, together with peripheral devices and memory, may be used for different tasks; but also serve to illustrate how a microprocessor can possess some distinct advantages in problem solving when compared with other "conventional" methods.

Because of the complex nature of the modern world it is sometimes difficult to decide whether one particular approach to a problem represents an advantage, or a disadvantage, when compared with a second approach. However, certain "commonsense" guidelines can be established in which a solution to a problem may be regarded as possessing advantages if it results in one, or more, of the following:

a) Reduced production cost for the same, or better, performance.

b) Increased accuracy ⎫
c) Increased efficiency ⎬ assuming that these *are* required.

d) Easier operation and reduced human effort (particularly in reducing routine, repetitive operations).

e) Increased reliability with reduced maintenance costs.

8.2 Digitised Weighing Scales

Fig. 8.1 illustrates an automatic digitised weighing scale now used in many grocery stores. In use, the produce to be weighed is placed on the weighing platform, and the price (cost per unit weight, lbs or kg) entered in via a push button keyboard. The scales automatically weigh, and then display the weight, price and cost ($= $ price $\times$ weight) on a seven-segment LED display. Typically, digital scales can weigh items up to 10 lb (4·5 kg) with an accuracy of $\frac{1}{8}$ oz (50 gm). The maximum price is £9·99$\frac{1}{2}$ (i.e. cost per unit weight) which, even with moderate inflation, is more than adequate.

Digital weighing scales possess some distinct advantages over the older, analogue scales, of which one type is illustrated in fig. 8.2. In analogue scales the weight of an article is displayed by a pointer moving over a curved scale. Analogue scales require the user to make a *measurement* (to compare the pointer with the scale as opposed to *reading* a digital display) and in

Fig. 8.1 Digital weighing scale

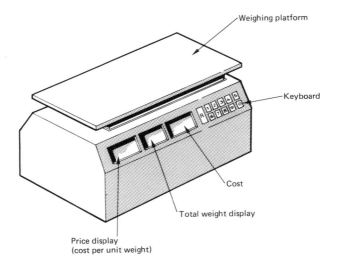

Weighing platform

Keyboard

Cost

Total weight display

Price display
(cost per unit weight)

Fig. 8.2 Analogue weighing scale

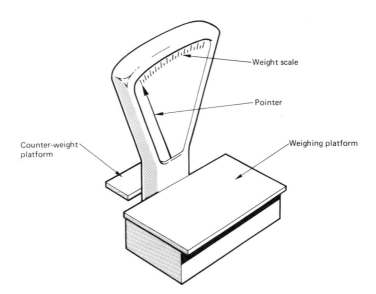

Weight scale

Pointer

Counter-weight platform

Weighing platform

many cases some form of (mental) calculation is necessary to determine the cost. Both of these activities are subject to human error and, furthermore, represent a tedious repetitive operation. Many analogue scales will only weigh up to a maximum of 3 lb or 5 lb (10 lb or 15 lb with added counterweights) with a resolution of $\frac{1}{4}$ oz (100 gm). Whilst cheaper than their digital counterpart, analogue scales require a higher degree of maintenance and are prone to "adjustments" by the user.

Fig. 8.3 illustrates the schematic diagram of a digital weighing scale. In operation the movement of the weighing platform, against a balance spring (not shown), is measured using either a strain gauge, potentiometric or

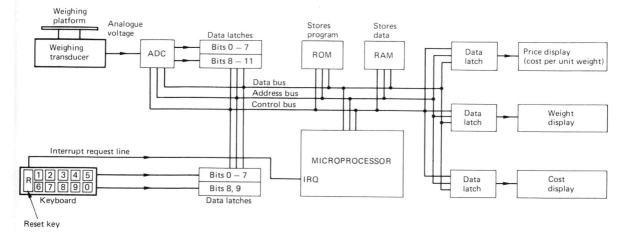

Fig. 8.3 Digital weighing scale: schematic

optical transducers. The output from the transducer is an analogue voltage which is converted to a digital signal using an analogue-to-digital converter. (Note that in certain optical systems a digital signal is obtained directly, obviating the need for an ADC.) The ADC is usually a dual-slope integration device (see 7.10.4) controlled directly by the microprocessor.

To obtain a resolution of $\frac{1}{8}$ oz in 10 lb (1 in 1280) the ADC must have a resolution of at least 11 bits ($2^{11} = 2048$). In practice a 12-bit ADC is used to reduce errors in the uncertainty of the LSB. Since a 12-bit ADC requires more data lines than the standard 8-bit microprocessors allows, the results of the conversion are stored in two data latches which serve as the ADC input port. The input from the keyboard numerals is likewise entered into data latches which function as the keyboard input port. The input from the reset key is connected directly to the interrupt request line (IRQ) on the microprocessor.

During use, the microprocessor inputs the price data from the keyboard and stores it in the RAM. An ADC is then performed and the weight of the article calculated by multiplying the ADC data by a (calibration) constant. The calculated weight is also stored in the RAM. Next the cost is calculated, by multiplying the weight by the price, and this too is stored in the RAM. Finally the price, weight and cost are retrieved from memory and stored in the display latches. Since the display latches are connected directly to the seven-segment displays, the displays then show the price, weight and cost of the article.

Fig. 8.4 illustrates the flowchart of a program, to be stored in ROM, which will perform the operations described above. On power-up (switching on), the microprocessor is automatically reset, following which control is passed to the start (START) of the program. The microprocessor interrupt vectors are set such that the control is also passed to the start of the program if the interrupt request line (IRQ) is activated. This occurs if the *reset key* is pressed, indicating that new price data is to be entered.

The first step in the program is initialisation, in which the RAM is cleared (all locations set to zero) and all the LED displays blanked. The keyboard

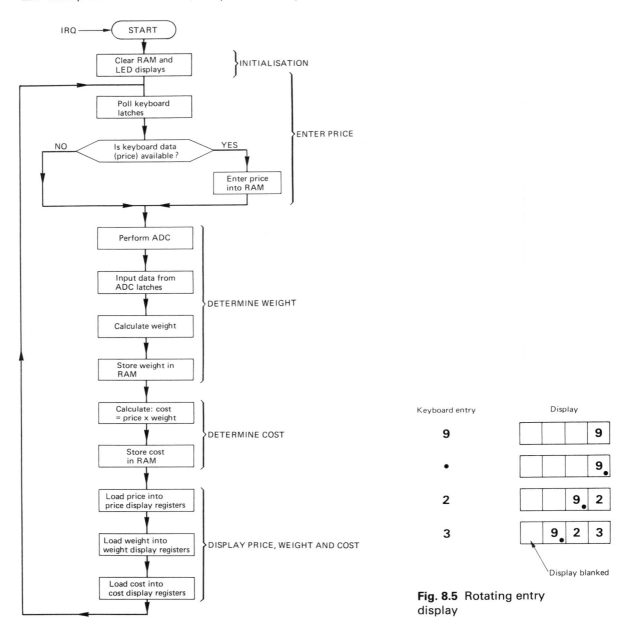

Fig. 8.4 Program flowchart for digital weighing scale

Fig. 8.5 Rotating entry display

latches are then polled to see if input data (the price) is available. If such data is available, this is entered into memory one digit at a time using a *rotating display entry*. (A rotating display entry is one in which the first digit entered into the system is displayed in the least significant bit LSB column. When second, and subsequent, digits are entered, the display is rotated left such that the last digit entered occupies the LSB position, fig. 8.5.) During data entry, either key lockout or key rollover (see 7.2.2) is employed to ensure that errors, due to the pressing of several keys simultaneously, do not occur.

The remainder of the program is self-explanatory and requires no further comment other than to point out that the program operates in a continuous loop until the reset key is pressed or the power removed. The time to execute one loop is, typically, 5–10 msec.

8.3 Microprocessor-controlled Central Heating System

Fig. 8.6 illustrates a typical central heating thermostat as used in many homes and offices. The bending of the bimetallic strip, with temperature, closes and opens the switch contacts which, in turn, switch on and off the heating system. The temperature at which the contacts open and close may be adjusted by a cam moving against the bimetallic strip. The cam is usually connected directly to a control knob which is graduated in °C or °F. In operation, the switch contacts are closed (heating on) until the ambient temperature reaches the set value θ_{set} following which the contacts open, switching the heating off.

Fig. 8.6 Domestic thermostat

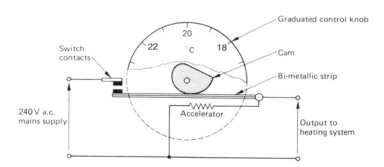

In theory, this device should maintain the room temperature constant. In practice the room temperature will vary in a sinusoidal fashion (fig. 8.7). This sinusoidal variation is due to both hysteresis in the bimetallic strip switching, and the effect of the *thermal mass* of the room(s) and surrounding air, which creates a *thermal delay* between the switching on and off of the heating system and a consequent change in temperature in the vicinity of the thermostat. To reduce these temperature fluctuations (typically ±3°C which *are* very noticeable) an *accelerator* heater is attached to the bimetallic strip. The accelerator is usually a high-value radio resistance (220 k) which dissipates approximately 0·125 watts when connected across the mains supply. Its action is to artificially increase the ambient temperature of the bimetallic strip, such that the thermostat switches the heating off at an earlier stage in the heating cycle, thus reducing the "overshoot" above θ_{set} (fig. 8.7). However, the accelerator resistance does not effect the cooling region of the cycle.

Fig. 8.7 Comparison
of thermostat
performance

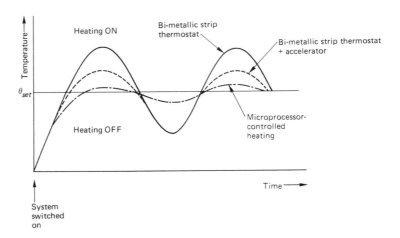

Fig. 8.8 illustrates a microprocessor-based heating controller. The temperature-sensing element is a thin-film platinum resistance (a Platfilm) whose resistance changes linearly with temperature. Platfilm sensors are cheap and are manufactured to a high tolerance ($\pm 0 \cdot 001\%$). Consequently they have a guaranteed performance and are readily interchangeable. The variation of resistance with temperature is given by

$$R = (100 + 0 \cdot 035\,T)\Omega \tag{8.1}$$

where T is the temperature in °C.

The system operation is as follows. The resistance of the Platfilm sensor is determined by an ADC, which measures the voltage developed across the resistance when a constant current is passed through it. For typical domestic applications, the system need only be capable of measuring temperature over the range −15°C to +35°C with an accuracy of 0·2°C. This requires that the ADC has a resolution of 1 in 250 $[(35 - (-15))/0 \cdot 2 = 250]$ which is easily accomplished with an 8-bit ADC.

The heating system (which will consist of a heater, fan, water pump, etc.) is controlled by one or more isolating switches, which physically isolate the low-voltage microprocessor circuits from the mains voltage used in the heating system. The isolating switches are usually opto-isolators which switch either relays or solid state switches such as triacs or thyristors.

The relatively high cost of the microprocessor system cannot justify its use as a straightforward replacement for the simple bimetallic strip thermostat. Consequently the microprocessor is also used to perform other, necessary tasks which are normally carried out by additional control devices. These tasks include the switching on and off of the overall heating system during specified periods, creating temperature profiles (fig. 8.9), etc.

Consequently, in addition to the ADC and isolating switches, the microprocessor is equipped with a control keyboard and several seven-segment LED displays. With the keyboard and display, a series of heating programs may be entered. When information is not being entered, the seven-segment displays are used to display the controller clock (which gives the date and

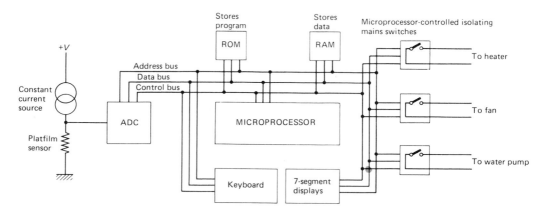

Fig. 8.8 Microprocessor-controlled heating system

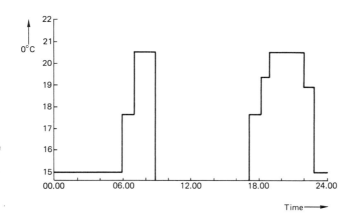

Fig. 8.9 Typical domestic temperature profile designed to provide maximum comfort with minimum cost

time of day), the system status (i.e. the particular program cycle under current execution), as well as the measured temperature.

Fig. 8.10 shows the flowchart of a suitable control program. Following power-up, the microprocessor is automatically reset and control passed to the start (START) of the program. The first step in the program is initialisation which clears the RAM and blanks the seven-segment displays.

The keyboard is then polled for input instructions, or data, which, if present, are entered into RAM. If no input data is available, the program executes a dummy routine, DELAY 1, which takes the same time to execute as the routine which inputs data and stores it in RAM. The purpose of introducing DELAY 1, and all other delays in the program, is to ensure that the time taken to execute the main program loop is constant irrespective of the path taken. The reason for this is that the loop time (typically 0·1 sec) is used as a timing element by the controller clock which is incremented each loop by 0·1 sec. Incrementing the control clock is carried out following the keyboard poll.

The program then compares the control clock (which gives time of day) to see if the overall heating system is to be switched on or off. If the system is

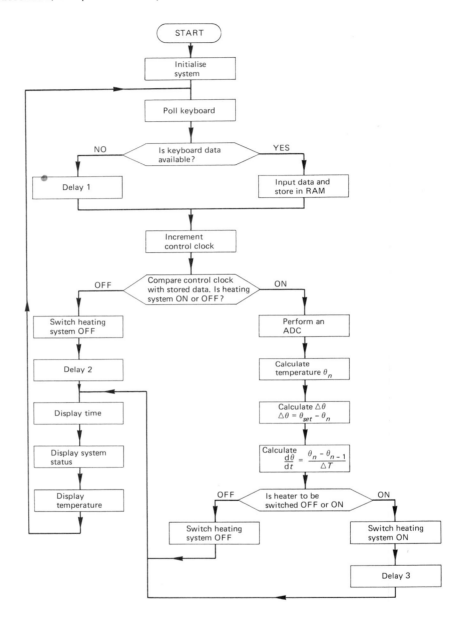

Fig. 8.10 Program flowchart for microprocessor-controlled heating system

OFF the microprocessor opens the isolating switches, executes DELAY 2, and then updates the seven-segment displays before returning to the start of the main program loop.

If the system is to be switched ON, an ADC is performed on the output of the Platfilm sensor. The digital data is converted to a temperature θ_n where n represents the current (nth) reading.

The difference between the measured and set temperatures $\Delta\theta$ is calculated together with the rate of change of temperature. The rate of change of temperature is calculated by dividing the difference between the current (nth) and previous ($n-1$th) temperature readings by the loop execution time ($\Delta T = 0 \cdot 1$ sec).

Both $\Delta\theta$ and $\mathrm{d}\theta/\mathrm{d}t$ are necessary to determine whether the heating system is to be switched on or off if temperature fluctuations about θ_{set} are to be minimised. For example, during the heating cycle the heater must be switched off before the measured temperature reaches θ_{set}, otherwise the system response will be the same as the simple bimetallic strip thermostat. Similarly, during the cooling cycle, the heater must be switched on before the temperature falls below θ_{set}. Following the switching on or off of the heating system, the program updates the seven-segment displays before returning to the start of the main program loop.

Typical heating systems, using the approach outlined above, can provide for a full seven-day heating program with up to eight separate on/off sequences per day. Depending upon the physical surroundings, room temperatures may be maintained to within $\pm 0 \cdot 25°C$. Additionally the system will provide for hot-water-only heating cycles (not shown in fig. 8.10).

8.4 Waveform Synthesis

Fig. 8.11 illustrates the schematic circuit of a "conventional" signal generator. It consists of a variable frequency oscillator (VFO) which is tuned by, typically, a variable capacitance or resistance. The output from the oscillator may undergo some form of *waveform shaping* to produce sinusoidal, square, sawtooth, etc. waveforms. A switch S_1 enables the user to select one particular waveform, whilst a variable attenuator allows the signal output level to be varied continuously from zero to a maximum.

Fig. 8.11 "Conventional" signal generator

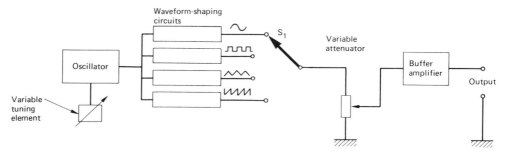

Such circuits are used to generate signals over the frequency range $0 \cdot 1$ Hz to 18 GHz, although at the higher frequencies ($\geqslant 1$ GHz) only sinusoidal waveforms are encountered. Output power levels may range from a few tens of mW at radio frequencies to many watts for audio signal generators.

Whilst this type of circuit is extremely versatile, well tried and proven, it nevertheless does have the disadvantage that, without additional complex circuitry, only simple waveforms may be generated. Furthermore, the direct control of such a generator by a computer or microprocessor—an ever-increasing requirement—cannot easily be accomplished.

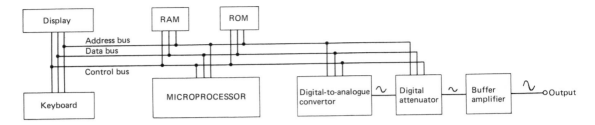

Fig. 8.12 Microprocessor waveform synthesiser

Fig. 8.12 illustrates an *incremental* microprocessor waveform synthesiser. The keyboard and display are used to input and output control instructions and information respectively. The ROM and RAM store the systems program and data. In operation, a sequence of numbers, which represents the envelope of the required waveform, are written, in succession, to the digital-to-analogue convertor (DAC). The analogue output of the DAC is thus a synthesised waveform which is fed to a digitally controlled attenuator before output via a buffer amplifier. The digital attenuator is an active analogue circuit (usually incorporating an operational amplifier) whose response is given by

$$V_{out} = V_{in}/k \tag{8.2}$$

where k is the value of the digital (usually 8-bit) control signal.

As an example consider the synthesis of a sawtooth waveform. This is easily accomplished by the program loop, shown in fig. 8.13, which first writes (or stores) the contents of a counter in the DAC data latches and then increments the counter. In the program shown, the accumulator is used as the counter. For an 8-bit microprocessor, the counter counts from 0 to 255 and then automatically resets when the counter overflows. The output from the DAC is thus a series of incremental steps (fig. 8.14) whose envelope is a sawtooth waveform. Provided that the incremental step, which corresponds to one least significant bit (LSB), is sufficiently small, the DAC output may, for most practical purposes, be considered as a pure sawtooth signal.

Fig. 8.13 Flowchart of program to synthesise a sawtooth waveform

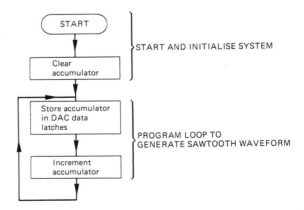

Fig. 8.14 Synthesised sawtooth waveform

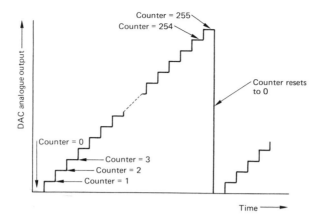

To vary the frequency of the sawtooth wave a variable software-controlled delay is introduced into the program loop (fig. 8.15). The delay effectively stretches the period of each cycle to obtain the desired frequency.

A reverse sawtooth may be synthesised in a similar fashion by decrementing, instead of incrementing, the loop counter. A triangular wave may be synthesised by first incrementing the loop counter from 0 to 255 and then decrementing the counter from 255 to 0. Fig. 8.16 shows the flowchart of a program to synthesise a variable frequency triangular wave. A square wave, the simplest waveform to synthesise, can be generated by writing 0 and 255 alternately to the DAC.

Fig. 8.15 Flowchart of program to synthesise a variable-frequency sawtooth waveform

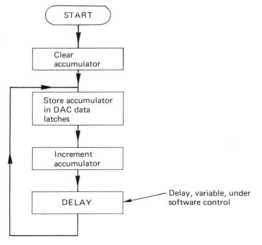

Two approaches may be used to synthesise sine (or cosine) waveforms. In the first the value of the sine function is calculated from a series expression of the form:

$$\sin(x) = x - \frac{x^3}{3!} + \frac{x^5}{5!} - \frac{x^7}{7!} + \cdots \tag{8.3}$$

for incremental values of x. The computed value of $\sin(x)$, multiplied by a

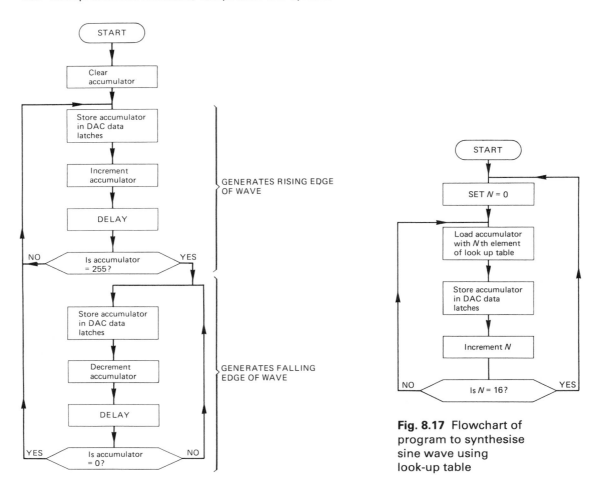

Fig. 8.16 Flowchart of program to synthesise a variable-frequency triangular wave

Fig. 8.17 Flowchart of program to synthesise sine wave using look-up table

suitable constant (see below), is then written to the DAC data latches. This particular method is rarely used, since the time taken to evaluate the function is, in practice, prohibitively long. Instead a second method is used in which the values of the function are first stored in a *look-up table* and then written to the DAC in sequence. Table 8.1 gives a look-up table for synthesising a sine wave incremented in steps of 22·5°. The table, suitable for an 8-bit microprocessor, is generated from the following expression:

$$\text{sine function value} = 127 + 127 * \sin(N * 22·5) \tag{8.4}$$

where $N = 0, 1, 2, \cdots 15$. To synthesise a sine wave the look-up table function values are written, in sequence, to the DAC.

The reason for using an expression of the form given in (8.4) to create a sine look-up table is that most DACs cannot handle negative numbers (the basic sine function is negative between 180° and 360°). The look-up table thus corresponds to a sine wave whose origin is shifted such that its zero level (x-axis) has a value of 127 (corresponding to sin (0) and sin (180)), with

Table 8.1 Look-up table to synthesise a sine wave

Position in table (N)	Angle (degrees)	Function value
0	0·0	127
1	22·5	176
2	45·0	217
3	67·5	244
4	90·0	254
5	112·5	244
6	135·0	217
7	157·5	176
8	180·0	127
9	202·5	78
10	225·0	37
11	247·5	10
12	270·0	0
13	292·5	10
14	315·0	37
15	337·5	78

the function varying between 254 (corresponding to sin (90)) and 0 (corresponding to sin (270)).

Fig. 8.17 shows the flowchart of a program which uses Table 8.1 to synthesise a sine wave. The program uses a counter N to sequentially select the elements of the look-up table. In practice one of the microprocessor index registers would be used as the N counter. Fig. 8.18 shows the resultant synthesised waveform which is a "coarse" sine wave due to the small number of elements (a total of 16) used in the synthesis. In practice a look-up table with 360 (1° resolution) or 720 (0·5° resolution) elements would be used to generate a "smooth" sine wave. As with the sawtooth wave, a variable delay may be included in the main program loop to vary the frequency of the generated signal.

Using look-up tables any periodic or aperiodic (pulse) waveform may be easily and conveniently synthesised.

The astute reader may have already wondered why a digital attenuator is included in the system, since the DAC itself may be used to vary the amplitude of the synthesised signal. There are three reasons for this. The first is that, if the DAC is used as an attenuator, the resolution of the synthesised signal is reduced. For example, a sine wave, synthesised by an 8-bit DAC, has a resolution of 1 in 256 ($\equiv 0·4\%$) if the full dynamic range of the DAC is used. If, however, the DAC is used to attenuate the signal to, say, 0·25 of its maximum amplitude, the resolution is now only 1 in 64 ($\equiv 1·5\%$). If the attenuation is 0·1, the resolution is 1 in 25 ($\equiv 4\%$). Second, the digital attenuator may be used to amplitude-modulate (AM) the synthesised signal—a useful feature to have in any signal generator. Finally, the separate attenuator makes for easier software management and development since both the frequency and the amplitude of the resultant signal may be varied independently.

The circuit shown in fig. 8.12, with its single DAC, represents an inefficient use of the microprocessor and would not be used in practice. Practical microprocessor-controlled synthesisers use several DACs to synthesise several waveforms simultaneously. The synthesised signals may then be mixed to produce a waveform whose complexity is only limited by the imagination of the user. As a further refinement, special frequency synthesiser integrated circuits are available which may be interfaced, directly, with most microprocessors. These integrated circuits contain, typically, three separate programmable frequency synthesisers with their own programmable digital attenuators and mixers. In addition variable bandwidth noise generators are also included which are used in many applications.

Fig. 8.18 Synthesised sine wave

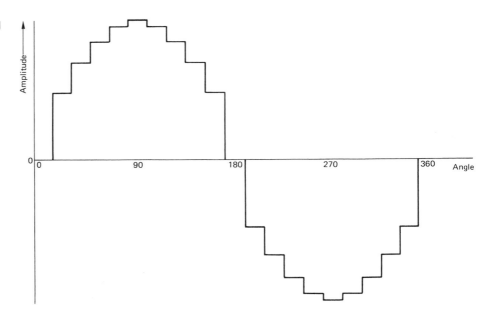

The microprocessor synthesiser, whilst an extremely versatile instrument, does have one major shortcoming, when compared with conventional signal generators. This is that, at present, microprocessor synthesisers are limited to the synthesis of signals whose frequency is $\leqslant 50$ KHz. Synthesis of higher-frequency (i.e. r.f.) signals can be achieved by (frequency) multiplication but this is of little practical use since the synthesised bandwidth is limited. Furthermore, such an approach tends to defeat the general objective that a microprocessor should provide an effective, versatile and cheap solution to a particular problem.

Problems 8: Microprocessor Applications

1   Draw the flowchart of a program which may be used to synthesise a square wave.

2   The Z80 instruction to output the contents of the accumulator to a peripheral port, located at address ADDR in page zero, is OUT (ADDR),A.

   Using the flowchart developed in the previous problem write an assembly code program to synthesise a square wave, on a Z80 system, in which the DAC is driven by an output port located at 40H in page zero.

3   The 6502 instruction to output the contents of the accumulator to a peripheral port, located at the absolute address ADDR, is STA $ADDR.

   Using the flowchart given in fig. 8.13 write an assembly code program to synthesise a sawtooth waveform, on a 6502 system, in which the DAC is driven by an output port located at the absolute address $E000.

4   Write a Z80 assembly code program to synthesise a triangular waveform using a DAC located at 0040H.

5   Using the look-up table given in Table 8.1 write an assembly code program to synthesise a sine wave on a 6502 system in which the DAC is located at $E000 and the look-up table is stored at $2000 to $200F.

Answers

Chapter 2: Computer arithmetic

1 *a*) 0111 *b*) 0100 *c*) 1111 *d*) 0000

2 *a*) 136 *b*) 91 *c*) 255

3 *a*) 1100100 *b*) 10001001 *c*) 1100·001

4 *a*) 263_8 *b*) 060_8 *c*) 367_8

5 *a*) 21_{hex} *b*) $B0_{hex}$ *c*) FD_{hex}
      d) $C36_{hex}$ *e*) $59D7_{hex}$

6 *a*) 0010 1100 1001 1110 *b*) 0011 0011 1111 1011
      c) 1010 0000 0100 0111 *d*) 1111 1101 1011 1000

7 *a*) 513 *b*) 225 *c*) 585 *d*) 65 518

8 *a*) 0101 0000 0010
      b) (i) 93 (ii) 457 (iii) 8601

9 0000 to EFFF for RAM, F000 to F0FF for ROM.

10 *a*) 4096×8 bits of 4 Kbytes (ROM); 8704×8 bits or 8·5 Kbytes (RAM) *b*) 16

11 *a*) 1100 1010 *b*) 0001 0100

12 *a*) 11110 *b*) 1001101 *c*) 1·1 *d*) 101·110

13 *a*) 0011 0111 *b*) 1011 0111 *c*) 0000 1011
       d) 0111 1111 *e*) 1111 1111 *f*) 0000 0000 and 1000 0000

14 *a*) 0010 1011 *b*) 1101 0101 *c*) 0101 0000
       d) 0001 0011 *e*) 1110 1101 *f*) 0010 0101
       g) 1100 0010 *h*) 1110 1000

15 *a*) 1C6A *b*) 2D2

16 *a*) 1000 *b*) 7FFE

17 *a*) $\cdot 1 \times 2^5$, 0101 0100 0000
       b) $\cdot 101 \times 2^2$, 0010 0101 0000
       c) $\cdot 11 \times 2^{-2}$, 1110 0110 0000
       d) $\cdot 1100100 \times 2^7$, 0111 0110 0100

18 *a*) 43 862
       b) p011 0100; p = 1 (for even parity)
          p011 0011; p = 0
          p011 1000; p = 1
          p011 0110; p = 0
          p011 0010; p = 1

Chapter 3: Logic devices, circuits and operations

1 *a*) 1 *b*) 0 *c*) 1 *d*) 0 *e*) 1 *f*) 1

2 *a*) (i) 0 (ii) 1 (iii) 0 (iv) 0 a 5-input AND gate
  b) (i) 0 (ii) 1 (iii) 1 (iv) 1 a 5 input OR gate

3 *a*)

A	B	F
0	0	0
0	1	0
1	0	0
1	1	1

b)

A	B	F
0	0	0
0	1	1
1	0	1
1	1	1

4

A	B	F
0	0	1
0	1	1
1	0	0
1	1	1

$F = 110101$

5 $F = A.B.C.D.E$
  a) The circuit of fig. 3.42 can be used.
  b) Use two NAND gates connected as shown below to produce the AND function; then connect 5 of these combinations as in fig. 3.42.

6 *a*) (i) 0 (ii) 1 (iii) floating output
  b) (i) 0 (ii) 1

7 *a*) D_0 *b*) D_6 *c*) D_7
  When inhibit signal is a 1, outputs from all AND gates are 0 and hence output from OR gate is 0.

8 *a*) Q_{n+1} column 0 1011; $\bar{Q}_{n+1}$ column 1 0100
  b) Q_{n+1} column 1 01110; $\bar{Q}_{n+1}$ column 0 10001

9 *a*) Circuit is set with $Q = 1$, $P = 0$
  b) Circuit is reset, $Q = 0$, $P = 1$
  c) Race condition occurs.

10 *a*) 1 *b*) 0 *c*) 0 *d*) 1 *e*) 1

11 *a*) 1,0 *b*) 1,0 *c*) 0,1

13 $Q = 0$ until clock goes to 1, when $Q = D = 1$ and remains 1 until second clock pulse when $Q = D = 0$.

14 *a*) $Q = 0$ *b*) 0 *c*) 1 *d*) 0 *e*) 1 *f*) 0

15 500 kHz, 250 kHz, 125 kHz, 62·5 kHz, 31·25 kHz

16

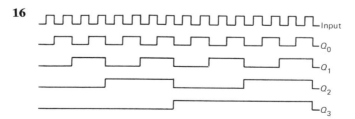

17

Pulse	Q_0	Q_1	Q_2
1	1	0	0
2	0	1	0
3	1	1	0
4	0	0	1
5	0	0	0
6	1	0	0
7	0	1	0
8	1	1	0
9	0	0	1
10	0	0	0

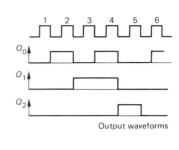

Output waveforms

18

Time	Q_4	Q_3	Q_2	Q_1	Q_0
0	0	0	0	0	0
after 1 clock pulse	1	0	0	0	0
2	1	1	0	0	0
3	0	1	1	0	0
4	0	0	1	1	0
5	1	0	0	1	1

Chapter 4: Microprocessor architecture and system operation

2 *a*) 4 bytes *b*) 2048 Kbytes

3 2 Kbytes of ROM; 1 Kbyte of RAM; 4 input and 3 output ports

4 *a*) 0000 0000 1111 1111 on the address bus, 0110 1101 on the data bus; $\overline{WR} = 1$, $\overline{RD} = 0$.
b) 0000 0001 0000 0000 on the address bus, 0001 0001 on the data bus; $\overline{WR} = 0$, $\overline{RD} = 1$.
c) 0010 0000 0000 0000 on the address bus, 1011 1011 on the data bus; $\overline{WR} = 0$, $\overline{RD} = 1$.

5 *a*) (i) ROM, 1K, 0000 to 03FF
b) (i) RAM, 256, 0800 to 08FF

10 *a*) If the WE and RE lines are enabled simultaneously, and the data bus of the microprocessor and the I/O port attempt to drive opposing signals to the port, some IC gates may be destroyed.
b) No, since the Z80 will not attempt to read and write simultaneously.

11

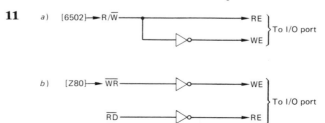

Chapter 5: Microprocessor programming

1 LD   A,C000H
   AND A,F0H
   LD   C000H,A

2 LDA $C000
   AND   #$0F
   STA $B001
   LDA $C000
   LSR
   LSR
   LSR
   LSR
   STA $B000

3 LD   A,E000H
   OR   0FH
   LD   E000H,A

4

Line No.	Label	Source	Code	Comments
1	START	LD	A, TABLE	⎫ LOAD 1ST ELEMENT OF TABLE INTO
2		LD	D, A	⎬ MINV (D) AND MAXV (E)
3		LD	E, A	⎭ REGISTERS.
4		LD	IX, (TABLE)	⎫ LOAD ADDRESS OF 1ST ELEMENT OF TABLE ⎬ INTO INDEX REGISTER.
5		LD	A, LENGTH	⎫ LOAD LENGTH OF TABLE INTO H
6		LD	H, A	⎬ REGISTER (COUNTER).
7	LOOP	DEC	H	⎫ DECREMENT COUNTER: IF <0 (END OF
8		JP	M, END	⎬ TABLE) THEN END ROUTINE.
9		INC	IX	⎫ INCREMENT INDEX COUNTER AND THUS LOAD
10		LD	A, (IX+00H)	⎬ ACCUMULATOR WITH NEXT ELEMENT IN TABLE.
11		CP	D	IS A<MINV (D REGISTER)?
12		JP	P, MAX	IF NO TEST FOR A>MAXV.
13		LD	D, A	STORE NEW MINIMUM IN D REGISTER.
14		JP	LOOP	EXAMINE NEXT ELEMENT IN TABLE.
15	MAX	CP	E	IS A>MAXV (E REGISTER)?
16		JP	M, LOOP	IF NO EXAMINE NEXT ELEMENT IN TABLE.
17		LD	E, A	STORE NEW MAXIMUM IN E REGISTER.
18		JP	LOOP	EXAMINE NEXT ELEMENT IN TABLE.
19	END	LD	A, D	⎫ STORE MINIMUM VALUE AT SYMBOLIC
20		LD	MINV, A	⎬ ADDRESS MINV.
21		LD	A, E	⎫ STORE MAXIMUM VALUE AT SYMBOLIC
22		LD	MAXV, A	⎬ ADDRESS MAXV.
23		RET		RETURN FROM ROUTINE.

6

Line No.	Label	Source Code	Operand	Comments
1	START	LDA	#$00	CLEAR ACCUMULATOR.
2		LDX	#$08	MULTIPLIER BIT COUNT = 8
3	NXTBIT	LSR	MPLY	SHIFT NEXT MULTIPLIER BIT INTO CARRY.
4		BCC	SHIFT	IS MULTIPLIER BIT = 1.
5		CLC		⎱ IF YES ADD MULTIPLICAND TO
6		ADC	MPLD	⎰ ACCUMULATOR.
7	SHIFT	LSR	A	⎱ TRANSFER LSB OF ACCUMULATOR
8		ROR	RLOB	⎰ TO RLOB (VIA CARRY FLAG).
9		DEX		⎱ DECREMENT BIT COUNTER: IF = 0
10		BNE	NXTBIT	⎰ EXIT FROM ROUTINE.
11		STA	RHOB	STORE HIGH BYTE OF RESULT.
12	END	RTS		EXIT FROM ROUTINE.

8 To create a delay of 1 msec a subroutine is required which will use 1000 clock cycles of a 1 MHz clock. There are many possible solutions to this problem of which the following is one example.

Line No.	Label	Source Code	Operand	Comments
1	DELAY	LDX	#$8D	LOADS X REGISTER WITH 14_{10}, USES 2 CLOCK CYCLES.
2	LOOP	NOP		⎱ PROGRAM EXECUTES THIS LOOP USING 7 CLOCK
3		DEX		⎰ CYCLES PER LOOP WITH THE EXCEPTION OF THE
4		BNE	LOOP	⎰ FINAL LOOP WHEN ONLY 6 CLOCK CYCLES ARE USED.
5		NOP		⎱ LINES 1–4 USE A TOTAL OF $2 + (140 \times 7) + 6 =$
6		NOP		988 CLOCK CYCLES. THREE NOP USE $3 \times 2 = 6$
7		NOP		⎰ CLOCK CYCLES.
8	END	RTS		⎱ LINES 1–7 USE A TOTAL OF $988 + 6 = 994$ CLOCK CYCLES. RTS REQUIRES 6 CLOCK CYCLES GIVING A TOTAL SUBROUTINE TIME OF 1000.

9 To create a delay of 2·25 msec the subroutine PAUSE must use 4500 T-states in a 2 MHz system. The following subroutine is only one of many possible solutions.

Line No	Label	Source code	No. of T-states	Comments
1	PAUSE	LD D,F8H	7	LOADS D REGISTER WITH 248_{10}.
2	LOOP	NOP	4	⎱ THIS LOOP IS EXECUTED 248 TIMES
3		DEC D	4	USING $248 \times 18 = 4464$
4		JP NZ,(LOOP)	10	⎰ T-STATES.
5		LD D,0H	7	⎱ THESE 4 INSTRUCTIONS ARE
6		DEC D	4	USED TO INSERT 19
7		NOP	4	⎰ T-STATES.
8		NOP	4	
9		RET	10	RETURN FROM SUBROUTINE.

Total number of T-states $= 7 + (248 \times 18) + 19 + 10 = 4500$.

11 In this solution the comment field is omitted. For comments see solution to problem 5.8.

Line No.	Memory location	Object code	Label	Source code	Operand
1	0400	A2 8D	DELAY	LDX	#$8D
2	0401	EA	LOOP	NOP	
3	0402	CA		DEX	
4	0403	D0 FC		BNE	LOOP
5	0405	EA		NOP	
6	0406	EA		NOP	
7	0407	EA		NOP	
8	0408	60	END	RTS	

N.B. In line 4, FC ≡ branch 4 memory locations backwards.

Chapter 6: Computer storage devices

3 Approximately 31 msec (30 msec average sector access time +0·96 msec to read the sector).

6 312·5 hours

9 *a*) 3·41 mins (50 msec to program 1 byte).
  b) 10·24 mins (10 msec to program 1 byte).

10 MOS since it consumes less power and is cheaper.

12
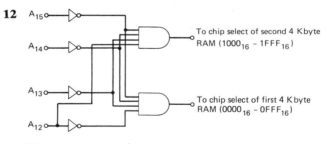

[Other circuits are possible]

Chapter 7: Peripheral equipment

5

Hex number	1 = segment illuminated; 0 = not illuminated								No. written to I/O port
	not used	$g = 2^6$	$f = 2^5$	$e = 2^4$	$d = 2^3$	$c = 2^2$	$b = 2^1$	$a = 2^0$	
0	0	0	1	1	1	1	1	1	3F
1	0	0	0	0	0	1	1	0	06
2	0	1	0	1	1	0	1	1	5B
3	0	1	0	0	1	1	1	1	4F
4	0	1	1	0	0	1	1	0	66
5	0	1	1	0	1	1	0	1	6D
6	0	1	1	1	1	0	0	1	79
7	0	0	0	0	0	1	1	1	07
8	0	1	1	1	1	1	1	1	7F
9	0	1	1	0	0	1	1	1	67
A	0	1	1	1	0	1	1	1	77
B	0	1	1	1	1	1	0	0	7C
C	0	0	1	1	1	0	0	1	39
D	0	1	0	1	1	1	1	0	5E
E	0	1	1	1	1	0	0	1	79
F	0	1	1	1	0	0	0	1	71

7 a) $2^{16} \times 1\ \mu\text{sec} = 65 \cdot 5\ \text{msec}$
  b) $2 \times 16 \times 1\ \mu\text{sec} = 32\ \mu\text{sec}$
  c) $2^{(16+1)} \times 1\ \mu\text{sec} = 131\ \text{msec}$

8 a) $2 \cdot 05\ \text{msec}$ b) $16 \cdot 38\ \text{msec}$.

9 There are several possible handshaking arrangements of which the following represents a typical solution.
Control line 1 (CT1) is used by the microprocessor to signify that data is available.
Control line 2 (CT2) provides the return handshake from the peripheral. Note that the low level of CT2 is used to signal two conditions.

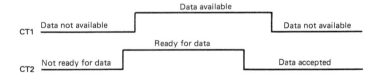

Chapter 8: Microprocessor applications

1

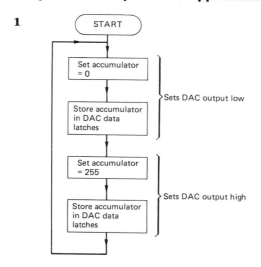

2

START	LD	A,00H	; SET ACCUMULATOR = 0.
	OUT	40H,A	; STORE ACCUMULATOR IN DAC DATA LATCHES.
	LD	A,FFH	; SET ACCUMULATOR = 255.
	OUT	40H,A	; STORE ACCUMULATOR IN DAC DATA LATCHES.
	JP	(START)	; REPEAT PROGRAM LOOP.

3

START	LDA	#$00	; SET ACCUMULATOR = 0.
LOOP	STA	$E000	; STORE ACCUMULATOR IN DAC DATA LATCHES.
	INA		; INCREMENT ACCUMULATOR.
	JMP	LOOP	; REPEAT PROGRAM LOOP.

4

START	LD	A,00H	
LOOP 1	OUT	40H,A	Creates rising edge of triangular waveform
	INC	A	
	CP	FFH	
	JP	NZ,(LOOP1)	
LOOP 2	OUT	40H,A	Creates falling edge of triangular waveform
	DEC	A	
	CP	00H	
	JP	Z,(LOOP2)	
	JP	(LOOP1)	

5

START	LDX	#$00	; X REGISTER USED AS N COUNTER.
LOOP 1	LDA	$2000,X	; LOAD ACCUMULATOR WITH NTH ELEMENT OF TABLE.
	STA	$E000	; STORE NTH ELEMENT IN DAC DATA LATCHES.
	INX		; INCREMENT X (N COUNTER).
	CPX	#$10	; IS N = 16?
	BNE	LOOP 1	; NO—GET NEXT ELEMENT IN TABLE.
	JMP	START	; YES—RESET N COUNTER.

Appendix A
6502 Microprocessor Instruction Set

1 ALPHABETICAL ORDER

ADC	Add with carry	**JSR**	Jump to subroutine
AND	Logical AND	**LDA**	Load accumulator
ASL	Arithmetic shift left	**LDX**	Load X
BCC	Branch if carry clear	**LDY**	Load Y
BCS	Branch if carry set	**LSR**	Logical shift right
BEQ	Branch if result $= 0$	**NOP**	No operation
BIT	Test bit	**ORA**	Logical OR
BMI	Branch if minus	**PHA**	Push A
BNE	Branch if not equal to 0	**PHP**	Push P status
BPL	Branch if plus	**PLA**	Pull A
BRK	Break	**PLP**	Pull P status
BVC	Branch if overflow clear	**ROL**	Rotate left
BVS	Branch if overflow set	**ROR**	Rotate right
CLC	Clear carry	**RTI**	Return from interrupt
CLD	Clear decimal flag	**RTS**	Return from subroutine
CLI	Clear interrupt disable	**SBC**	Subtract with carry
CLV	Clear overflow	**SEC**	Set carry
CMP	Compare to accumulator	**SED**	Set decimal
CPX	Compare to X	**SEI**	Set interrupt disable
CPY	Compare to Y	**STA**	Store accumulator
DEC	Decrement memory	**STX**	Store X
DEX	Decrement X	**STY**	Store Y
DEY	Decrement Y	**TAX**	Transfer A to X
EOR	Exclusive OR	**TAY**	Transfer A to Y
INC	Increment memory	**TSX**	Transfer SP to X
INX	Increment X	**TXA**	Transfer X to A
INY	Increment Y	**TXS**	Transfer X to SP
JMP	Jump	**TYA**	Transfer Y to A

2 OP CODE AND TIMING FOR 6502

(n = number of clock cycles   # = number of bytes per instruction)

MNEMONIC	note	IMPLIED OP n #	ACCUM OP n #	ABSOLUTE OP n #	ZERO PAGE OP n #	IMMEDIATE OP n #	ABS. X OP n #	ABS. Y OP n #	(IND,X) OP n #	(IND),Y OP n #	Z. PAGE, X OP n #	RELATIVE OP n #	INDIRECT OP n #	Z. PAGE, Y OP n #	N	V	B	D	I	Z	C	MNEMONIC
ADC	(1)			6D 4 3	65 3 2	69 2 2	7D 4 3	79 4 3	61 6 2	71 5 2	75 4 2				•	•				•	•	ADC
AND	(1)			2D 4 3	25 3 2	29 2 2	3D 4 3	39 4 3	21 6 2	31 5 2	35 4 2				•					•		AND
ASL			0A 2 1	0E 6 3	06 5 2		1E 7 3				16 6 2				•					•	•	ASL
BCC	(2)											90 2 2										BCC
BCS	(2)											B0 2 2										BCS
BEQ	(2)											F0 2 2										BEQ
BIT				2C 4 3	24 3 2										M7	M6				•		BIT
BMI	(2)											30 2 2										BMI
BNE	(2)											D0 2 2										BNE
BPL	(2)											10 2 2										BPL
BRK		00 7 1															1					BRK
BVC	(2)											50 2 2										BVC
BVS	(2)											70 2 2										BVS
CLC		18 2 1																			0	CLC
CLD		D8 2 1																0				CLD
CLI		58 2 1																	0			CLI
CLV		B8 2 1														0						CLV
CMP				CD 4 3	C5 3 2	C9 2 2	DD 4 3	D9 4 3	C1 6 2	D1 5 2	D5 4 2				•					•	•	CMP
CPX				EC 4 3	E4 3 2	E0 2 2									•					•	•	CPX
CPY				CC 4 3	C4 3 2	C0 2 2									•					•	•	CPY
DEC				CE 6 3	C6 5 2		DE 7 3				D6 6 2				•					•		DEC
DEX		CA 2 1													•					•		DEX
DEY		88 2 1													•					•		DEY
EOR	(1)			4D 4 3	45 3 2	49 2 2	5D 4 3	59 4 3	41 6 2	51 5 2	55 4 2				•					•		EOR
INC				EE 6 3	E6 5 2		FE 7 3				F6 6 2				•					•		INC
INX		E8 2 1													•					•		INX
INY		C8 2 1													•					•		INY
JMP				4C 3 3									6C 5 3									JMP
JSR				20 6 3																		JSR
LDA				AD 4 3	A5 3 2	A9 2 2	BD 4 3	B9 4 3	A1 6 2	B1 5 2	B5 4 2				•					•		LDA
LDX	(1)			AE 4 3	A6 3 2	A2 2 2		BE 4 3						B6 4 2	•					•		LDX
LDY	(1)			AC 4 3	A4 3 2	A0 2 2	BC 4 3				B4 4 2				•					•		LDY
LSR			4A 2 1	4E 6 3	46 5 2		5E 7 3				56 6 2				0					•	•	LSR
NOP		EA 2 1																				NOP
ORA				0D 4 3	05 3 2	09 2 2	1D 4 3	19 4 3	01 6 2	11 5 2	15 4 2				•					•		ORA
PHA		48 3 1																				PHA
PHP		08 3 1																				PHP
PLA		68 4 1													•					•		PLA
PLP		28 4 1													•	•	•	•	•	•	•	PLP
ROL			2A 2 1	2E 6 3	26 5 2		3E 7 3				36 6 2				•					•	•	ROL
ROR			6A 2 1	6E 6 3	66 5 2		7E 7 3				76 6 2				•					•	•	ROR
RTI		40 6 1													•	•	•	•	•	•	•	RTI
RTS		60 6 1																				RTS
SBC	(1)			ED 4 3	E5 3 2	E9 2 2	FD 4 3	F9 4 3	E1 6 2	F1 5 2	F5 4 2				•	•				•	•	SBC
SEC		38 2 1																			1	SEC
SED		F8 2 1																1				SED
SEI		78 2 1																	1			SEI
STA				8D 4 3	85 3 2		9D 5 3	99 5 3	81 6 2	91 6 2	95 4 2											STA
STX				8E 4 3	86 3 2									96 4 2								STX
STY				8C 4 3	84 3 2						94 4 2											STY
TAX		AA 2 1													•					•		TAX
TAY		A8 2 1													•					•		TAY
TSX		BA 2 1													•					•		TSX
TXA		8A 2 1													•					•		TXA
TXS		9A 2 1																				TXS
TYA		98 2 1													•					•		TYA

(1) Add 1 to n if crossing page boundary   (2) Add 2 to n if branch within page; Add 3 to n if branch within another page

Appendix B
Z80 Microprocessor Instruction Set

INSTRUCTION		OBJECT CODE	BYTES	CLOCK PERIODS
ADC	data	CE yy	2	7
ADC	(HL)	8E	1	7
ADC	HL,rp	ED 01xx1010	2	15
ADC	(IX+disp)	DD 8E yy	3	19
ADC	(IY+disp)	FD 8E yy	3	19
ADC	reg	10001xxx	1	4
ADD	data	C6 yy	2	7
ADD	(HL)	86	1	7
ADD	HL,rp	00xx1001	1	11
ADD	(IX+disp)	DD 86 yy	3	19
ADD	IX,pp	DD 00xx1001	2	15
ADD	(IY+disp)	FD 88 yy	3	19
ADD	IY,rr	FD 00xx1001	2	15
ADD	reg	10000xxx	1	4
AND	data	E6 yy	2	7
AND	(HL)	A6	1	7
AND	(IX+disp)	DD A6 yy	3	19
AND	(IY+disp)	FD A6 yy	3	19
AND	reg	10100xxx	1	4
BIT	b,(HL)	CB 01bbb110	2	12
BIT	b,(IX+disp)	DD CB yy 01bbb110	4	20
BIT	b,(IY+disp)	FD CB yy 01bbb110	4	20
BIT	b,reg	CB 01bbbxxx	2	9
CALL	label	CD ppqq	3	17
CALL	C,label	DC ppqq	3	10/17
CALL	M,label	FC ppqq	3	10/17
CALL	NC,label	D4 ppqq	3	10/17
CALL	NZ,label	C4 ppqq	3	10/17
CALL	P,label	F4 ppqq	3	10/17
CALL	PE,label	EC ppqq	3	10/17
CALL	PO,label	E4 ppqq	3	10/17
CALL	Z,label	CC ppqq	3	10/17
CCF		3F	1	4
CP	data	FE yy	2	7
CP	(HL)	BE	1	7
CP	(IX+disp)	DD BE yy	3	19
CP	(IY+disp)	FD BE yy	3	19
CP	reg	10111xxx	1	4
CPD		ED A9	2	16
CPDR		ED B9	2	21/16*
CPI		ED A1	2	16
CPIR		ED B1	2	21/16*
CPL		2F	1	4
DAA		27	1	4
DEC	(HL)	35	1	11
DEC	IX	DD 2B	2	10
DEC	(IX+disp)	DD 35 yy	3	23
DEC	IY	FD 2B	2	10
DEC	(IY+disp)	FD 35 yy	3	23
DEC	rp	00xx1011	1	6
DEC	reg	00xxx101	1	4
DI		F3	1	4
DJNZ	disp	10 yy	2	8/13
EI		FB	1	4
EX	AF,AF	08	1	4
EX	DE,HL	EB	1	4
EX	(SP),HL	E3	1	19
EX	(SP),IX	DD E3	2	23

INSTRUCTION		OBJECT CODE	BYTES	CLOCK PERIODS
EX	(SP),IY	FD E3	2	23
EXX		D9	1	4
HALT		76	1	4
IM	0	ED 46	2	8
IM	1	ED 56	2	8
IM	2	ED 5E	2	8
IN	A,port	DB yy	2	10
IN	reg,(C)	ED 01ddd000	2	11
INC	(HL)	34	1	11
INC	IX	DD 23	2	10
INC	(IX+disp)	DD 34 yy	3	23
INC	IY	FD 23	2	10
INC	(IY+disp)	FD 34 yy	3	23
INC	rp	00xx0011	1	6
INC	reg	00xxx100	1	4
IND		ED AA	2	15
INDR		ED BA	2	20/15
INI		ED A2	2	15
INIR		ED B2	2	20/15
JP	Label	C3 ppqq	3	10
JP	C,label	DA ppqq	3	10
JP	(HL)	E9	1	4
JP	(IX)	DD E9	2	8
JP	(IY)	FD E9	2	8
JP	M,label	FA ppqq	3	10
JP	NC,label	D2 ppqq	3	10
JP	NZ,label	C2 ppqq	3	10
JP	P,label	F2 ppqq	3	10
JP	PE,label	EA ppqq	3	10
JP	PO,label	E2 ppqq	3	10
JP	Z,label	CA ppqq	3	10
JR	C,disp	38 yy	2	7/12
JR	disp	18 yy	2	12
JR	NC,disp	30 yy	2	7/12
JR	NZ,disp	20 yy	2	7/12
JR	Z,disp	28 yy	2	7/12
LD	A,(addr)	3A ppqq	3	13
LD	A,(BC)	0A	1	7
LD	A,(DE)	1A	1	7
LD	A,I	ED 57	2	9
LD	A,R	ED 5F	2	9
LD	(addr),A	32 ppqq	3	13
LD	(addr),BC	ED 43 ppqq	4	20
LD	(addr),DE	ED 53 ppqq	4	20
LD	(addr),HL	22 ppqq	3	16
LD	(addr),IX	DD 22 ppqq	4	20
LD	(addr),IY	FD 22 ppqq	4	20
LD	(addr),SP	ED 73 ppqq	4	20
LD	(BC),A	02	1	7
LD	(DE),A	12	1	7
LD	HL,(addr)	2A ppqq	3	16
LD	(HL),data	36 yy	2	10
LD	(HL),reg	01110sss	1	7
LD	I,A	ED 47	2	9
LD	IX,(addr)	DD 2A ppqq	4	20
LD	IX,data 16	DD 21 yyyy	4	14
LD	(IX+disp),data	DD 36 yy yy	4	19
LD	(IX+disp),reg	DD 01110sss yy	3	19
LD	IY,(addr)	FD 2A ppqq	4	20
LD	IY,data 16	FD 21 yyyy	4	14

INSTRUCTION		OBJECT CODE	BYTES	CLOCK PERIODS
LD	(IY+disp),data	FD 36 yyyy	4	19
LD	(IY+disp),reg	FD 01110sss yy	3	19
LD	R,A	ED 4F	2	9
LD	reg,data	00ddd110 yy	2	7
LD	reg,(HL)	01ddd110	1	7
LD	reg,(IX+disp)	DD 01ddd110 yy	3	19
LD	reg,(IY+disp)	FD 01dddd110 yy	3	19
LD	reg,reg	01dddsss	1	4
LD	rp,(addr)	ED 01xx1011 ppqq	4	20
LD	rp,data16	00xx0001 yyyy	3	10
LD	SP,HL	F9	1	6
LD	SP,IX	DD F9	2	10
LD	SP,IY	FD F9	2	10
LDD		ED A8	2	16
LDDR		ED B8	2	21/16*
LDI		ED A0	2	16
LDIR		ED B0	2	21/16*
NEG		ED 44	2	8
NOP		00	1	4
OR	data	F6 yy	2	7
OR	(HL)	B6	1	7
OR	(IX+disp)	DD B6 yy	3	19
OR	(IY+disp)	FD B6 yy	3	19
OR	reg	10110xxx	1	4
OTDR		ED B8	2	20/15*
OTIR		ED B3	2	20/15*
OUT	(C),reg	ED 01sss001	2	12
OUT	port,A	D3 yy	2	11
OUTD		ED AB	2	15
OUTI		ED A3	2	15
POP	IX	DD E1	2	14
POP	IY	FD E1	2	14
POP	pr	11xx0001	1	10
PUSH	IX	DD E5	2	15
PUSH	IY	FD E5	2	15
PUSH	pr	11xx0101	1	11
RES	b,(HL)	CB 10bbb110	2	15
RES	b,(IX+disp)	DD CB yy 10bbb110	4	23
RES	b,(IY+disp)	FD CB yy 10bbb110	4	23
RES	b,reg	CB 10bbbxxx	2	8
RET		C9	1	10
RET	C	D8	1	5/11
RET	M	F8	1	5/11
RET	NC	D0	1	5/11
RET	NZ	C0	1	5/11
RET	P	F0	1	5/11
RET	PE	E8	1	5/11
RET	PO	E0	1	5/11
RET	Z	C8	1	5/11
RETI		ED 4D	2	14

INSTRUCTION		OBJECT CODE	BYTES	CLOCK PERIODS
RETN		ED 45	2	14
RL	(HL)	CB 16	2	15
RL	(IX+disp)	DD CB yy 16	4	23
RL	(IY+disp)	FD CB yy 16	4	23
RL	reg	CB 00010xxx	2	8
RLA		17	1	4
RLC	(HL)	CB 06	2	15
RLC	(IX+disp)	DD CB yy 06	4	23
RLC	(IY+disp)	FD CB yy 06	4	23
RLC	reg	CB 00000xxx	2	8
RLCA		07	1	4
RLD		ED 6F	2	18
RR	(HL)	CB 1E	2	15
RR	(IX+disp)	DD CB yy 1E	4	23
RR	(IY+disp)	FD CB yy 1E	4	23
RR	reg	CB 00011xxx	2	8
RRA		1F	1	4
RRC	(HL)	CB 0E	2	15
RRC	(IX+disp)	DD CB yy 0E	4	23
RRC	(IY+disp)	FD CB yy 0E	4	23
RRC	reg	CB 00001xxx	2	8
RRCA		0F	1	4
RRD		ED 67	2	18
RST	n	11xxx111	1	11
SBC	data	DE yy	2	7
SBC	(HL)	9E	1	7
SBC	HL,rp	ED 01xx0010	2	15
SBC	(IX+disp)	DD 9E yy	3	19
SBC	(IY+disp)	FD 9E yy	3	19
SBC	reg	10011xxx	1	4
SCF		37	1	4
SET	b,(HL)	CB 11bbb110	2	15
SET	b,(IX+disp)	DD CB yy 11bbb110	4	23
SET	b,(IY+disp)	FD CB yy 11bbb110	4	23
SET	b,reg	CB 11bbbxxx	2	8
SLA	(HL)	CB 26	2	15
SLA	(IX+disp)	DD CB yy 26	4	23
SLA	(IY+disp)	FD CB yy 26	4	23
SLA	reg	CB 00100xxx	2	8
SRA	(HL)	CB 2E	2	15
SRA	(IX+disp)	DD CB yy 2E	4	23
SRA	(IY+disp)	FD CB yy 2E	4	23
SRA	reg	CB 00101xxx	2	8
SRL	(HL)	CB 3E	2	15
SRL	(IX+disp)	DD CB yy 3E	4	23
SRL	(IY+disp)	FD CB yy 3E	4	23
SRL	reg	CB 00111xxx	2	8
SUB	data	D6 yy	2	7
SUB	(HL)	96	1	7
SUB	(IX+disp)	DD 96 yy	3	19
SUB	(IY+disp)	FD 96 yy	3	19
SUB	reg	10010xxx	1	4
XOR	data	EE yy	2	7
XOR	(HL)	AE	1	7
XOR	(IX+disp)	DD AE yy	3	19
XOR	(IY+disp)	FD AE yy	3	19
XOR	reg	10101xxx	1	4

* Execution time shown is for one iteration.

x   represents an optional binary digit.

bbb   represents optional binary digits identifying a bit location in a register or memory byte. (000 = LSB, 111 = MSB)

ddd   represents optional binary digits identifying a destination register.

        111 = A   000 = B   001 = C   010 = D   011 = E   100 = H   101 = L

sss   represents optional binary digits identifying a source register—same coding as ddd.

ppqq represents a four hexadecimal digit memory address.

yy   represents two hexadecimal data digits.

yyyy   represents four hexadecimal data digits.

When two possible execution times are shown (i.e., 5/11), it indicates that the number of clock periods depends on condition flags.

Index